GEMS OF THE VIEUX CARRE

Dedication

This book is dedicated to America's
most interesting people, the Tourists.

Gems of the Vieux Carre

The story of four historical romances of the Frence Quarter of old New Orleans depicting living conditions and home life of the Creole and their slaves in pre-Civil War days.

by

Pierre Paul Ebeyer

Author of New Orleans' most complete book, the "Paramours of the Creoles."

WINDMILL PUBLISHING COMPANY
4700 Airline Highway -:- New Orleans, La.

Printed by
The Illustrated Press
New Orleans - - - U. S. A.

The birth of the book:

"GEMS OF THE VIEUX CARRE"

By The Author

"Good morning, Alex."

"Good morning, Pierre. My, but you seem to be meditative."

"I am; and I have much reason to be."

"Why?"

"Well, before the war, I wrote a book, 'PARAMOURS OF THE CREOLES'."

"I know that."

"During the war I wrote on Napoleon's escape from St. Helena."

"The book you did not publish."

"No, I did not."

"Why?"

"Because Napoleon was being compared to war-time mongers, and the public was not interested in him."

"Do you intend publishing it?"

"Yes, in France."

"I see, but why the meditation?"

"Because I've been constantly deluged with requests concerning the homelife of the old Creoles. For instance, one man said, 'Mr. Ebeyer, your 'PARAMOURS OF THE CREOLES' furnishes us with a wonderful insight into the life of the French Quarter. I never once dreamed it was that interesting! But why not also furnish us with a complete insight into the homelife of the Creoles themselves? Certainly one would imagine it to be an extremely interesting subject.'

"And a woman wrote, 'Tell us how those old cultured people lived with slaves in the old brick mansions behind the beautiful iron lace-work.' "

"Well, Pierre, you would be an ideal one to write on that subject, since you were born among and reared with Creoles and ex-slaves in the French Quarter; and especially since you lecture on this subject."

"Speaking of lectures reminds me of a talk I gave recently to the foremen of Consolidated Vultee Aircraft Corp., on the Creole. Most of them had read Paramours.

"When I had concluded my talk, a Mr. Taylor, I believe his name was, walked up to the platform, shook hands and, after thanking me, said, 'Mr. Ebeyer, after reading your Paramours of the Creoles, I inquired at bookshops for a story on the home and plantation life of the Creoles. Failing there, I visited the library and searched their files thoroughly. Nowhere can I find a book that covers, let me say, the life of the Creoles as you have so thoroughly and so frankly portrayed it for us tonight. You owe it to the Creoles, to yourself, and to posterity, to put in book form your seemingly singular knowledge of those people.

" 'Further,' he continued, "New Orleans's billion dollar legacy," as you so aptly call the French Quarter, will remain here long after all Creoles with knowledge of their forefathers' manner of living have passed on. If you, or someone equally well informed, does not put this information in writing, it, too, will pass on; and much that could be of interest concerning your beloved French Quarter will be lost forever. I demand, as an American citizen,' he continued excitedly although he was smiling, 'that you-put-in-writing-what you've told us tonight.' "

"He was certainly insistent, Pierre; you must have spoken well."

"I did mention secrets that need no longer be secrets. However, I pondered the question. The more I thought, the more the idea appealed to me. And Mr. Taylor's words, 'You owe it to the old Creoles, to yourself, and to posterity' continually rang in my ears—in fact, plagued me.

"A week or two later, I ran into a Mr. White, who had been in the audience that night, just as he emerged from one of the old buildings in the Vieux Carre. After explaining who he was, he enthusiatically said, 'I have visited these old buildings on numerous occasions, and each time I have received a thrill. But after learning from your lecture how the Creoles lived, I am now so interested that when I re-enter these buildings, I see them peopled with the old Creoles and their slaves. In my mind's eye, I see the Creole drive through the old carriage entrance in his black carriage. A slave emerges from the slave quarter and rushes up to the horses, the Creoles alighting and slowly walking up the winding stairway. Entering the second-story rooms, I see the Creole opening large windows while his wife, after donning bed clothes, lowers the mosquito bar preparatory to their retiring. I could also realistically picture these people stealing into the next room where a baby was asleep in the arms of a slave wet-nurse. Returning, I see them as they kneel and pray before retiring and also realize they must have kissed good-night after entering the bed under the mosquito bar, for I learned from your talk about the almost unbelievable affection of the Creoles.

"'In fact,' he continued, Alex, 'I now feel a queer unaccountable emotion whenever I'm in these old Creole homes. And I find myself transported exoterically into another world, the interesting world of the old, cultured Creole.'"

"That's easy to understand, Pierre. But, what is your problem?"

"To write so that I might fix indelibly in the reader's mind episodes of the Creoles so that they, the readers, might, as did Mr. White, fully absorb all phases of Creole life, and experience the same queer, unaccountable emotions he estactically felt."

"Why not write as you spoke."

"That wouldn't do for, in lecturing, I had occasion to refer continually to the Paramours. Repetition in speech is sometimes pardonable, but never in two different books."

"I understand. In other words, you want a forceful method of relating."

"That's it. I want a vehicle in which I can completely and faithfully picture every movement, every thought, every emotion of the Creoles."

"Well, the most forceful urge of the human emotions is reproduction."

"That I know. But, even though I shall explain their candidness in sex conversation, a candidness derived from the French, yet, I cannot use this vehicle alone."

"Well, the reproduction urge leads to love or affection. Why not show the Creole homelife in one of the Quarter's old romances. For instance, that story we often speak of, "INSEPARABLE'.""

"One story would never suffice. There is entirely too much of interest to be told in—"

"Two or three, then. Surely, you're not in want of romantic material with your knowledge of Creole love affairs."

"Now, that's an idea. In addition to 'INSEPARABLE' I could use the romance of that vivacious, impulsive 'PETITE' for the second story; The Redcoat Britisher who married a Creole in 'AND OBEY' for the third; and for the fourth, those two lovable characters of Lizette and Phillippe in the story, 'MINE'.""

"Pierre, aren't those romances known to the Creoles as the four most beautiful of the thousands of love affairs of the French Quarter, the most outstanding? I believe I once heard someone refer to them as such."

"Definitely yes, for my old French grandmother continually referred to them as the 'GEMS OF THE VIEUX CARRE' as she would relate them to me in her broken English while I sat on her lap for hours as a youngster in the patio under waving fronds of banana trees.

"Yes, the old Creole title, 'GEMS OF THE VIEUX CARRE' it will be. With this vehicle, I shall be able to portray their lives in a soft, interesting, fiction-like way instead of in dry biography. And I shall be able to cover the entire field."

"For instance?"

"Well, their various superstitions—their impulsiveness that led to duells—their clannishness—their plantation life—the extremities they went through for their children—the men making goddesses of their women—their strange courtships and their stranger honeymoons—their soft easy philosophy of life—their extreme religiousness—their candidness of sex subjects—their serious view on being a God-parent—their pleasure in being of service to others—their actions during epidemics—their living with slaves—their extreme affection —their fine furniture—their famed hospitality—to sum up, their Creole culture! In fact, Alex, when one will have completed 'GEMS OF THE VIEUX CARRE', one will see the French Quarter as only you and I and possibly a few other Creoles now view it—as it was in days of yore."

"I believe that. And Pierre, in addition to this, one will read of the Quarter's four most beautiful romances."

"A drink to the birth of the new book! What shall it be, Alex?"
"As of yore, the Creoles' favorite, 'Scotch and Soda'."

STORIES

"INSEPARABLE"

"PETITE"

"AND OBEY"

"MINE"

"INSEPARABLE"

Contents

		Page
I.	PAUL AND GRACE	1
II.	BELLE	6
III.	JEAN	10
IV.	THEIR CHILDHOOD	12
V.	A GREAT AWAKENING	15
VI.	REFLECTION	20
VII.	A PRAYER	22
VIII.	PRACTICAL JEAN	24
IX.	TOO DAMN DANGEROUS	26
X.	A REALIZATION	29
XI.	A RUDE AWAKENING	32
XII.	RENE'S VISIT	35
XIII.	ON THE GARDEN WALL	38
XIV.	A POSSIBLE SOLUTION	44
XV.	RELIGIOUS REASONING	48
XVI.	THE INEVITABLE	54
XVII.	KISS ME AND KISS ME AGAIN	61
XVIII.	EMILE'S VISIT	66
XIX.	A TEN-HOUR DRIVE	68
XX.	SEND FOR THE MINISTER	71

"PETITE"

Contents

		Page
I.	EMILE AND GRACE	76
II.	LAFITTE, THE PIRATE	81
III.	ANTOINE	87
IV.	PETITE	93
V.	SLAVE PSYCHOLOGY	98
VI.	THE BALL	101
VII.	THE SONG OF PETITE	110
VIII.	THE ENGAGEMENT	113
IX.	THROUGH THE SWAMPS AT NIGHT	125
X.	LOVE-SONG TELEGRAPH	140
XI.	THE DUEL	145
XII.	HALLUCINATION	154
XIII.	THE BATTLE	162
XIV.	ASK FOR MY FORGIVENESS	165

"... AND OBEY"

Contents

		Page
I.	PAUL AND GRACE—PETITE AND ANTOINE	172
II.	A KISS IN THE HOSPITAL	177
III.	JOHN AND JEANNETTE	183
IV.	THE ENGAGEMENT	189
V.	CHOOSING FURUITURE	194
VI.	A DUAL WEDDING	200
VII.	MADEAU, THE FORTUNE-TELLER	205
VIII.	JOHN'S VISIT TO MADEAU	213
IX.	RESULTS	219
X.	THE DUEL	225
XI.	PUNISHMENT	228
XII.	JEANETTE'S RESOLUTION	238
XIII.	IN ENGLAND	246
XIV.	REUNION	248
XV.	A FRIEND BEFRIENDED	254
XVI.	GET THE HELL OUT OF HERE	264

"MINE"

IN THREE PARTS

Part One—"The Epidemic"

		Page
I.	THE REQUEST	275
II.	PHILIPPE	281
III.	LIZETTE	284
IV.	THE ORGAN-GRINDER	288
V.	THE KING AND THE QUEEN	291
VI.	MARDI GRAS	294
VII.	THE CHOLERA EPIDEMIC	302
VIII.	THE PRAYER	304

Part Two—"As You Desire Me"

I.	THE ENGAGEMENT	309
II.	YELLOW FEVER	314
III.	BASIN STREET	320
IV.	GREEN EYES	324
V.	THE MARDI GRAS PARADE	329

Part Three—"The Great Revelation"

I.	REVELATION	334
II.	A MOMENTOUS DECISION	338
III.	MINE	342
IV.	GRATITUDE	346

Author's Note: The four stories are in sequence, and to read them otherwise than in their proper order would, in a large measure take much of the pleasure and meaning out of the book.

The endings are all very sensational. Reading them first would ruin the effect of the stories.

All names are fictitious.

INSEPARABLE

CHAPTER I

Ici Repose Jean Moveau
Nee Janv. 21, 1843

Ici Repose Belle Mastero
Beloved of Jean Moveau
Nee Janv. 5, 1845

Ferme Pour Toujours

"Just what does that mean, Emile?"

Emile, a Creole, had been born in the old French Quarter, known in New Orleans as the "Vieux Carre." He was middle-aged, with a fair education. In a low, sad emotional voice he answered, " 'Ici' means 'here'; 'repose' means 'reposes' and—"

"What does it all mean in English?"

" 'Here reposes Jean Moveau, born January 21, 1843.' The next inscription reads, 'and Belle Mastero, beloved of Jean Moveau, born January 5, 1845.' The last line means, 'closed forever.' "

"Husband and wife, Emile?"

"Not in the true sense; that is, the law would not recognize them as such, although the community, without one exception, did."

Grace, not seeming to understand, stood before Emile, her blue eyes searching his. He turned his head intentionally; so she stood on her tiptoe and, reaching up with her small hand, gently turned his face and looked directly into his eyes, which were moist. They were in the old St. Louis Cemetery. The hot sun beamed on the whitewashed tombs, which in turn reflected the heat in all directions. Some tombs of all descriptions were so old that they had sunk almost to their full height into the soft earth, completely burying the inscriptions on the marble fronts; while others were of recent construction, since it was the year 1861, and this community had been visited by many yellow fever epidemics in the past ten years. And, too, many tombs housed the bodies of notable personages, and still another held the two wives and one child of a famous Governor of Louisiana.

Grace's reaction, amid these surroundings, was a feeling of tenderness and bewilderment, especially when she glanced at her companion's sad face and asked, "Emile, please, what is the story?"

He, hearing the sadness of her voice, answered, "I'm sorry, Grace! I didn't mean to sadden you, but—"

"Please, Emile, let's go."

She, a girl of twenty-two, from the North, had heard the history of the Creoles from Emile. Only the day before she had been a guest at a Creole wedding. She was in love with Emile, having for the first time been initiated into the manners and culture of a Creole, whose life is dedicated to the feminine sex, women being, in his eyes, God's greatest creation.

They had ridden together to and from the wedding on the rear seat of a barouche. Adele, a girl more than ninety-nine per cent white, married Pierre, who was entirely white. Their wedding would have been illegal in Louisiana; so they had driven to Mississippi, where Adele was unknown.

Grace's deep affection and honesty of purpose displayed the day before had quickly found a response from Emile, who, in the barouche, had held her in his arms during the long trip, while he softly caressed her smooth face and neck, occasionally placing a kiss on her lips, eyes, nose, and finger tips—just often enough to cause her affectionate nature to desire more—so much so, that her movements were ever responsive to his.

Together, hand in hand, these two, Emile with bowed head, and Grace, in silence, slowly walked past the tombs, out of the cemetery to the barouche, where Emile had tethered the beautiful twin roan horses to a hitching post.

Having placed her on the front seat, Emile was untying the tether when Grace asked, "Shall I drive?"

"No thanks, I feel much better."

"I'm glad to see you more composed."

"I feel so much better, Grace, that now I can tell you their story."

"Wouldn't it be advisable to wait for another time?"

"It is quite long; and, if you don't mind, I should like to take you to my studio, which was Belle's home, and is exactly today as she left it; the furnishings were originally hers."

"My, that would be the ideal place! You know, when you read on that tomb, 'Closed Forever,' I realized they must have been great lovers and that their romance would be interesting."

While Grace was talking, Emile was driving through narrow streets, passing beautiful brick mansions, built directly on the sidewalk, with their old patios or backyard gardens seen through the carriage entrances. Over the sidewalks were porches, where castiron lace-work, made by slaves, abound in many intricate designs. From the banquettes (sidewalks), black and colored slaves happily waved to Emile and Grace. Before the War Between the States and in this little community of tranquility, everyone knew each other. Presently the barouche was driven into one of those carriage entrances; and before the horses had really come to a stop, a slave was holding their bridle.

Emile quickly stepped out and in a moment was at Grace's side, helping her to alight. They went up four steps; then he opened a large mahogany door that led into a white hall with a high ceiling, from which hung a superbly designed crystal chandelier with its many candles.

Grace entered; Emile, following and placing his arm around her shoulder, gently guided her to his studio. On the walls were oils, among them paintings of Robert E. Lee; Bienville, the founder of the city; and a girl with exquisitely shaped features, her jet black curly hair falling to her bare shoulders and then spreading seemingly in an effort to conceal the rounded beauty, the outline plainly showing. Her eyes were large and dark, neither blue nor black, but very expressive under long lashes and seemed to follow one from every angle of the large room. The artist, one of the most renowned of that time, had begged and pleaded for months with the subject's parents for permission to paint her, as did other artists of the day. Her parents were adamant in refusing, for, as they said, "Permit one and we shall have to permit all, since all are our friends." They finally consented to an oil being made of her only on condition that the picture would remain a family possession. Since the artists really wanted it for personal purposes, none would accept, except the celebrated one who felt he would have the satisfaction of painting the most beautiful girl in New Orleans—a colored girl over ninety-eight per cent white.

Looking further, Grace noticed an old rosewood secretary which was open; many papers, brown with age, protruded from every pigeon hole. Behind the upper doors and through the glass one could see old books, all printed in France, and every one of which bore evidence of having been handled over and over again.

Turning, Grace saw a large door over which was a very large fan-shaped transom that hung down, supported by heavy hand-forged hinges, permitting an abundance of air to enter from the patio, which was abloom with tropical flowers of all varieties and hues. In the center was a beautiful fountain, with a marble statue of a nude woman on a pedestal pouring water from a ewer. The outer rim was encircled with jets forcing streams high into the air; the spray blown against the pale green fronds of the banana trees later fell on the purple flowers of the wisteria, the drops glistening in the noonday sun like beads of pearl. In a corner was a large yellow and black spider in the center of a beautiful symmetrical web four feet or more in diameter; the web glistened from the fine spray as though covered with millions of jewels, the color changing with every motion of the web caused by the soft, light summer wind. It was a scene one would never imagine there, judging from the outside appearance of the mansion; yet it held such beauty as would inspire a poet.

Grace's face was aglow; and, turning, she smiled at Emile and again faced the patio as though looking for fairies. Emile was most pleased with her reaction, for secretly he aspired to make her mistress of all of this. He startled her with, "Grace, you like it?"

"I love it, all of it. My! I'd love to live here forever." Realizing the inference, since she and Emile were sweethearts, she unconsciously placed her hand to her mouth and said, blushing, "Emile, I don't mean—"

, "Yes, you do, Grace; and I hope very soon to see whether you're a lady of your word. This house formerly belonged to Belle Mastero's parents; and this very room was hers, exactly as you see it now with its rare old books, its borderless rug, its beautiful mahogany tester bed, its chaise lounge, its—"

"Pardon me, may I sit in it?"

"By all means, Grace; but wait. Let me turn it so that it faces

my rocker. There, now make yourself comfortable; that's it."
Grace sank into the down-filled loose cushion, covered with blue
brocaded velvet, and as her beautiful glistening, golden tresses
rested on the dark covering, in perfect contract, Emile continued,
"Grace, you are beautiful."

"Beautiful? How can you possibly say that when you have
such a picture as this?"—pointing to the picture of the colored
girl. "Tell me," she continued, "Who is she?"

"It is Belle."

"The one marked 'Beloved' in the cemetery?"

"The same, Grace."

"And does the name 'Belle' have a special meaning? You
see, I've never heard that name before."

"It does have a special meaning. You see, when she was born,
her head was covered with jet black hair that immediately curled
after her head was dry. In handing her to her mother, the proud
woman said, 'Elle est belle,' meaning, 'She's beautiful.' Later,
when visitors came to see the baby, they also used the same
expression with the consequence that someone suggested the
name; so over the old brass and copper fount at the Saint Louis
Cathedral she was christened Belle."

"Very appropriate; and you knew her?"

"Personally, and also Jean; in fact, I was so closely connected
that I knew their every secret, every thought, as you will realize
as I unfold their romance to you."

"I know what Belle looked like. What was Jean's appearance?"

"He was a powerful man, but not what you would call handsome. His eyes were as blue as yours, with the same expression
of affection, an inheritance from his father, a nobleman from
Normandy. His complexion was also like that of his father—fair.
From his mother, he inherited a spirit of charity that was a
by-word in this section."

"That characterization alone would denote a good man."

"Yes, it would; but, let me start at their childhood, for it was
then that their devotion for each other began. I believe it the
equal of any in history or in fiction."

"Equal to that of Romeo and Juliet?"

"I believe so, Grace."

CHAPTER II

BELLE

"You know, to begin with, I must go back to seventeen years before Belle's birth. Her mother, Blanche by name, was the child of a colored woman well over ninety per cent white, whose protector, or boy friend, was a white young man nineteen years of age. One year after Blanche was born this young man married a Creole, with the result that her mother committed suicide. From that time Blanche was reared by the young man and his parents, who had grown to love her as though she were their legitimate heir. She grew to womanhood, and when she was eighteen year old, she accompanied them on a trip to Brazil where she met a wealthy young Spaniard named Antonio Mastero, who almost instantly realized that he loved her.

"On one of their rides he proposed marriage; and as she was colored, she refused, although she admitted she cared for him. She did not give the reason, for her grandparents had cautioned her against mentioning it on the trip, never once dreaming what would happen."

"She didn't have colored features?"

"No, Grace; in fact, she was so fair that her mother had christened her 'Blanche', meaning white."

"Oh! I see. What happened next?"

"Well, he made known his wishes to her grandparents and told them that he wished them to consider his proposal a few days, for he was compelled to visit his ranch.

"When he returned, they had unexpectedly left, much to Blanche's sorrow; but they had left a note, explaining in detail that their granddaughter was colored, and ended by expressing the wish that it remain a secret in Brazil. Blanche also left a note, confessing her love completely and ended by asking his forgiveness for not having informed him at the beginning of her true status.

"After he had read the notes, he immediately sold his ranch to a party whom we afterwards found to be his brother, chartered a small boat, and set sail for this city, arriving one week ahead of them, since their boat made other coastal stops.

"You can imagine their surprise and Blanche's elation when from the deck of the ship they recognized Antonio, who, after the gang plank had been lowered, raced up to Blanche and threw his arms around her."

"This happened seventeen years ago, Emile?"

"Yes, Grace, seventeen years ago they were married."

"Isn't there a law in Louisiana prohibiting colored and white marrying?"

"Yes, there is; but Antonio when asked if he was colored or white, when applying for a marriage license, promptly answered colored. His adoration for Blanche was such that he would have gone to any length to make her his bride; and since she reciprocated his love by changing her religion, there would be no confession. So his statement that he was colored would go unchallenged and remain a secret."

"Oh, I see; and were they happy?"

"One of the most affectionate, loving and unselfish couples I've known; both had the same temperaments; and, Grace, it is necessary that I explain to you a bit of science so that you'll understand Belle better. You see, when both parents of a child have, for instance, weak lungs, that weakness doubles in the child with the consequence that it is subject to lung disease. The same holds true for the heart or any other organs of the body; so in Belle, that affection, the desire to love and be loved, together with complete unselfishness, was doubled, so to speak, with the consequence that her temperament was just as remarkable as her beauty. She was truly an unusual child."

"And she lived in this house?"

"Yes; she was born on the second floor, in the front room."

"And where are her parents?"

"They are living now in Brazil."

"This is a personal question: Are you keeping this home for them?"

"No, you see when they left, I accompanied them to the boat. When we had completed our farewell, they gave me an envelope which I was asked not to open until I had reached home. On examining its contents I was amazed to find a deed transferring the house to me. Also I found a note asking me to occupy it, for they would prefer knowing that a friend was in their home."

"My, that was wonderful of them; they must have liked you very much; in fact, as far as I can judge, everybody likes you."

"Well, I do have many friends; but, Grace, I'm particularly interested in only one liking me now."

"As far as she is concerned, she loves you and is candid enough to admit it. But tell me about Belle."

"Well, just next door, in that very house, lived a couple who had a boy. They had bought a slave woman as a wet nurse. The boy was two years old at the time Belle was born, past nursing age; so the slave was sold to Belle's parents, who used her for nursing Belle. It afterward developed that it was the slave's idea—for after she had seen the black-haired baby girl, she seemed to have but one desire and that was 'to hold her to her breast'. It wasn't long before she came to love the white child like her own."

"I imagine that was only natural."

"Yes, it was; and that love influenced Belle's entire career, for, since all Negro and some colored people were taught from the time they learned to speak to understand chanting and to chant themselves, it was only natural that the slave taught her ward that science."

"Science, Emile?"

"Yes, it is quite a science. You see, those folks used chanting as a means to convey secrets, that is, secrets from the white people, for through chanting they could give messages to other folks of their kind, these messages being interposed among hymns and other chants; they were senseless to those not initiated."

"And no one taught the whites?"

"No, for the reason that Marie Laveau, the queen of the Voodoos, forbade them to do so; and to incur her wrath was akin to suicide. She was dead by this time, and there was no one to replace her immediately. So Belle's nurse was free to teach the child; and an exceedingly good job she made of it, for we find Belle at the age of six chanting to the boy next door. She started by using a hymn. Now and then an experienced chanter interpreted her, asking what were six and three. Listening, one would hear the boy answer something like this, 'I was playing marbles, and playing for keeps, and I won nine.' This, Grace, he sang to any notes that came to his mind."

"I see; but wasn't he the one who was also nursed by Belle's nurse?"

"Yes, the same one, and his name was Jean."

"Oh, I see, what a wonderful thing, those two nursed by the same woman and yet they were not related! But tell me, who taught the boy chanting?"

CHAPTER III

JEAN

"Jean when three years old became an orphan through losing his father at sea. He had grown to be so attached to his governess, a former school teacher, that his mother, when she remarried, left him with her, placing the property in his name in trust since her husband's duties called him to New York. Every month Mam'selle Delphine received an allowance for his support. Since she also taught others and had a fair income, the allowance was banked in Jean's name. Mam'selle Delphine, an octoroon, had learned chanting when a child. She was well educated, for her time; so it was natural that other colored people constantly sought her advice; and much of their conversation was carried on in the form of chanting.

"Since she was without relatives, it was only natural that she lavished all of her love on Jean, just as the slave nurse lavished hers on Belle.

"Since the two women seemed to live only for Jean and Belle, it was natural that they should interest themselves in the children's future. As I later found out, the nurse and the governess were in constant communication from the day the slave began nursing Belle, planning their future which was to have them live together as man and wife, especially since some rumors were afloat to the effect that the Louisiana legislature would repeal the law prohibiting the marriage of colored and white persons, since pressure was being brought to bear by influential white men who were interested in colored girls over ninety per cent white.

"One of the first things the two women did was to teach chanting to the children, for with that art they could converse or express themselves freely; and Grace, we must bear in mind that all of their actions—I mean those of the governess and the nurse—were motivated by what one might well call maternal love, even though the children had not been born to them."

"I can understand that, Emile; but didn't Belle's mother, Blanche, since she was colored, know chanting?"

"No, for the reason that she had been reared by her white grandparents."

"Oh! yes, that is right; I had forgotten."

"And her father, being a Brazilian, never had heard of it, as it was only a custom here."

"But one would imagine that Belle as a child would have told her parents the secret of chanting."

"She did try as a youngster, I mean when she was three years old; but her father, who knows about it now, told me that he thought it was a childish idea, as children are fond of imagining things; so he paid no attention to her. Of course, we can understand how, especially when she attended school, she realized what a wonderful tool she had and the necessity of keeping it a secret. To cite one instance, let me tell you about the time she mounted a spirited horse that was tethered to the hitching post you saw outside. Jean, Belle, and I have often discussed this case. The horse began to balk and kick and Belle realized she was about to fall and probably be trod upon. To receive help from her parents would have meant chastisement, while to chant her difficulties to Jean meant instant succor and, of course, sympathy for her bruises should she sustain any."

"The little devil. But chanting for her school problems certainly didn't help her education."

"You forget, Grace, that Mam'selle Delphine heard those chants, and when she realized they were detrimental to Belle's education, she quickly interposed, for after the twelfth grade, she had taught the children the various sciences; such as botany, astronomy, geology, physics, and the anatomy of the human body; you notice, Grace, how interested these women were, especially Mam'selle Delphine, in keeping the children constantly in each other's company."

CHAPTER IV.

Their Childhood

"You know, Emile, if we did not understand that their intentions were honorable we should condemn them for secretly plotting."

"Especially if you knew all of their plots. For instance, Grace, when Belle was seven years old, the women had planned and put into effect an act that was tri-fold in its result. Each afternoon, after their baths, they sent the children to the Cathedral; they walked there hand in hand; and Jean, like a little gentleman, took the best of care of little Belle. Upon entering the church, Jean reached for the Holy Water, putting some on her fingers so that she could make the sign of the cross too; again, we find Belle depending upon Jean.

"These visits not only placed the children together from a religious standpoint, which certainly had a moral and psychological effect, but also definitely prevented a twenty-four hour separation, for every day they were in each other's company at least once."

"But, you said it had a triple effect. One we know was Belle's dependence and Jean's guardianship. Another was daily association. Now what was the third?"

"The confidence of Belle's parents since, although Protestant, they reasoned that religion could harm no one, regardless of its denomination. As the women sent the children to church, her parents were pleased. Their confidence was such that they placed Belle almost entirely in their hands.

"As for Jean, Mam'selle Delphine had taught him that the feminine sex was gentle and their every whim, their every desire should be fulfilled by man; and further, that their comfort and ease should be of paramount importance. You see, Grace, this teaching was not only done by word of mouth, but was also inculcated by Mam'selle Delphine's seeing that her instructions were carried out. She began these lessons practically in his babyhood."

Grace, who had been listening intently, now realized why Emile treated her with so much courtesy; and the thought flashing through her mind that it was possibly Creole culture and not love that prompted his actions, made her frown, as though she were in pain.

Emile, seeing this, arose immediately, and in a moment, was sitting by her side on the chaise lounge.

"Please, honey," he blurted, resting on both elbows and holding Grace's head gently in both hands, "what ails you?"

"Oh, Emile, I begin to realize that your attentions are Creole mannerisms and not what I thought they were."

"Why Grace, you silly little darling! See, I kiss the two tears that have collected in your heavenly blue eyes. And then your pretty lips."

Grace, feeling a sudden ecstacy, immediately threw both arms around Emile's neck, holding him tightly. They might have remained so indefinitely had not Emile suddenly broken the charm by gently removing her arms, and kissing her again. Then he asked, "Shall I continue the story?"

"Please, Emile," was her simple answer.

"You know, Grace, seeing those tears in your eyes together with your hurt expression reminds me of a similar expression caused by one of Belle's escapades, one that her father called cute. It seemed that Belle had a habit of leaning out of the attic window. I say attic window, but that third story consisted of four rooms, since the large attic was ceiled, floored and partitioned; and it was as livable as any other part of the house. The reason for this style of architecture was for the purpose of paying taxes on only two stories. This system is universal in this French Quarter. However, Belle had been admonished repeatedly by her parents, who explained the danger of leaning out of the windows; but, like all children, admonishing is as far as it went. Then, too, there was the possibility of Jean's being near should she find herself in trouble, and he would immediately answer her chant requesting aid. This day she leaned too far and losing her balance, slid onto the roof. Grasping the window sill with one hand, she was able to avoid slipping further. But neither could she draw herself back into the window. In fear, she began chanting at the top of her childish voice, looking

to the right and left for Jean, who was in the rear of his home.
Although Jean heard her, it so happened that her father, who was
in the second story, heard her voice coming from the direction
of the attic rooms, and, like all fathers of a mischievous child,
feared for the worst. He raced up the stairs and peering at the
window saw her predicament and was, for once, the first to reach
her; so, you see, may I repeat, that her dependence on Jean
was such as to be conducive to mischievousness and the consequence was such that she was constantly seeking Jean's aid.
These continual happenings, psychologically speaking, created
in Belle, a feeling of dependency; and in Jean, one of protection."

"Emile, you say continual happenings?"

"That's right, Grace; one could never guess what Belle would
do next, for even as a young girl she had shown exceptional will
power. It was only from Jean that she accepted advice."

"Was she in love?"

"No one knew at that time, for accepting advice and help from
Jean might have been a reaction caused by his constant protection, a protection that was responsible for her reaching womanhood safe and sound, because at sixteen we find her being consulted by her parents with reference to receiving young men
friends, evidently with a view of marriage."

"You mean they wished her to give up Jean?"

"Well, it seems that Belle's parents believed that Jean and
Belle were only friends, for I later discovered that love was never
mentioned between them; and I believe that had they been asked
about it they would have answered that they really didn't know.
It seems, too, that the colored women had hinted marriage at
one time or other; but since Belle and Jean were both young and
since they were constantly in each other's company, one would
imagine that they experienced a subconscious satisfaction when
neither went with the opposite sex. If and when one of them
did, as would probably happen in the future, they would cer-
taintly experience a change, for then they would be awakened to
the stark realism of what their lives really meant to each other."

"And, what did happen?"

CHAPTER V

A Great Awakening

"Well, as I've remarked before, our State forbids marriage of white and colored persons, so that Belle's parents naturally wanted her to marry a colored man, let us say, at least her equal in percentage of white blood, as in Belle's case, ninety-eight and one-half or, to put it demically, 98.4375 white; the difference between her mother of 96.875 and 100 per cent for her white father."

"But, Emile, that ninety-eight and one-half is practically white and certainly wouldn't really have made any difference."

"I know that, Grace; and yet, since it was the law, they were compelled to abide by it. I sincerely believe that this was one reason why Belle's parents never once dreamed of anything but friendship existed between her and Jean, for Jean was a real Creole, reared in an atmosphere of Creole culture with its ideals. So he believed in justice; and, whether love or friendship existed between them, he would have stepped aside so as to permit a legal marriage, as he confided to me when later seeking advice. You see, it was only natural that her parents concerned themselves with her future."

"And when did they do that?"

"On her sixteenth birthday. They called her into the parlor and explained that the time had come when she should be thinking of making a home for herself."

"Wasn't sixteen rather young?"

"No, that age was not too young when one considers that a courtship in this section lasted about four years; twenty years of age was not too young to marry."

"What was her reaction?"

"She told me that she acquiesced to dispose of the subject until she was able to consider it further, so when in trouble, she did what she always had done. She immediately chanted a favorite hymn; and when she felt safe, she chanted to Jean her parents' request. Jean's mind made a quick decision, which was that she should meet him in my home, reasoning that since I was a disinterested party and further as I had known them and their fami-

"And they came?"

lies for years, I could possibly be able to reach a just decision."
my slave had let them in. So you can imagine my surprise when
I entered and saw them. Belle was seated on the sofa; Jean, on
a chair. They greeted me with 'Hello, Emile!'

" 'Hello Damon and Pythias,' was my reply.

" 'Is it Damon and Pythias, Emile?'

" 'I've often wondered, Jean. What do you think, Belle?'

" 'Emile, I'm sure I don't know. I'm so worried that I just
can't think. I told Jean my dilemma, and he recommended that
we come to you.'

" 'Told or chanted? You see I know your secret.'

" 'Chanted, Emile.'

" 'Well, since you've come to me for advice, suppose you tell
me your troubles.'

" 'Mother and especially father insist that I receive young men
with a view to courting. I've refused all callers for over a year,
because I knew none who wouldn't bore me; as you know, all of
us are acquainted with each other in this small community.'

" 'I see, since you two don't know whether it's a Damon and
Pythias friendship, you are equally ignorant of the possibility of
its being love. What has been your reaction, Jean, considering
you are white?'

" 'It was terrible; I already feel as though I've lost everything
in the world; in fact, I feel such a loneliness that if I were a
woman I'd burst into tears. And yet, I do not now know whether
my affection for Belle is love; and, even if I did, my duty
towards her would be to aid her in becoming a legally wedded
wife. My God, Emile, what a thought!'

" 'That remark alone, Jean, requires much thought; and the
fact that your expression was full of pain would further corrobo-
rate it, as did the smile that flashed over Belle's face, something
that you possibly don't know. I've often thought of you two, as
many in our little town have, and my reasoning has always led
me to the conclusion that someone would, to use my favorite
expression, get hurt. Since this has struck you as a bombshell, I
recommend that you postpone a decision until your hearts have
time to determine the true status of the case. Now, if I thought
I'd influence you two, I'd avoid telling you what I know will be
the outcome. In other words, knowing definintely the inevitable
decision you two will reach, I am not influencing you.'

" 'What will be the outcome?' asked Jean as he stopped in front of me, as he had been pacing back and forth.

"Grace, the blood had left his lips, and they were trembling. Belle, still seated, was twisting her handkerchief into knots, and I could see that she was biting her lips. Realizing what those symptoms meant, I replied, 'Before I answer, I wish you, Jean, to sit next to Belle. That's right, right there. You two are as nervous as cats, and I want you to take a drink. What shall it be, Belle?'

" 'I'll just take a sip from Jean's glass.'

" 'A sip from Jean's glass, eh! Still depending on Jean to make your decisions. And you, Jean, what shall it be?'

" 'Soda and whiskey.'

"I mixed the drink and handed it to Jean, remarking that I had made it somewhat strong so that it might not only quiet their nerves, but also sharpen their wits. I told them that I had found that drinking liquor, up to a certain point, had that effect on me. I was paying particular attention as to how, or rather, the manner he would give her the sip. Watching him closely, I noticed that his hand was trembling, only until the glass was near her lips, when, with extreme care, he gently placed it where she could sip. When she had had enough, she made a motion and then placing the glass, the part that had touched her lips, against his, he drained it as though it were water. 'Now Emile,' he said, 'What's the verdict? I feel as though I am a convicted man.'

" 'Well, to begin with, you two have known each other for ten years; and during that time Belle has relied upon you for all decisions, even minor ones, as she has so well proved when she said she would sip from your glass, permitting you to make the decision as to the liquor; and you, Jean, have rendered those decisions, accepting the responsibility as though Belle belonged to you, taking it for granted, as did Belle also, that this condition would continue through life. No doubt, now and then, both of you questioned that; but I believe you brushed it aside as an unpleasant thought, realizing that each would be lost without the other. The proof of it is that at the slightest inkling of a separation you both went completely to pieces.

" 'As I have said before, I've been expecting this and had

reached a conclusion long ago. My answer to both of you is definitely love in its most profound and unselfish form. Those words are not adequate to express the devotion that you two will experience from this night on for, again in your subconscious minds there has been growing, minute by minute, day by day, and month by month, since childhood, an understanding which is now so deeply rooted that regardless of consequences no storm, no matter what its intensity, could possibly destroy it. As I've said before, all of this grew in the subconscious mind and is now bursting forth in tempestous fury in the conscious mind since it has found an opening, that opening being the possibility of a separation. You, Belle, and you, Jean, have been made cowards by love and adoration; but, as what I've told you this night becomes more comprehensive, you two will become extremely brave, realizing that, like a soldier defending his home, you have more than existence to fight for.'

"You know, Grace, when I'd finished talking, and I talked with complete conviction that they might absorb the truth, for I loved them both as my two dearest friends, I turned to prepare a whiskey and soda for myself, my nerves then being on edge, when I was suddenly turned around by powerful Jean, who kissed me squarely on the lips, followed by Belle who threw her arms about my neck and sobbingly thanked me. She was beautiful, Grace, more than beautiful—so much so, that I found myself wondering how so much beauty could be in one human being, especially after seeing her in tears."

"You know, Emile, you could write of her?"

"I'd fail, Grace, for the public enjoys reading of people like themselves, that is average people; not a woman like Belle."

"With so much beauty, it's surprising that other suitors did not force themselves on her."

"They tried, in every conceivable manner. At least eight of them approached me. One, in particular, a handsome man over ninety-nine per cent white, René Guichard, by name, called on me only recently and actually offered me part interest in his plantation if with my assistance he would be successful in marrying her."

"And what was your answer?"

"To the effect that if I could be of service he need not pay me.

I further suggested that he do all in his power to forget her as I was positive her fate was sealed and that no coercing, no presents, no persuasion, nor anything else could possibly change or alter matters."

"Did he take your advice?"

"No, for René still managed to force himself into the family pew every Sunday, encouraged, of course, by her parents."

"Emile, tell me, as Belle was sixteen years old, and Jean eighteen, wasn't it possible that sexual desires at one time or another had crossed their minds?"

"I'm certain I can answer in the negative, for the women in the ninety per cent and above were reared strictly as the Creole girls were, that is, in perfect ignorance of sex; and men like Jean were taught from very babyhood that those of the feminine sex, to repeat, were God's greatest creatures and to permit a sex thought concerning any of their feminine friends to enter their minds would have been as abnoxious as having one in regard to one's sister."

"You don't mean that their instruction really began from babyhood?"

"I certainly do, for I well remember my mother's method when her friends visited us; their baby girl was placed in the same carriage with my brother, and he was made to understand that his trinkets were to be given to the girl to play with. This sounds far-fetched, Grace, but it is the truth. However, let's get back to Belle and Jean."

CHAPTER VI

REFLECTION

"When they left, I shook their hands and wished them good luck, ending by admonishing them that they had a grave problem to solve and that, although they themselves should make their own decision, they were free to call on me at any time. The night was black except for the flickering of the gaslights; fire-flies moved to and fro seeming to add to the scant illumination by which they were to wend their way homeward. Since it had rained, the gutters and narrow muddy streets were filled with water. The night was extremely silent and that silence was broken only by the occasional song of a frog seemingly calling for more rain. In the distance shone the faint glow from the lamp of a horse-car; and to the right and left were strongly bolted battened windows. Now and then a slave silently went past on his master's business.

"Along the deserted street Belle and Jean walked hand in hand in deep reflection. Occasionally, some pleasant thought made Jean squeeze Belle's white soft hand. Promptly she acknowl-edged it. On they walked until they reached the corner where the wooden banquette that served for a sidewalk had been washed away, and there they stopped. Stooping, Jean gently raised her in both his arms while she instinctively placed her arm about his neck. Neither broke the silence, a silence that to them was something holy, for had not God placed them together since their childhood. When they reached the banquette on the op-posite side Jean gently placed her on her feet and they resumed their walk hand in hand, just as the Cathedral clock was striking the midnight hour. Overhead lightning flashes revealed the black rolling clouds that seemed to melt instantly into rain as if to drench the earth. Running, still hand in hand, they reached and took shelter in the vestibule of the Cabildo, facing Jackson Square and the turbulent Mississippi; and they began thinking how they were moving like the great river to a destiny unknown. They stood there still in silence, a beautiful, understandable silence. Presently the lamp man advanced with his small ladder to relight the blown-out gas lamp; and, as he left, a barouche filled with sailors rolled towards the river. Later, a gig with a longely occupant, possibly a doctor, rolled from out of the darkness back into blackness. And as those wheels turned so did the wheels of that old Cathedral clock. How long they had been there, neither would have known had not the clock struck two; nor had they realized the rain had ceased and the beautiful heaven was again aglow with stars."

"That was beautiful. Please, what happened next?" Emile paused, seeming to live the scene himself.

"Well, Grace, they finally reached home and stopped. Jean reached for Belle's free hand, and holding both in his, whispered, 'Belle, we have come to a beautiful understanding, and I want you to retire and sleep if you can, for tomorrow may be an eventful day for you and me.'"

CHAPTER VII

A Prayer

"When Belle entered, her second mother met her. Not speaking a word, she led the girl to her room. While Belle was disrobing, the old mammy was busy turning down the coverlet on the bed—a coverlet she had made with her own hands especially for her 'chile'. Throwing aside the linen sheets, Belle slipped quietly into bed while mammy covered her as she would a baby.

" 'Don't talk, chile,' she said as Belle's lips began to move. 'I knows all about it. Tomorrow I'll go to see Mr. Emile for you; he'll tell us what to do.'

" 'We've been there, mammy.'

" 'You and Jean?'

" 'Yes, both of us.'

" 'He fixed it?'

" 'Yes, mammy.'

" 'I'se glad. I had de mis'ry ever since yo chanted. Now say yo prayers and go to sleep, honey chile.' So saying, she opened the door leading to her room and retired, leaving Belle, who rose, walked to the *prie-dieu*, knelt, and prayed. Listening, the old slave heard her say:

" 'God, my Father, I beseech Thee on bended knees to lead Jean and me in the future as You have done in the past. I pray Thee not to separate us, my God. But, should it be Your will to do so, I ask Thee to take us both to Thy home, Thy breast. Amen.'

"So saying, she tiptoed back to bed, slipped under the coverlet, and lay there, not to sleep, but to think—to think that without Jean life could not go on. She was glad she had asked God to take them to His home. Then the thought came, if that were His will where would their bodies be placed? Shuddering, she called, 'Mammy!'

" 'Yes, Chile, I'se comin'. What yo want, Honey?'

" 'Mammy, I've asked God to take us rather than to separate

us; and, Mammy, should He do it, probably by the next epidemic, promise me that you will see that we are placed together.'

" 'Honey Chile, I promise. But look, de light keeps burnin' in Jean's room.'

" 'I know, I've been watching. He loves me, Mammy, and I love him—hear me, love—love it is'—and turning over she buried her head in her pillow and sobbed, her slim body moving convulsively. Mammy, that dark black Mammy stooped and petted her.

" 'Yo should be happy, honey. Now turn over, let me wipe yo tears; there now. You knows, honey, what I'd do?'

" 'No, Mammy, what would you do?'

" 'I'd goes to my man and tells him to take me, bring me where he want, does what he want wid me, but takes me.'

" 'That would be sinning, Mammy.'

" 'Not when two peoples loves like you two does.'

" 'We do love each other; my, for the first time in my life my entire body thrilled when he squeezed my hand. Mammy, maybe I shouldn't say it, but I was wishing that he would throw his arms about me, that he would squeeze me and kiss me. That would have been heaven. And, Mammy, you know what he did when Emile told him that our affection for each other was not friendship, but love?'

" 'What he do?'

" 'He turned Emile around and kissed him right on the lips.'

" 'He do?'

" 'Yes, Mammy.'

" 'And what yo do?'

" 'I was crying, and I threw my arms around Emile's neck and thanked him.'

" 'Yo both was glad it was love?'

" 'Yes, and now, I don't know whether to be happy or sad.'

"Yo be happy, chile. Now der candle is burnin' out. Go to sleep. Goodnight, honey.' "

CHAPTER VIII

PRACTICAL JEAN

"When Belle entered her door, Jean remained outside until he felt she had reached her room. Then he turned to his door, entered, and proceeded to his room from which he could look down into hers. Yes, the candle was lighted; and unless he judged incorrectly, it would remain so for some time. Falling into his favorite rocker, he permitted his head to rest in both hands and began to muse.

" 'What a fool I've been! Practical Jean, I'm called—practical. And yet, maybe it was better—yes better that it should be romance now that I'm eighteen than at fifteen or sixteen as with other Creoles who choose colored girls as mistresses. Yet, still I cannot understand why I've never had the urge to love, hold, pet, caress, and kiss—kiss, my what a pleasure that would have been—pleasure? Hell, no; that would have been heaven— heaven? No, that would have been wrong; or—would it? Let's see, be practical again, Jean, be practical. Reason this thing out. Now first, does she love me? There's no doubt about that, for didn't she cry when Emile said it was undoubtedly love; and my, how beautiful she was when I placed my handkerchief to her eyes, and how sad they were when she summoned up sufficient courage to look at me. The sadly smiling lips all but said kiss me, kiss me! Me, I should kiss them! Who am I that I should kiss them, give them their first kiss! No, My God, no, not I—but—oh hell, here I go butting my head again—practical Jean; and yet, 'tis true, if two people desire a thing and that thing only concerns them, harming no one, then practically speaking, they should have it.

" 'Let's see, would God have condoned my action? Well, He's our Father; and since our Father wants us to be happy, since He wants us to receive every good thing life can give, He would, as I would for my children, condone it. Under that condition, I have done Belle an injustice by abstaining—oh hell, what's the use, you can't think now, Jean. Go to sleep—sleep! How odd, that can't be done! I know—liquor. Emile said liquor up to a certain extent sharpens the wits. Liquor—that's it—whiskey and soda—and a cigarette.

" 'Now, back to my darling, Belle. Let's see, we love each other—that's definite. She knows it; I know it, and Emile knows it. Now, what shall we do—what can we do? Maybe if I could talk to her—Yes, her candle is still burning—No, damn it, it isn't, I have just seen it go out. Jean, a troubled mind can't think—another drink, straight this time, and another and another—more, more, more—enough; now, to bed.' "

CHAPTER IX

Too Damn Dangerous

"Grace, I would have condemned Jean for that drinking had I not realized that since Belle relied upon him to do the thinking for her, he had, so to speak, a double load on his mind—that is—"

"I know, to be in her shoes' and also his."

"That's right, with the consequence that he had become weary; and weariness of the mind is synonymous with muscle-weariness, both cases bordering on collapse. Ordinarily, Jean was not a drinking man; but he, like others of his day, kept whiskey and soda in his home. However, what I've told you was the way his act was explained to me. Grace, those two were as honest, clean, unselfish, and just as any couple I've ever known."

"Do you think we can be that way?"

"You have been; I've tried."

"What do you mean, you've tried? Remember, I know what you did for Jeanne and Paul. You see, you have me placing the girl's name first."

"Yes, I've noticed that. But now to answer your question— I know this entire story; and, as everyone with a secret that need not be one any longer is eager to tell it—so am I. Now then, since you are the one I care for most, I want naturally to unburden my story to you."

"Unburden, Emile? I believe it's your turn to say 'I'm sorry.'"

"All right, I'm sorry. Do you forgive me?"

"On one condition only."

"What may that be?"

"That you kiss me."

"Then, I consider myself forgiven, for here it is—one, two, three, as Jeanne once said Paul kissed her."

"But those are sweetheart kisses."

"What kind do you want?"

"Marriage ones."

"But, we're not married."

"Please, Emile."

"No, Grace; it's too damn dangerous."

"Why?"

"Because this story has had a terrible effect on us, and subconsciously we are permitting it to get the better of us."

"I never thought of it in that way."

"Because it was subconscious."

"Oh! I see. Then this is the reason I wanted to be hugged and loved and kissed."

"Yes, this is the reason everyone wants to be hugged and loved and kissed; it is the call of nature without which this earth would be depopulated."

"And when two people feel that way?"

"They should marry, Grace—er—er—if possible."

"And, if not possible?"

"Then, it's strictly up to the individual."

"And, also to society."

"Grace, I'm not speaking of Creole men in general, but of myself in particular when I tell you that, if I were one of two lovers that cared for each other devotedly—remember, I said devotedly—and were unable to wed, I would say, 'To hell with society.'"

"You might, at first—but not after you had considered it well —not you."

"But now the public has grown to be more reasonable."

"Is the public really more reasonable?"

"I think so."

"But, Emile, suppose we were parents?"

"If we were, we would naturally prefer to see our children marry. But, would we if we knew that their love for someone else was as true and lasting as, for instance, that of Belle and Jean, and that marriage was impossible? In other words, would we want our children unhappily married to someone they didn't love, which would inevitably turn to hate when one considers this kind of marriage, remembering the sexual duties they must perform. It must be misery even though they might 'fight it out for the sake of the children' who would be reared in an atmosphere of hate. In such a case the interested parties would invariably find someone more to their liking; and presto, intrigue, clandestine meetings, discovery, divorce, and disgrace for the entire family would follow."

"Even so, I still believe you'd think differently. But tell me, is it really you or Jean who is practical?"

"Both."

"And do you think we will love as much as they?"

"That's not a fair question, Grace; but we can try."

"Why try?"

"Well, because love actually and literally grew with Jean and Belle while you and I know each other only four days."

"But, as from the start we've loved, we'll hardly finish a bad second."

"Nicely said—but shall we continue the story?"

"Please, Emile."

CHAPTER X

A Realization

"Belle did not sleep, but preferred to lie awake, not thinking of the future, but exulting in the fact that she loved and was loved in return."

"Wouldn't one think that she would plan the future instead?"

"Hardly, for two reasons, as she explained to me. She answered when I asked her the same question, 'I've grown so accustomed to have Jean solve my problems and never once has he failed, that it is only natural I feel he will find a way out of this dilemma; and then, you know how I feel towards my religion. Since I prayed, as God knows I did, from the very bottom of my heart, I just feel that my prayer will be answered.'

"I then asked her if a doubt existed as to whether it might be friendship instead of love, a doubt that seems to cloud the mind of every lover. She replied, 'I could have accepted his action toward you when you pronounced it love as proof of his affection; but, if I knew nothing else, the trembling of his lips when I left you and looked into his eyes was most significant, although I really was disappointed in his not drawing me to him and holding me as though I were his.'"

"Did she sleep at all that night?"

"Not at all, for soon the sun shone through the fanshaped window; and rising, she peered across the brick wall to the room where Jean was sleeping and prepared for church. It was a beautiful, mild morning. Although it was midsummer, a gentle breeze was blowing from the Gulf, carrying with it as it entered her room the fragrance from the garden."

"It has the same flowers and plants today?"

"The annuals that don't reseed every year are re-planted; but the Louis Philippe roses, the wisteria, rosa montana, honeysuckle, trumpet, and ficus repens that climbs, spreads, clings, and covers every brick were planted by her when she was a child, and her mammy, since her mammy also had charge of the garden; she made Belle, with her little hands, fill in the earth so as to make her feel important, explaining that the plants would not grow unless they were planted by tender young hands. However, to return to the story—mammy helped her dress for early Mass at the Cathedral. As I was walking towards the French Market for my morning coffee, we met. 'Good-morning, Belle,' I said and continued, 'how did you get home through the rain?'

" 'Emile, that rain was wonderful.'

" 'Wonderful?' I asked.

" 'Yes, for Jean picked me up in his strong arms to cross the flooded street; and I felt a thrill I've never experienced before. I placed my arms around his neck; and when my eyes met his, he turned his head, but drew me tight—tight—tight—to him. As I held him close around his neck I placed my head next to his. I'll confess,' she continued, 'I was wishing all the banquettes were flooded.'

" 'It didnt take you too long to realize how much you really mean to each other.'

" 'I'm sure we do not know the extent and probably never will; but I've realized that in preference to leaving him, I prefer death; and so I've asked our Father to take us both from this earth.'

" 'You said us, Belle.'

" 'Yes, because I know the torture I would experience without him, and I would not want him to experience the same misery. I prefer that God take him first, for when my time would come, which would not be long after, I could close my eyes knowing that I was not leaving him.'

"Then I said, 'Belle, you seem certain of the extent of Jean's love?'

" 'Emile,' she answered, 'lovers, true lovers, feel and experience the same emotions, whether they are men or women.'

" 'When did you discover this?' I replied, knowing full well her answer, for I could see a seriousness now that was entirely new to her.

" 'Since he held me in his arms. His pressing me close to him caused me to place my face next to his.'

" 'Beautiful reasoning,' I answered, 'but the bells are ringing, and you had better hurry.'

"With that, off she went. I looked after and admired her as

did all whom she passed; the men removed their hats; the women bowed in return, for all knew her; and although they knew she was colored, they appreciated her attractiveness, purity, and religious devotion."

"From what you've told me, you were lucky to know her."

"I assure you, it was a plesaure to know her, but also to know Jean, who was equally admired, for he was charity itself, never refusing, under any circumstances, to be of aid to white or colored, male or female."

"May I interrupt?"

"Surely, Grace."

"Did Jean have admirers? I mean women who thought of him as a sweetheart?"

"Many—many, not so much for his appearance, although he was the equal in that sense to the average Creole, but more for his culture, refinement, and, as I've said before, true kindness. They realized, however, that his life seemed to be dedicated to Belle, especially since he was unconscious of their many wiles. It became common gossip that he was known by those that really knew him as practical. Then, too, he had been reared by a colored foster mother; and even though his birth certificate stated he was pure white, as it was recorded in the Cathedral, nevertheless, it did leave a subconscious reaction.

"Now, let us get back to Jean—he was awakened that morning by the strains of the organ over whose mellow tones he heard the voice of Belle, she having returned from Mass. She was singing the song of the battle cry of the French Republic, the Marseillaise. Never before did both voice and words thrill him as they did now. Her choice of song, too, was to him an omen of great significance. He had lain just as he had awakened so as not to miss a single note; and when the last strain had floated over the air, he jumped up and walked to the door. Opening it, he jarred it purposely so that Belle would know that he was awake. It wasn't long before he knew that she had heard him, for softly she began chanting hymns, in which she told him all that had happened since they had separated."

CHAPTER XI

A Rude Awakening

"She sang well, Emile?"

"Very well, Grace, having taken lessons from one of our best instructors."

"And did Jean answer her chant?"

"Not then, for he had received a message from me asking him to call at my home that evening at seven o'clock."

"Why did you send for him?"

"Because I had a visitor that morning, and I thought it better that he remain with me that evening."

"Don't keep me in suspense. What happened?"

"Well, Jean called and after a few pleasant remarks asked me my reason for summoning him. I told him that I knew he trusted me and that every move I made as far as he and Belle were concerned was purely in their interest. He admitted that, stating this was the reason why he always came to me for advice, ending with 'Emile, what's wrong?'

" 'Jean,' I said, 'I want you first to promise me that you will permit me to do your thinking for the next few hours.'

"Sensing that what I had in mind was serious, he replied, 'I promise.'

" 'Well,' I said, 'René is calling on Belle tonight.'

" 'What!' he roared, rising from his chair.

" 'Now, be seated, Jean, and don't forget your promise. Listen well to me for Belle knew nothing of this.'

" 'That's a relief, although I should have known better.'

" 'If you remember, when Belle's parents spoke of her receiving company, she said she had acquiesced so as to have time to consult you and to think.'

" 'Yes, I remember.'

" 'Well, her father invited René to call tonight, and René visited me this morning; hence my note to you.'

" 'And just what did he expect?'

" 'He expected plenty, but I had him sit in that same chair and reasoned with him for over an hour.'

" 'What did you two say?' And he continued, 'This is down-right hell.'

" 'It's not so bad as all that for, although Belle will conduct herself as a lady, I assure you she will in no uncertain terms convey the idea that he is only welcome as a friend; in fact, Jean, those were my exact words to him when he informed me of his invitation.'

" 'What was the conversation?'

" 'Why, when he first entered I thought I recognized a smile of triumph. He started with, 'Well, Emile, I've received an invitation from Belle.'

" 'Not from Belle,' I said

" 'Then from whom?' he asked.

" 'From her parents. You know, René, you came to me once before on this same mission. Do you remember my suggestion?'

" 'Yes, I do; but I'm afraid my heart won't take your advice.'

" 'You know what will happen?'

" 'No, I don't.'

" 'Do you want me to tell you?'

" 'Yes, do.'

" 'René, you're in love, and you honestly believe it to be what we might call maximum. That's right?'

" 'Yes, I don't think I could care more.'

" 'Well, you can; and unless you protect yourself now, you will find that each day you entertain the possibility of Belle's becoming a sweetheart of yours, your affection will increase to such an extent that when the truth eventually dawns upon you, you will receive a severe blow, one that might prove fatal; Jean and Belle were here to visit me last night, and there is an affection between them that can and only will be dissolved by death.'

" 'But, Emile, Jean cannot possibly marry Belle; and you know as well as I that she, at least, is certainly deserving of that. I've been clean all my life, am prosperous, and can certainly give her a home commensurate with what she deserves.'

" 'René, if I didn't know you better, I would believe that this argument is the best you can offer. However, I know you're not thinking, for you can't help but realize that marriage minus love is and always will be a total failure. I know definitely that some day I shall love, too, but I'll be damned if I marry someone that is in love with someone else. Let me tell you further, should

Belle marry you by a miracle, and I mean by a miracle, your kisses would only be obnoxious to her unless—'

" 'Unless what?'

" 'Unless she is able to imagine you to be Jean.'

" 'My God!'

" 'I'm sorry that I must tell you the truth as I see it, since you evidently came to me for it.'

" 'Well, you certainly have brought it home forcibly. But tell me, is there some way that I can possibly perform that miracle? There must be, Emile. Think.'

" 'Miracles have been performed, René; but can't you see, mon ami, that those two have grown together as one and that their affection is not a spontaneous one, but one born of ten years of constant association. From childhood they have experienced together the smiles and the tears, the bitter and the sweet; and there is more yet that I could explain, but I think you understand.'

" 'Yes, I do. I suppose I should hate you, but I can't.'

" 'No, don't hate me, René, for I am very fond of you; and it is that fondness that causes me not to want to see you hurt. Tell me, what are your plans now?'

" 'To keep my engagement; and if future events turn out as you have pictured them, then I will desist.'

"Jean, listening intently, relaxed and sighed with relief; 'Emile,' he eventually asked, 'what can I do to repay you?'

" 'Nothing, for I have helped three friends.'

" 'And you had a reason for waiting until now to tell me.'

" 'Yes, just that you may not witness René calling. The only thing that one can say against you is that you have a temper, and that temper may cause regrets—you know the swords.' "

CHAPTER XII

RENE'S VISIT

" 'I know, Emile, you think of everything.'

" 'Not I; but Belle, who visited me immediately after her father had informed her of René's coming visit. She had blood in her eyes, if I may use that expression; and Jean, you would have grabbed and loved her. It was the first time I've seen her in anger, and I enjoyed it so much that I threw up my hands and said, 'My—my.'

" 'And what did you tell her?'

" 'Well, every time she started to say while rising, 'Think of it, Emile . . . ', I interrupted with, 'Belle, please be seated.' However, I told her that René had visited me and related our conversation, as I've done to you. As you no doubt realize now, she left here feeling reassured.'

" 'Yes, I know her; and you certainly have had a busy day. If you will permit, I should like to leave you to your meditation. Goodnight, good friend.'

"So saying, Grace, he left; and as he had guessed, I began to meditate and promptly fell asleep in my chair. Awakening at three o'clock, I undressed and jumped into bed. You see, I was weary."

"And did René visit Belle?"

"Yes, for at eight o'clock sharp he drew the pull; and the old bell on a spring rang. Belle's father, as was the custom, opened the door and welcomed René. He was handsome, Grace, as he was the result of colored and white mating. Mr. Mastero escorted him to the parlor upstairs which faces this patio, making him feel at home. As he entered, Belle bent low and curtsied.

"The custom at that time was for the parents to remain as chaperons; and although René was supposed to call on Belle, yet the conversation was mainly between the two men. For one-half hour Belle had hoped her father would leave them alone long enough for her to explain to René the impossibility of that for which he sought. However, since the conversation had turned to hunting and fishing, a subject of great interest to them, she realized the evening would pass without her completing her mission. Finally, she purposely coughed, which caused her father to realize he and René were doing the unpardonable in not including Belle in their conversation, as men will do when conversing on their favorite subject; and he said, 'Belle, dear, you don't feel well?'

" 'Only a slight cold. And, father, I believe I would feel better if we walked out into the open air, to the river possibly, as it has been a long time since I've seen it at night.'

"Her parents believing this to be a sign of success, quickly assented, so that upon leaving the house Belle managed to be at René's side. Down the street they went, the old folks arm in arm, while René helped Belle to step from the banquette to the street and back from the street to the banquette. When they were passing the Baroness Pontalba apartment building, Belle increased the distance between them and her parents; so René, sensing the reason, said to Belle, 'I saw one of your friends today.'

" 'You mean Emile?'

" 'Yes, how did you know?'

" 'I saw him, too.'

" 'When?'

" 'Just after you had left.'

" 'And, er—er—did he speak of our conversation?'

" 'Yes, he told me everything; and, Master René, I am terribly sorry.'

" 'Miss Mastero, I'm sorry, too, in more ways than one, believe me.'

" 'I do believe you, René; and so that you will know that I really mean it, I'll ask you to call me Belle and I'll call you René, just like sister and brother; and, René, the reason why Emile told me of the conversation was that he was afraid I might be discourteous to you.'

" 'I don't think that possible.'

" 'To be truthful, I might have been had I not heard of your er—er—'

" 'Love, Belle?'

" 'I'm sorry it happened, really I am.'

" 'I know it, and I now realize what Emile meant when he said I would care for you more each day that I entertained the idea that I might court you. You are sweet, Belle, sweet, sweet, sweet.'

"Reaching the river, Grace, Belle changed the conversation to steamboats; and so passed that evening."

CHAPTER XIII

ON THE GARDEN WALL

"Grace, for the first time Belle realized the potentialities of the river, even though she had known it all her life. While sitting on the old bench used by oyster luggermen during the day, she felt how happy she would be if Jean had been by her side, if only to give her hand an occasional squeeze that spoke more than words. Yes, she would ask him to come here tomorrow with her. So that night she remained awake sitting near the door patiently waiting for Jean's return

"Towards eleven o'clock he came; and peering through the darkness into Belle's room, as was his custom, he saw the reflection of the candlelight. Realizing that she had remained up for him and that it was too late to converse through chanting, he quietly stole down the slave stairway, and climbed the trellis which supported the white moonflowers that were beginning to gather the evening dew. Reaching the top of the thick brick wall, he called softly, 'Belle, Belle.' Hearing him, she quietly tiptoed to the window and looking up was surprised to see him seated on top of the wall.

" 'Wait, Jean,' she whispered, 'I'll get the ladder.'

"But before she could move, a dark figure had crossed the patio and was returning with it. Her ever faithful slave mother, Grace, placed it against the vine-covered wall and held it while Belle climbed; and Jean, reaching down, clasped one of her hands in an effort to support her.

"There was no moon, only the bright stars overhead, forming a canopy. Red Mars, the God of War, twinkled brightly, reminding them of the battle they were fighting only for the other's happiness. Reaching the top, Jean helped her to a sitting position, placing his arm about her to steady her. Belle, in that position, put her hands over his head and, bending her head backward so that she might look into his blue eyes, said, 'Darling.'

" 'Please, Belle,' he murmured as his arm tightened, 'don't say darling yet.' And he continued, 'God knows I love you, adore

you, Belle; but until I am able to have the right to have you call
me by that beautiful and tender name, without harming you, it
hurts.'

"'Oh, Jean, I love you, too. Why can't we do something, anything?'

"'I've been thinking, Belle, thinking deeply, having stopped at
the front of the Cathedral and offered a prayer to our dear Lord,
a prayer from the bottom of my heart, asking Him for guidance.
The more I seek, the less I find; and there are times when I
would accept what I believe to be the inevitable, by destroying
myself, if it were not for the suffering I would cause you.'

"'No, no, Jean,' she softly cried, 'please, not that.' Then
turning her face upward, she prayed, 'God, my Father, please
don't let Jean do that.'

"That beautiful face, that upturned face, captivated Jean; and,
forgetting everything else, he drew her closer to him, and softly
let his lips touch hers, murmuring, 'Sweet, if you could be mine
forever.'

"She whispered, 'You are wonderful, wonderful.'

"And Jean looking up said, 'Look, up there is Etoile Polaire, the
North Star, with its two ever faithful guardian stars revolving
around and around. Belle, my darling, you will ever find me
forever guarding you, as faithful as those two stars.'

"And, in a soft voice, Grace, he continued, 'I didn't have to
tell you that, did I?'

"In an undertone, just above a whisper, Belle answered, 'No,
I know it, I know it. But I love to hear you say it. It sounds
so sweet, and, Jean, please hold me closer. Oh! Jean, darling,
would that we could live forever thus—you are so sweet—you
and I that love so very much. Tell me, tell me now that you
will find some way, any way—Oh! Jean, sweet, kiss me—again
and again.'

"Then Jean answered, 'Belle, darling, we will find a way,
we must find one—'

"Belle, becoming serious, interrupted with, 'Jean, promise me
that you will take me to the levee tomorrow night.'

"'I promise. And, Belle, one more kiss—there, now, let me
help you down; and until tomorrow, adieu, my sweetheart,
adieu.'"

"Emile, that must have been beautiful; it gives me a thrill."

"It gave me one, too, when I first heard it; in fact, it still does."

"Continue."

"The next morning, I awakened early, having spent a restless night. I had a premonition that something would happen to Belle and Jean. I know premonitions to be fear, but I also know that the fear is backed up by past events, too many to be held in the conscious mind; or, rather, the subconscious mind seems to judge them collectively, hence a premonition.

"However, at nine o'clock I decided to call on Belle. Reaching her home, instead of entering through the hall door, as was my custom, I walked through the stable entrance in order to avoid her parents. Coming to the fountain, I saw Belle cutting flowers; and when she raised her head, I quickly placed my finger on my lips, indicating silence, which she quickly understood. We walked toward the door and entered.

"When she had closed it, I said, 'Belle, I have a premonition that something unpleasant is about to happen to you and Jean.'

" 'You may be right, Emile, for I feel terribly moody.'

"And, Grace, she told me, as I've told you, of their meeting on the garden wall, and ended by saying, 'Now, since thinking it over, why should we, Jean and I, be deprived of the pleasure permitted every other living soul. Out of millions, we two should be singled out—that positively is not just; and since it is not just, it is not God's work.'

" 'Right you are, girl; but don't do anything rash.'

" 'Emile, you know we love you, don't you?'

" 'Yes, I do.'

" 'And you also know that we always come to you for advice?'

" 'Yes, I know that, too.'

" 'Then, if I should ask you not to advise me today, would you be angry?'

" 'Definitely no, but . . .'

" 'Now, Emile!'

" 'All right, Belle; the subject is ended.'

" 'Not for me, for I want you to tell me that you will always think of Jean and me as you do today, regardless of what might happen. Will you promise?'

"Thinking that I might be able to prevent a catastrophe, for I knew Belle's will, I answered, 'That will require some meditation.'

" 'But, aren't we human?'

"I had gained a point, for now I was able to advise again.

" 'I grant you that, but—'

" 'And if I want Jean, all of Jean, and I know he does want all of me, would we be harming anyone?'

" 'No you wouldn't, but—'

" 'Then, before we're driven to distraction, or possibly worse, with Jean's consent, I will become to him what my mother is to my father—what your mother was to your father.'

" 'But Belle—'

" 'No buts, except—except Oh! please don't condemn us.'

" 'I won't.' With that, I said goodbye in my usual manner, feeling as though I had taken a licking. I had failed, Grace; and yet, she was right. "Damn it,' I heard myself saying, as I walked home with measured steps."

"What followed?"

"That evening Jean called for Belle, and off they walked towards the river."

"But her parents permitted them to go out unchaperoned?"

"Oh! yes, you see, the confidence that they placed in Jean was just another thorn in his side. In other words, to betray that confidence, that trust, would have been dishonorable in its worst sense."

"Yes, I can understand, especially since they had been seen together almost daily from infancy and, as you've said, were regarded more as friends. What happened next?"

"Well, they lay, resting on their sides facing each other, on the grassy levee of the deserted river front; from there they could see the ferries, with their red and green lights, shuttling back and forth from shore to shore. Occasionally, a steamboat passed, its powerful stern wheel whipping the water.

"The same stars they saw overhead again burned brightly tonight; and again the challenge of Mars entered Belle's heart— this time a burning challenge which had been fanned by the desire to re-experience the thrills, the ecstacies of the night before; only this time, she wished to imbibe it to its fullest extent.

"Jean, tiring of his position, dropped full on his back, his head resting on the soft grass. Belle, seeing him in that position, felt an urge, and broke the silence with, 'Jean, never once in our lives have you refused me anything, have you?'

" 'No, Belle.'

" 'Will you continue to please me?'

" 'Yes.'

" 'Will you promise?'

" 'Yes, I promise.'

" 'On your word of honor?'

"The last question caused Jean to realize that Belle had something of grave importance on her mind; so he asked, 'Belle, is it that important?'

"Turning and leaning over Jean so that their chests met, she answered, 'Jean, please darling, tonight, forget about our welfare, about—Oh! Jean, I love you so—tonight be my sweetheart; love me, hold me, kiss me, Jean—please be my lover—see, I kiss you, on the lips, too—'

" 'But, Belle—'

" 'Jean darling, please,' she pleaded, "you've never argued before. Can't you realize what we're missing?'

" 'Yes, but,'—and as Jean started to rise to a sitting position, Belle held him down and with her face so close that he could feel her burning breath, she insisted, 'Remember your promise!'

" 'I know, but listen well to what I have to say. No one who has ever lived on this earth longed—yes, longed, you understand, to take a girl into his arms more than I long to take you. If I had one hour with you alone, I would be satisfied to repent the remainder of my life. If I would be harmed and not you, you would not have needed to ask me. You have your entire life ahead of you—'

" 'Jean,' she interrupted, softly, gently passing her hand on the side of his face and neck. 'There is the great Mississippi River with its inviting, cool water that has come miles and miles from the summits of beautiful, pure, snow-capped mountains. We're pure, too, darling.' She paused to let her lips touch his. 'If after one hour of love, we feel that we have become stained, then, like that pure snow, we can mix and become part of the muddy water.'

" 'You mean—'

" 'Yes, I mean that if we decide that we can't live together and we know we can't possibly live apart, I will gladly, hand in hand, with you, darling, walk into the river—into oblivion.'

"Moving his hands from her sides, he raised them to her face. Holding it gently, he drew that bit of loveliness down and kissed her passionately. Then, again moving his hands, he placed his arms around her while she rained kisses on his face and neck until, from exhaustion, she turned over, her back lying flat on the soft grass. Just then, Grace, a lone whistle from a steamboat blowing for a landing directly in front of them caused them to rise; and Jean, gazing directly into her blue-black eyes, grabbed her hand and said simply: 'I'm glad,' and led her toward home just as day was breaking.

"As they reached the Cathedral, its chimes began to peal, calling all the faithful to prayer; and, still hand in hand, they walked through its massive doors, entered a vacant pew, and knelt in prayer, beginning with a prayer of thanks."

CHAPTER XIV

A Possible Solution

"Emile, when you said their devotion was possibly the equal of any in history, you didn't miss it far, did you?"

"It was the most beautiful romance I know."

"And one that gave you a different outlook on life—one different from that of any man I've known. You know, I wish I could have experienced that romance."

"Not I; for the misery experienced is in ratio to the ecstasy; that is, the deeper the love, the deeper the misery—believe me, it is misery."

"In what way?"

"Well, the more one loves, the more one misses one's lover when one is separated from her. So Belle and Jean, in addition to having this yearning for each other's company, which certainly was misery, also faced the fact that they saw no solution of their problem; but rather the opposite, which must have at times caused a hopeless feeling, akin to despair. I am satisfied, it was this feeling that made Belle propose what she did on the river front—a proposal of ignorance."

"But didn't she know that she would sin?"

"No, Grace. Let me explain you something that I know exists nowhere else but in this quarter. You see, the girls about Belle's age knew absolutely nothing of sex, going from home to school an school to home. They are given a room, like the one next to this, in which were an organ and a piano. This was all they had with which to amuse themselves and their friends."

"You mean the room through this door has an organ and a piano?"

"Yes; that very room was what we might call Belle's recreation room. In there she and her friends would sing and dance or enjoy any other amusement they wished. As their parents were extremely careful about their friends, they were kept in total ignorance of the sexual duties of married life. Belle, being more intelligent than the average girl in this section, had absorbed an inkling here and there; but her total knowledge of sex was like hundreds of loose threads, no two connecting. In other words, she knew that something existed between man and woman that bound the ties of matrimony; but exactly what that something was she did not know."

"My, I wouldn't want to be that ignorant of the subject."

"Where you've come from, you are taught in a different way, which I have always contended was the correct thing to do, for I am convinced that ignorance of the subject is the reason why so many Creole husbands today are protectors of colored girls, and have two families."

"Just how do you connect that?"

"Well, Grace, their ignorance is only dispelled a night or two before the marriage, which results in total shock; so much so, that I know of many cases where the bride's fear caused her to leave the groom waiting at the church."

"But, couldn't the girl reason that her parents had had the same experience and lived through it?"

"Yes, in some cases she did; but in all cases, the sudden shock not only made her fear her husband physically, but also made her supersensitive about modesty with the consequence that as months went by friend husband became totally discouraged and took unto himself a second family with an octoroon or quadroon whose mother was a mistress, and who had reared her child also to become one for the next generation, teaching her from the day of puberty, sex knowledge, so that when the time came, what was a shock to the Creole woman was a pleasure to her."

"That is as it should be."

"Yes, for nature is not filth, but beauty."

"Now, I can understand Belle's action. She wanted to be what a wife was, even though she was ignorant of a wife's duty. When you spoke of the yearning they had for each other's company, truthfully speaking, I don't yearn for you."

"Grace, you're not thinking."

"I'm not?"

"Listen, I call for you in the early morning at Jeanne's and return you to her at night. Now, let me ask you, how long have we been separated during our waking hours?"

"Why, none—Oh! I see. You were right, I was not thinking.

Under that condition, we really don't know how great our love is."

"No, nor shall we know unless some event happens that will give us something to gauge by."

"But I do thrill under your kissing."

"So do I when I caress you; but you will find that it will take not the pleasure side to furnish a gauge, but rather the painful. In fact, it was just such a painful reaction that caused Jean to meet me at the coffee stand in the market. Refusing my offer of coffee and *brioche*, he nervously waited until I had finished, when he asked, 'Emile, have you time?'

"'Always, for you, Jean,' I answered.

"Then drawing me to one side, he related the entire episode of the night before as I've described it to you. He said further, 'I've been awake all night, sitting in a chair. Every time I dozed off, I awoke with a start for, if I didn't have a vision of Belle insane, I had one of her death.'

"'Oh! It can't be that bad, Jean.'

"'But, Emile, imagine a girl like Belle taking such a drastic action. Can't you see that it was a mental reaction and that those reactions have mounted in the past and will mount in the future to such severity that eventually their enormity will cause insanity. My God, man, help us, for I feel as though my mental powers are about to collapse.'

"'Now, pull yourself together,' I told him, seeing his condition was certainly bordering on insanity. I fully realized exactly what he meant; and as a friend of theirs, I was obliged to find a way to a happy conclusion. Certainly I could not nor would not permit two God-fearing people to go insane, as I was convinced they would, considering that in solving their problem I was certainly harming no one."

"Not even Belle's parents?"

"No, not even her parents for, had they known Belle's situation, I'm sure they would have welcomed any assistance I could have given."

"I understand. What did you do then?"

"Just then the melodious chimes of the Cathedral rang out—a notification of the beginning of seven o'clock Mass. We had been walking towards the church and noticed, among the Creoles, several Italians who were entering. When I asked Jean who was to officiate, he said Father Slovani.

"Then the thought came to me that possibly a personal interview with the good priest might solve their problem. My stopping short caused Jean to look inquiringly at me. He said, 'Emile, you've thought of something—I know it.'

" 'Yes, Jean, and I may have struck the very thing.' When I said that, he caught me by my shoulders with both hands and excitedly shouted, 'What is it? Please, Emile, what is it?'

" 'Calm yourself and listen. We know Father Slovani is a just and methodical thinker; and I was wondering if you and Belle would accost him together, explaining everything from beginning to end, whether he could not possibly get you two a special dispensation. I don't know of its having been done, but there must be a first to everything. It's certainly worth trying.'

" 'Why didn't we think of that before?' Then he thanked me; and, leaving me standing, he actually ran to tell Belle of the possible solution."

"And did Father Slovani obtain the special dispensation?"

"You're the same old Grace. Do you want me to ruin the story or will you wait until later to know?"

"Later, dear."

CHAPTER XV.

RELIGIOUS REASONING

"Racing through the streets, Grace, he told me that he had arrived home breathless and that he had to wait until he became composed before he was able to convey his message. And then, he said, he was so anxious that he almost revealed their secret of chanting for, instead of singing hymns first, he immediately proceeded to chant his message, and, had it not been for Belle, who had seen him and waved to him to stop, their secret would not have been a secret any longer. However, he later explained everything and told Belle to prepare to meet him at the Cathedral for four o'clock, that being the earliest time reserved by the priest for visitors. From that time, until they met, their excitement was so great that, strange to say, they both experienced cold sweats as they thought of their possible future happiness and of their possible future failure; for, as Belle has since told me, one minute she was elated and the next she was depressed.

"They met at the appointed time and knelt and prayed in their own way; and when they had finished, they walked to the priest's home. Arriving there, they used the old iron knocker; and a colored girl answered. When they explained that they desired an audience with Father Slovani, she escorted them to a room whose walls were colored with pictures of Saints. In fact, everywhere were signs of religion. Realizing their environment, Belle said, 'Jean, if we're not successful in this room, I for one am ready to abandon the idea of matrimony.'

"Just then Father Slovani entered. 'Good evening,' the priest greeted them in French, and continued, 'what can I do for you today?'

"'Father,' stammered Jean, 'You know both Belle and me?'

"'Surely I do. Why I christened both of you and have seen you perform your duties monthly, having been your confessor for years. I've known your every movement and have wondered at your cleanliness of thought, although you have been closely associated since childhood. I've attributed it to your purity of mind, Belle, and to your culture, Jean.'

" 'Thanks, Father,' said Jean. 'But that purity of mind will cease to exist unless you find a way to help us.'

" 'I have always done so in the past and have confidence of again being able to do it.'

"When he uttered those words, Grace, Belle fell on her knees before the venerable priest and with upturned face pleaded, 'Please, Father, please find some way that Jean and I can marry.' She continued, 'Don't, Father,' for he had begun to talk, 'Listen further to what we have to say.'

" 'All right, Belle, but rise and clear those eyes of tears.'

"Jean helped her to her feet, and both sat together on an old black horsehair sofa. The priest looked on and noticed how tenderly Jean had assisted her and how he had drawn her head down to his shoulder and placed his arm around her. He broke the silence with, 'Jean, you seem more composed. Suppose you tell me your trouble.'

" 'Father,' Jean began, 'Belle and I have found that we love each other devotedly, and we are definitely convinced that we cannot live apart, having felt the pangs of hell the last few days, caused by an incident that awakened us to the fact that we may be separated. Further, we have considered everything thoroughly, Father, and have come to the conclusion that we have only three lines of conduct from which to choose.'

" 'What are they?'

" 'First, to destroy ourselves.'

" 'Good God, don't tell me it is that serious!' And he continued, 'You would never see the face of your Maker.'

" 'I know, Father; but the human mind can stand only a certain amount of punishment, after which it is unaccountable. However, another would be to be married by a Justice of the Peace out of the State.'

" 'You cannot do that, for your church would recognize you two as living in adultery, and you would disown your religion by recognizing the magistrate over the church.'

" 'I know that also, Father. Now, the last one would be for us to forget the world and to live only for each other, preferring a happy life, and glad we had done it, to a miserable one, and sorry we hadn't; or what we have prayed for, and what Belle has

pleaded for on her bended knees before you, Father, a holy
uniting in matrimony, a—'

" 'Compose yourself, Jean—'

" 'Please let me finish, Father. As you know, we have been
placed together by God, as you have often told us. If it was
God's will that we should grow together as one, then it is also
His wish that we should live together in happiness—not in the
hell that you have always told us is for the wicked.'

"Beads of perspiration had collected on his brow and some
had trickled down his cheek to Belle's face; the girl looked up
with a most sympathetic expression and wiped his forehead with
her small lace handkerchief. The old priest noted all of these
things. Years ago he had learned to read the expressions of his
grateful flock; and in the soft manner that had become a part
of him, he sadly said, 'Jean, if it were in my power, I would perform that ceremony, now, yes right this very minute; but you
forget that we have State laws and that even I, a priest, must
respect—'

"Jean was stunned and winced as though struck by a blow.
'State laws?' He muttered, 'State laws, did you say, Father? You
would compare a pure, clean affection—an inseparable affection
to laws that are broken daily—to the stills that flourish over the
State that, drop by drop, furnish the "demon rum," as you call
it from your pulpit. And the State laws close their eyes to that.
And you would compare our love with State laws whose officials
close their eyes to slaves that are smuggled into this community
contrary to the United States laws. And you would further compare our plight to the State law forbidding lottery, of which you
are perfectly aware the State also closes its eyes, for, from your
very pulpit you admonish your flock not to gamble—not to buy
lottery tickets. I repeat, Father, it is most unfair—nay, grossly
unjust, for State laws not to permit legitimately the union of
two of its citizens, permitting them the full happiness God had
intended, as I said before, since from the cradle He has caused or
permitted to cause our uninterrupted association to where one
cannot now live without the other; it is unjust not to permit its
citizens their rightful heritage while winking its eye at harmful,
indecent corruption.'

" 'Now, Jean, it is not I that compares those laws. I realize it is your desire for cleanliness and Godliness that prompts such action as yours, and if I did no more good in my life's work in the church than to have inculcated into you two people your love of fairness and your desire of upright living, I would feel my earthly mission a full success. However, for me to marry you two, knowing one of you to be colored, the city and of course the State through the city would learn of it and have me, a priest of seventy-four years of age, excommunicated. Further, the wedding would be declared illegal.'

" 'Forgive me, Father. Surely you know us too well to believe we would want happiness at your expense. But, Father, that State law, that damnable State law would permit a colored girl of ninety-eight per cent white to marry a pure Negro, of which she is only two per cent, and yet not marry a white of which she is ninety-eight per cent. Why, Father, why this discrimination?'

"The old priest meditated a moment while stroking his grey-black beard and then answered, 'Well, the State's contention is that black children might be born.'

" 'What a damnable, lamentable excuse. Father, you have baptized over one thousand illegitimate babies of colored women and white fathers. You know and I know not one from that combination was black. You and I, and I dare say the State officials know, that no child of which Belle and I may be the parents could be born other than white.'

"Every word uttered by this eighteen-year-old lad rang truthful and convincing; and as they rang, echoed and re-echoed in Belle's ears, she realized the absolute futility of it all. Why, Oh why, she thought, could not things have happened last night as she had planned. Now, that awful pain—that uncontrollable suffering—that subconscious feeling of total despair would be over, for their bodies, their consciousless bodies would be floating peacefully along.

"She burst into sobbing—an uncontrollable sobbing that caused Jean to take her into his arms. He tried to console her, but just what could he say? Instead his eyes rested on the good priest who had turned completely around in an effort to hide his emotions. And as the priest returned his handkerchief into his black frock, he said, 'Let her cry, Jean, it will ease her.' And as

Jean gently petted her, his sympathy seemed to cause her to lose complete control of her emotions and shrieking at the top of her voice, she fell into hysterics.

"Jean, unconscious of everything except the misery undergoing in that spasmodic, shaking body, took her bodily in his arms and would have left the priest's house if that good Father had not motioned him into the next room, where Jean placed her on the bed.

"The maid, hearing the shrieks and having witnessed those scenes before when parents called on the good priest after the burial of a loved one, quickly entered the room with a sedative. Handing it to Jean she stepped back as he sat on the bed and gently raised her to where he could force the liquid between her teeth, after which he again gently laid her head on the pillow.

"After a few minutes Belle became calm, with only an occasional deep sigh. Gently placing his arm beneath her he said, 'Come, dear, let's go. We'll find a way, for we cannot and will not be deprived of what is rightfully ours.'

"Leaving, they made their way home, not again stopping, as was their custom, in the church."

"My, Emile, that must have been terrible."

"Terrible is not the word, for as Jean afterward said, 'Emile, the more Belle realized that our last hope was gone, the more sorrowful she became; and as I came to my senses, I realized that since we were deprived of a marriage in the eyes of the people and since we were the equal of anyone in the community in the eyes of God, then, by reasoning, no one could honestly or justly deprive us of a wedding in His eyes.'"

"We certainly can't deny the justice of that reasoning."

"Definitely not; and, between you and me, I don't believe the priest would; for, the next afternoon, when I met Father Slovani, he explained to me his position in their case. He further explained that he had heard a remark by Jean, one that he had never heard before, and that as long as he lived he would remember. He said, 'Emile, when those two had reached the door, Belle appeared about to collapse. Jean supported her; and in that fraction of a minute, Jean told her to brace up, for he knew what was taking place in her heart, and he wished he could hold it in his hands and kiss away its pain.'

" 'Emile,' the priest continued, 'it was only then that I fully realized the extreme affection they had for each other. So I immediately consulted my superior, hoping that we might find a solution for their dilemma; but we could do nothing.' "

CHAPTER XVI

THE INEVITABLE

"On reaching home, Jean led her directly to his room. Calling for his governess, he instructed her to have the slave mother bring over Belle's Bible.

"Belle was sitting in a chair, weak, dejected and sad. Jean went over to her; and stooping so as to look up into her face, he said, 'Belle, I've sent for your Holy Bible, and we'll have two witnesses. Now, you and I will marry and pledge our troth before Almighty God, on the Holy Bible, using the same vows administered by the priest. Do you want to?'

" 'Of course, Jean.'

" 'All right—prepare yourself, for here they come.'

"Grace, it must have been solemn to see those two old women enter, the old slave mother carrying the Holy Bible as reverently as she knew how. As they walked up to Jean, Belle rose, looked sadly at him, and said, 'I'm ready.'

" 'All right. Now Belle, place your hand on this Holy Bible, next to mine—that's right, right here—and repeat after me—I, Belle Mastero, before Almighty God and these witnesses and on the Holy Bible, take thee, Jean Moveau, for my holy wedded husband, and I do solemnly swear to honor, love, and obey until'—and he continued the vow to the end. Grace, she reverently repeated every word after him until she had completed the wedding vow. Jean then repeated his part with his whole heart and soul; and when he had finished, he laid the Holy Bible down, and kissed his in-the-eyes-of-God wife and led her to a chair, after which he opened the Bible at a beautiful colored page on which were printed pictures of doves, orange blossoms, and spaces for recording marriages. Filling in the blanks and having signed on the dotted line, he handed the pen to Belle, who, with shaking hand, signed. The two colored women then wrote their names as witnesses, the slave mother using an X.

"Jean, noticing Belle's exhausted condition, ordered her home and to bed—a bed she did not leave for forty-one days, for upon reaching her room, she collapsed completely, both mentally and physically."

"You mean she became insane?"

"Yes, Grace, insane. The slave mother immediately summoned Jean and then her parents, who were visiting at the time. They in turn summoned the doctor. After an examination, the doctor ordered a psychiatrist be called; so they sent a summons to the nearest one, who resided in Biloxi, Miss. Jean remained at her side the entire night, waiting patiently for the doctor, for he reasoned that he should tell him all. The next morning, I received a note telling me that it was imperative that I call immediately. On my arrival, Jean explained everything to me and asked that I remain with him until the doctor came. For almost one hour I had time to study Jean. I really expected the boy to follow Belle—so much so, that when the bell rang I answered it in person so as to inform the doctor who immediately ordered Jean to be seated and to relax. He then visited Belle, who didn't move and stared as in a trance. When he had completed the examination, he turned to find Jean who, all excited, blurted out, 'Will she live, Doctor? Will she get well?'

" 'That, I can't say, my boy,' he replied, 'but I want you to remain seated and above all to relax before I have two patients.'

" 'You mean me, doctor?'

" 'Yes, I mean you.'

"Just then Belle spoke, and everyone listened intently while she slowly said, 'Jean, my husband.' Then she stopped for a full minute, when her lips again began to move. Jean rushed over to the bed and said, 'Yes, darling,' with an anxiety that was sadly pathetic, but Belle spoke no more. Her eyes closed for the first time since the night before, and she fell into a deep sleep. Jean's head dropped and he cried bitterly. I started towards him, but the doctor stopped me, saying, 'Let him cry,' which he did without restraint. When he felt relieved, he stood up and faced the doctor, who said consolingly, 'Jean, my boy, if I can do anything for her, it will be through you. Now, should you also become my patient, I'm licked. So you see the necessity of your remaining calm.'

" 'I'll do as you say, Doctor.'

" 'That's fine. Now tell me everything that has happened,' and saying that, he asked permission of Belle's parents to use another private room, when Jean calmly said, 'Doctor, I would rather remain here and tell all. Don't go, please,' he begged her parents as they started to leave. 'You should also know.' Then he asked the doctor to be seated and started at the beginning, looking neither to right nor left, but straight at her beautiful innocent face—that face which looked so pale—as if to ask her to bear witness; he told of the chanting, their childhood, René's visit and its consequences, their visits to me, their talk on the river front, ending with their conversation in detail with Father Slovani; and their in-the-eyes-of-God wedding. One could see, Grace, he believed that to help Belle it was necessary to tell all in the hope that some little detail might prove a clue. Only once was he on the verge of a breakdown, and that was when he spoke of their marriage. So pathetic and truthful was he that Belle's father, for the first time realizing the great and unselfish love that existed between them, turned to a crucifix that hung on the wall and reverently said, 'God, my Father, I promise that, should it be Your will that my daughter recover, to recognize that marriage.' Then he walked over to Jean, and offered his hand, that being his method of sealing a pact."

"And did she recover, Emile?"

"Grace—"

"I'm sorry, continue."

"Jean sat limp, looking the doctor squarely in the eye, searching for some clue that might reveal his true verdict. He didn't have long to wait for the doctor, addressing all of us in general but Jean in particular, as if he, too, recognized the wedding, said, 'You two have been through hell, son, actual hell. Why she did not break sooner was due only to her unselfish desire not to hurt you. Now I cannot assure you as to when she will recover, for her illness was caused by shock, and from shock she will recover. As for her physical being, she is perfect.' Then he continued, 'Now, Jean, as I said before, I'm sure it will be through you that the shock will come. As to when, our Creator only knows; so I say to you, most emphatically, that you owe it to her, your wife, to keep sane, and to remain with her as long as possible.'

"My, Jean had a terrible load to carry."

"Yes, and he said to me after the doctor had left, 'Emile, I swear to you, our best friend, to remain at her bedside for the rest of my life, except when the nurse puts me out; and, when you reach home, say a prayer for her.'

" 'For your wife, Jean?'

" 'Yes, for my wife,' he murmured with a sad smile that would have touched a heart of stone."

"And you prayed, Emile?"

"All the way home, Grace, in my own way."

"And how was that?"

"Well, I spoke to our God, pleading their cause as though I were their lawyer, citing the fact that they were good and did not deserve their fate."

"But, don't you think God knew that?"

"Yes, I think so, Grace; but a prayer asking a favor never does any harm."

"Then you don't think He might have resented your asking Him, your interfering with His work"

"First, I wasn't sure it was His work. Second, no harm could be done when I meant to help my neighbor. You know, Grace, when I neared home, I began to think that should Belle recover, God might have a happy life in store for them in payment for the damage that nature and society alone caused."

"Emile—Oh, never mind."

"What were you going to say?"

"I was going to ask did they ever have any happiness, but I take back that question."

"I'm glad you did."

"May I ask this one: Did Jean remain by her side always?"

"Well, let me answer you this way: Twenty-four hours a day and day after day he remained at her bedside, sleeping in this rocker, the one I'm sitting in. On the seventeenth day, the physician demanded that some sort of furniture more comfortable than a rocker be provided for him, hence the chaise lounge you're in.

"On the twenty-eighth day he was forced to sit for at least one hour in the sunshine and on each day thereafter. He had become very thin, and it was only the constant reminder of the doctor to the effect that he was neglecting Belle by not eating that forced him to take food.

"On the forty-first day, Grace, the psychiatrist called, again hoping that something had happened. He also wanted to keep an eye on Jean, for, as he said to me on leaving, 'Emile, I'm going to have another patient.'

" 'But, Doctor, can't we do something to prevent it?'

" 'There's only one chance. Since you are his best friend, perhaps you can induce him to take a trip, explaining that it will be in Belle's interest. Unless something intervenes I expect a call in the morning for him.'

" 'It's that serious, Doctor?'

" 'I'm afraid so.'

" 'Then I will see what I can do.'

"Emile, what did you do?"

"Grace, I was very much worried; in fact, their trouble had bothered me to such an extent that, seeing things growing worse, I began to feel glum and morose—so much so that I passed acquaintances on the street without realizing who they were. However, I pulled myself together and walked into what I had regarded as the equivalent of a death chamber. On entering, I saw Jean and began to study him."

"And what was his appearance?"

"His face was haggard and drawn; and there was a far away expression about his eyes that bothered me; so I said, 'Jean, how do you feel?'

" 'Really, Emile, I don't know.'

" 'And Jean,' I continued, knowing that I was treading on dangerous ground, 'don't you think a visit to the country for a few days with me would do you good?'

" 'Emile, are you serious?'

" 'Yes.'

" 'And do you think that I would leave her?'

" 'Yes, I do if it were for her good.'

" 'You mean that my leaving her would be in her interest?'

"Grace, ordinarily I could have wormed out this situation; but, not being myself, I realized that an answer in the affirmative would lead to a final admission of my fear for his mind; so I said, 'In this respect, Jean, that you would see other sights and perhaps, like a vacation, they might improve your thinking powers—'

" 'You mean I should take a vacation? Surely you can't be serious.'

" 'Forget it,' I said, feeling I had again failed, and mumbling something about my calling again the next morning, I departed. On reaching home, my mind cleared somewhat; and I began to realize that his mind was not what it should be. However, since my brain was not equal to the situation, I dismissed the thought and, hitching my horse to the rig, drove to the lake for diversion."

"What happened next?"

"Well, towards six o'clock that evening Belle's parents received an urgent call to the bedside of a dying relative. It was the nurse's night off, and they were in a quadary as to what to do. Jean, hearing their plight, recommended that they go, stating that he would call the slave mother should he need her. This arrangement left Jean alone with Belle; and, had I known that, realizing his unbalanced mental condition, I certainly would have remained with him that night."

"Emile, you have me on my toes, again."

"Not toes, Grace; for you are squirming, and one doesn't squirm on one's toes."

"You see too much, but tell me what happened."

"Well, they were alone in this very room. On the dresser burned a candle, protected from the breeze by a beautiful cut crystal hurrican glass, its flickering light illuminating everything, especially Belle so that Jean could study her features again that night as he had for forty nights. Usually she rested on her side, but this night she laid flat on her back, her shapely uncovered arms resting comfortably at her side. It was nine o'clock, and except for the neighing of a horse now and then, everything was quiet. Mammy was in her room, fast asleep, having sat up the previous night with Jean and the nurse, hoping, always hoping that some sign would reveal a clue that might lead to the recovery of 'her chile'. Jean had taken a chair, that straight one, and placing it by the side of the bed, he sat on the edge, resting his arms on the bed, admiring her black curly hair, her closed eyes, cheeks that still were rosy pink, lips, those beautifully shaped red lips that were slightly apart, those alluring lips. Slowly he half rose, and gently his face dropped until his lips touched hers, warm and moist. Then drawing back into his former position, he again began to stare, whispering, 'Belle, darling, how beautiful you are lying there, so peaceful and quiet, your chest moving in constant rhythmic motion. I would do anything to have you back again. My God, that she should have to bear such a cross. I can't understand it, God; it doesn't make sense.' Then he sighed and continued, pleading, "We're alone, God, Thou, Belle, and I—. Please bring her back or please show me a way, Father; I'll Prómise anything, I'll do anything.' And, as an after thought, he added, 'Father, if we've done wrong, offended Thee in some way, forgive us, for we have always revered Thee. And further, Father, if we must atone, let me do it. I will give my right hand to have her back. Maybe my mind is deranged; but please, Father, take my hand, but restore her.'

"And, Grace, the more he thought of atonement, the more he became obsessed with the thought that forfeiting his hand would cure her. Pushing his chair backward, he knelt by the bed and pleaded, 'God, our Father, I'm almost convinced that my sacrifice will save her. Shouldn't Thou not show me a way tonight, then tomorrow I will do it—I promised'."

CHAPTER XVII

KISS ME AND KISS ME AGAIN

"Did he, Emile?"

Emile, disregarding her question, continued his story. "Jean having returned to his chair leaned forward and whispered to Belle, 'Darling, to think how cruel the last months have been to you—and all caused by a shock—a shock?' He asked himself, rising. 'A shock!' he explained, almost screaming. Then he added, 'My God, that's it, a shock.' Is that your answer, Father? Tell me, what kind of shock?'

"Grace, he walked to the mirror; and believing he had the clue, he gazed at himself. Trembling for fear he would lose the clue, he said, 'Jean, don't become excited. Be yourself—she needs you. Be calm, relax, and think—what could possibly shock her?—'

"Again kneeling, this boy with his disarranged mind, prayed, 'My God, help me—suggest what kind of shock—what to do, please, God, answer.'

"And thinking of the possibility of some wrong they might have committed, his mind reverted to the levee episode. 'My Father, had I done what she requested, all of this would have been averted. She would be mine now and I would be hers, alone in love, alone, alone.' And then, Grace, as an afterthought, he added, 'Alone—aren't we alone now—yes, alone, just she and I— My God, is that the answer?'

"His mind was muddled, Grace, for fear, love, justice, duty, all raced back and forth. Eventually he said, 'Do it, do it, if you care for her—you owe it to her!' And he reasoned, was she not his? Wouldn't that be a shock? Wouldn't she acquiesce if she were of sane mind? What was there to lose? It was about the only chance she had of regaining her senses. If he failed, then she wouldn't know it and wouldn't feel the pangs that come from failure—as in the past, pangs that raced through his heart at every beat—for he would do what she suggested, walk into the muddy river and become part of its rushing stream.

"Thus he continued to argue with himself. 'If successful, and

I have a premonition that it will be, it will cure her, for it was a shock that caused it and it will be a shock that will restore her. Then, too, were we not man and wife? For did we not take the same oath that others, luckier than we, take? Couldn't we safely take a vow to love each other until death do us part, when others kneeling before a priest would take the same vow, not being sure just how long their love would last. Yes, our vow, as sacred as any and as binding in the eyes of God as any, made us man and wife, if not in the eyes of man, certainly in His eyes.'

"Reasoning thus, Jean lay across the bed and, taking Belle's head in both his hands, spoke to her softly, now and then kissing, sometimes tenderly, sometimes passionately, her beautiful lips.

"Once or twice he thought he felt a reaction; but, like anyone with so much at stake, he believed it to be just wishful thinking, for he would immediately kiss her again without the result he had hoped for. Finally, slowly, without compunction, he gently unbuttoned and opened the gown from her rounded shoulders and saw the beautiful form of her creamy white, shapely chest; a form fully accentuated by shadows from the soft candle light. It was then that, feeling like a thief in the night, he quickly drew the gown together without rebuttoning it, left the bed, walked to the window, and stared into the night at the stars—stars that were shining on lovers all over the world."

"That was terribly, Emile."

"Yes, Grace. Then the thought crossed his mind that if he would become suddenly insane—and he reasoned that it was highly possible—and if something would happen that would cause her to become normal, what a hell it would be for her. The mere thought made everything go black. Then sensing he was about to drop, he backed towards the bed and fell in a dead faint, by the one he loved more than life itself."

"My God, was there no happiness in their lives?"

"Do you want me to ruin the story?"

"No, please continue."

"Well, Grace, when Jean fell, a blow seemed to strike Belle, no one knows where, but certainly in a vital place, for she opened her eyes and dazedly began looking around. The candle light attracted her attention and as she turned her head to look at it she noticed a form lying prone on its back. What was the form? Why the candle? Unconsciously, she rubbed her hand across her forehead so as to clear a very muddled mind. She again closed her eyes in an effort to think more clearly. Was she in her own home? Yes, for she recognized the dresser; or did she? Better look again. Reopening her eyes, she again gazed at the dresser. Yes it was definitely hers for it even had the burned mark on the stanchion holding the mirrow caused many years ago by a fallen lit candle. Lowering her eyes she noticed her pink dresser set. Instantly she recognized the porcelain stopper in one of the decanters which was broken and which fitted sidewise on the open neck. And, too, there was her massive Holy Bible. It, too, was hers for the candle revealed the well known frayed edges of the bookmark.

" 'The Bible, the Holy Bible,' she said, and continued, 'I know, it was something about that Bible. If only I could chant to Jean, he would—Jean—Jean!' she said aloud. Then as her mind began to clear she remembered her 'In-the-eyes-of-God marriage.' 'Now, Belle,' she said, almost inaudibly, 'calm yourself for your heart is thumping like a trip-hammer. Think, where is Jean? Is that him at your side? 'Take it easy, girl, take it easy,' she admonished herself. And, moving slowly, she turned to where she might see the face of the form. But, one arm had dropped across her chest. She began to tremble as she reached up and moved that arm. As she bent it upwards and over it dropped lifeless to its owner's side. 'It must be Jean—Jean, Oh! Jean, wake up,' she almost screamed as she forced her body upwards. In doing so, she had moved out of the path of the light and it shone obliquely from the holder on the dresser illuminating Jean's features to where the shadows plainly revealed the sunken eyes of the wasted face.

"Laboriously lifting herself, she gently stroked his face and softly called, 'Jean, Jean,' as her wits began to return.

"Now, thinking more clearly, she realized something direful must have happened and started for a wet towel. Slipping out of bed, she started towards the washstand when, through sheer weakness she fell on the floor in a heap. Forcing herself to a sitting position, she looked for something to hold to steady herself when she noticed the chair by her bed. Turning her head to look for other changes, she saw the chaise-lounge. And then it began to dawn on her, especially since she was so weak, that she must have been ill. And that Jean, that ever faithful Jean, had slept in her room throughout that siege, for a siege it must have been for her to be in that weakened condition.

"She further reasoned: Jean is sick—how sick? Quick, a wet towel. And, Grace, Belle crawled to the washstand, and, reaching for its marble top, laboriously drew herself to a standing position, bracing her body in the corner formed by the washstand and the wall. In this position she reached for the towel rack and secured a towel. Then dropping it into the pitcher she wet it thoroughly. By now, her head was spinning, caused by her supreme exertion, and everything in the room seemed to be moving.

"However, again clutching the marble, she permitted her now trembling body to fall gently to the floor when, again crawling, she reached the bed. She desired rest, just to sit there and catch her breath, so to speak, but, on that bed lay her Jean. And that thought renewed her will for, with every bit of remaining energy in that weak, trembling body, she drew herself onto the bed.

"Slowly, she moved to where she held him in her arms. And then she noticed he was completely robed and that his respiration was normal. Believing his ailment could not be very serious, she decided not to call for help, for he was hers, alone now, and alone they would remain. Instead, she reached for the wet towel and with it began to wipe his face, saying softly, 'Jean, Jean wake up. Then drawing him closer she held him tight and said, 'Jean, you're mine now, never to leave me; never.'

"Jean's eyes slowly opened; and believing it all to be a dream, he murmured, 'My God, would that it were true.'

" 'It is true, Jean—it is true. Look, I kiss you, I hold you. Oh, Jean, my beloved—don't sob so, please, don't cry.'

"Then holding him so that the light from the candle fell full on his face, she added, 'Darling, what hell you must have been through. Your face is drawn; your eyes, hollow—tell me—'

" 'For forty-one days, Sweet, you've been insane, collapsing immediately after our "in-the-eyes-of-God marriage." '

" 'Good God, for forty-one days you must have been in a living hell.'

"Let's forget it, sweet. Come, let's change positions and you lie in my arms where I can hold you, never to let you go. There—now, my, but it's wonderful to hold you so, to kiss you on your lips, on your neck—but, Belle, your gown has opened and—'

" 'Let it remain as it is, for Jean, my darling, I am yours forever and ever. Do whatever you will, but hold me tighter, my love. Kiss me and kiss me again. I pray that I may be what you've always wanted me to be, a dutiful and obedient wife; but, oh, Jean, don't ever go through that ordeal again.'

" 'Belle, my sweet, before I'll again permit you to experience what you've been through, I'll see my soul burning in hell. Now, Belle, get under the cover while I—'

" 'Jean, where are you going?'

" 'Where does your father keep his nightshirts?'

" 'In the armoir.'

" 'And, Jean,' whispered Belle, petting his face ever so gently, for he was by her side again, 'before you kiss me, please take back what you said about your soul burning in hell.'

"Leaning over, he gently answered, 'I'm sorry, my love; I'm sorry.'

CHAPTER XVIII

EMILE'S VISIT

"I returned late in the evening from driving. Turning my horse over to a slave, I entered my room full of foreboding. I was sure something serious was about to happen; in fact, my mind was so troubled that I began pacing the floor. As most people do when in trouble, I reached for my Holy Bible and read for about two hours. Then I felt that I was composed enough to sleep; so I slipped into bed. I began tossing from side to side as the clock chimed the hours and half hours; the last I heard was two-thirty."

"Emile, as you are usually calm, you must have been very much worried."

"I was, Grace. However, at ten o'clock next morning, I awoke with a start. I felt I should be with them; so, omitting my bath and shave, I dressed immediately and was on my way. Nearing their home, imagine my surprise to meet the doctor with a smile on his face.

" 'Doctor, you seem pleased this morning.'

" 'Very much so—but as it is a pleasant surprise and you evidently are on your way to visit them I'll—'

" 'Then she's better?'

" 'So much so that you should have seen her eating a heavy breakfast.'

" 'She must be hungry, I imagine.'

" 'No, it wasn't hunger, but the desire to gain strength quickly to nurse Jean. My, I've never seen such devotion. And, Emile, why don't you write the story of their lives?'

" 'The public wouldn't believe it, Doctor.'

" 'I'm not so sure of that. You know from the little I've observed the public likes the unusual.'

" 'Maybe!' I grunted, and shaking his hand I was off in a hurry to see them.

"Arriving at their home, I rushed through the hall and walked through the open door. In the fraction of a second, I realized the situation—Jean was in bed, and Belle was sitting at his side, stroking his hair. I shouted, 'Congratulations'—and both of them started as though wishing to come to me, when Belle, seeing Jean move, gently forced him down, saying, 'No, no, darling, Emile will come to you.'

" 'Please do,' he begged.

"And Belle, with her blue-black eyes again beaming in excitement directed me to the other side of the bed. 'No, Emile, not in the chair, but sit on the bed.'

" 'My!' I exclaimed, 'this is the happinest surprise I've ever experienced. Tell me all about it—er—er—that is—'

" 'Listen, I'm ashamed of nothing; and I know that Jean isn't either; so to you, we'll tell everything.'

"And so, Grace, they told me what I've been telling you. They also added that the joy of the past ten hours fully repaid them for all the heartaches they had endured.

" 'Well,' I said, 'you two deserve much happiness.' And as if I didn't know, I asked, 'Why are you in bed, Jean?'

"Belle answered, saying, 'When the doctor entered this morning, I was dressed in my négligée sitting on the edge of the bed and Jean was as you see him now. After examining me, he eyed Jean; and, placing both his hands on my shoulder, he said that Jean had stood by me day and night for forty-one days, during which time only his love for me kept him from being where I've come from. Therefore he should remain in bed for at least one week, and he placed him in my care.' "

CHAPTER XIX

A Ten-Hour Drive

"Emile, is that their Holy Bible on the table?"

"The very one, Grace."

"May I see the marriage record?"

"Surely—here on page four."

"But it is dated May nineteenth, eighteen sixty-one—why that is only two months ago."

"That's correct."

"And Belle and Jean are in that tomb?"

"What?"

"Don't be rude, Emile."

"I'm not rude. Will you repeat what you said?"

"I asked whether Belle and Jean are in that tomb?"

"Why, no, Grace, they are very much alive—happy as—"

"Did you say, alive?"

"Yes, I did."

"Alive, Emile?"

"Alive, Grace."

Grace moved to a sitting position on the chaise lounge, stared at Emile, and shook her head as if to clear it. Her eyes stared at him in bewilderment; then her little hands began to close into little fists. Her large blue eyes gradually began to narrow until they were mere slits. Realizing what Emile had said, she leaped from the chaise lounge and began beating him on his chest with both her fists, shouting, "You tricked me, tricked me—"

Emile began to laugh; and the more she struck her feeble blows, the more he laughed. Trying to avoid her, he moved about the room; and finally striking the chaise-lounge, he fell into it flat on his back. Grace tripped and fell halfway across him, which made him laugh so heartily that she, righting herself, sat at his side, looked down at him, and catching his spirit, smiled, and then burst into laughter.

When they became composed, Emile asked, "Why, Grace, whatever gave you the idea they were dead?"

"Never you mind, you big brute," she answered, kissing his face which rested between her hands, "for that you will take me to them right now."

"Don't be silly, honey," he replied; "why it's ten-thirty, and it is a good ten hours' drive."

Whereupon, she again began beating his chest with her small fists, crying, "You owe it to me; and I don't care how far it is."

He grabbed her little hands, held them, and rose from the chaise lounge. Then releasing them, he seized her by the waist, raising her completely off of the floor so that their faces met, and in that position he said, "Kiss me first and then say please."

"That's easy," she answered, kissing him full on the lips, and whispered in her sweet way, "Please."

Putting her down, Emile reached for the tassel, jerking it. When the bell rang, a slave entered. "Mammy, this is Grace, my sweetheart; and Grace, this is Belle's second mother."

Grace rushed over and hugged her, saying, "So you were the one that witnessed her marriage!"

"Yes, chile, I was, in dat room right up here," she replied, pointing to a second-story room in the adjoining house. She continued: "Then came the misser'ble days."

"Yes," Grace answered, "Emile has told me of her and Jean; and Mammy, he tricked me—tricked me into believing they were dead by showing me a tomb."

"He didn't trick yo, honey; he'll explain." And, looking towards Emile, she asked, "Yo wants me, Massa?"

"Yes, Mammy. Have my sulky hitched."

"But a sulky is fo one person," she rejoined.

"Tonight it will ride two."

"I sees," she chuckled and then asked, "What horse?"

"My favorite, Fidel."

With that, the slave woman left them. Grace turned to Emile and inquired, "What does Fidel mean?"

"In English, Fidelity."

"Always something with romance, Emile?"

"Yes, always romance." And he continued, "You know, Grace, every house in this old French city, a city within a city, can boast of at least one beautiful romance; in fact, the history of this city just teems with romance."

Just then, the sulky was driven to the door; and, Emile, placing Grace in his lap, gave the horse a command. Through the carriage entrance they rolled off to Belle and Jean.

When they had reached the road, Emile asked, "Comfortable, honey?"

"Comfortable and snug—and, Emile, happy. On what road are we?"

"The road to Baton Rouge, dear."

"A ten hours' drive?"

"Yes, a ten hours' drive to a plantation that Delphine purchased with every penny sent her for Jean's support."

"And, about that tomb?"

"Well, I could have told you about that in the cemetery; but every time I see it my eyes become moist, remembering Belle in her bed, her jet black curls in contrast with her beautiful white transparent skin, those curls spread over the large pillow—and she insane."

"Oh, I see. But what is it all about?"

"After their week of happiness, having been through so much hell, they resolved never to be separated again, either in life or in death; so the next morning they repaired to a tomb maker. Jean contracted for that tomb with every penny he had saved; so, as he told me, they would remain in death as they were in life—inseparable."

"Emile, I believe, as you said, their romance is second to none."

"Yes, I love it. Now, Grace, it is nearing midnight, and I want you to cuddle a little closer, then shut your eyes, and sleep."

Grace shifted about a bit, lifted the hand that was holding the reins, kissed it, closed her eyes, and slept.

CHAPTER XX.

Send for the Minister

When they reached the plantation, a slave ran up to the horse and held it by the bridle while Emile, stiff from sitting in one position for hours, gradually edged his legs out of the sulky, holding his precious load gently so as not to waken her, not noticing that one blue eye had opened and quickly closed again. To be hugged was wonderful, but to be carried by him, why that was real ecstasy.

Walking straight through the massive pillars on the veranda and through the large open door, Emile came to a stair leading to the sceond floor and would have climbed it had not Belle, seeing him, come running, shouting, "Emile, Emile."

Grace opened only one eye; and when she saw Belle, recognizing her from the picture in Emile's studio, she jerked herself out of Emile's arm and ran to meet her, crying, "Belle, Oh, Belle."

Emile stood staring and noticed that Belle reciprocated Grace's hug to the fullest extent. And when Belle said, "I believe you are Grace," his eyes opened wide and he stammered, "Say, what in hell is this all about?"

Belle answered, "A little bird told me all about Grace—how pretty and how sweet she was; but it did not do her justice."

"I don't think anyone could. But tell me, has Jeanne visited you?"

"Yesterday."

"I understand now; and, Belle, will you take Grace upstairs to freshen up a bit or shall I; you see we came in the sulky."

"All the way from the city in a sulky?"

"Yes, Belle."

"And where did Grace sit?"

"I didn't sit, but snuggled in Emile's lap and slept."

"You naughty children; but come, Grace, let's go upstairs." So, hand in hand, the two happy women ran up to the only vacant room.

"My," said Grace, "this is a beautiful room, and what a grand view of the Missisisippi River; but it seems to be furnished for a man."

"It is; this is Emile's room; and we let no one else use it. Grace, since it is the only one, and since you and Emile will spend some time with us, I am wondering just how to handle the situation?"

"Well, I know I'll not permit you and Jean to separate at night so that you and I can sleep together and Emile and Jean together; that is strictly out, for I imagine you sleep in his arms."

"Yes, in his arms. And may I congratulate you upon having Emile as a sweetheart?"

"Congratulations are in order, Belle; and he is the most darling, the most chivalrous man I've ever known. You know, I love Ceole culture; and, Belle, when he says do something, his tone of voice alone betrays he's addressing a woman; yet, at the same time, it is a command—and I love it. You know, I was sitting on his lap, looking up at him when he said, 'Grace, it is almost midnight, and a want you to cuddle a little closer, shut your eyes, and go to sleep.' I recognized that as a command, and cuddling closer I felt the urge to kiss his hand and did it. It thrilled me so that my body shook. Looking up, I realized that he, too, felt it, for he glanced down and smiled."

"Jeanne told me you were terribly in love."

"I am, Belle; in fact, I am really only happy when I'm with him."

"And she told me he was equally in love with you."

"She did? And what else did she say?"

"Oh!—Among other things she said you must not misconstrue his great affection as weakness for, in reality, it is love in its most serious form. She further added that Emile's life was spent in an environment where the men dominate, and for you not to obey would be a catastrophe for both of you; whereas, if you are humble, he will shower you with courtesies and affection, and you will never experience anything but extreme gentleness throughout your life."

"I've noticed you and Jeanne are humble.'

"Yes, and we wouldn't be different for the world, knowing full well that we would lose joys that other wives never receive."

"I want to be like that, too, Belle, and I will ask him to insist on the word 'obey', if and when we marry."

"You haven't set the date?"

"We've never spoken of it."

"But, Grace, he wants you."

"I know, but sh—sh—. Here he comes." Rushing to the door to meet him, Grace said, "Emile, this is to be our room."

Emile, staring into her eye, smiled and looked at Belle as much as to say, "You two have been plotting."

Looking back at Grace, he found her small hands feeling their way up slowly to his chest while the side of her face rested against him. Subconsciously he placed his left arm around her, tilting her face upward with his right hand, and was about to say something when she, looking humbly into his eyes, said, "Emile, will you have them put the word 'obey' in the ceremony?"

Emile dropped his right hand and lifted her into his arms, kissing her on the neck and walking towards the second-story veranda, where a large rocker awaited them. Then turning to Belle, he said, "Send for the Minister."

FINIS

PETITE

CHAPTER I

EMILE AND GRACE

"Still writing, Emile?"

"No, I've just finished the story."

"Have you named it?"

"Yes."

"Now tell me, may I kiss you?"

"Please do."

"Now do you want your rocker? See, I've made it comfortable with pillows."

"Thanks, but is it possible that you had a motive in suggesting the rocker? Come now, confess."

"Darling, I er—er—Oh, you know, I want to sit on your lap. See how the rain falls and the lightning flashes; you know how I fear it and—"

"You feel safer in my lap."

"You darling, you always help me in a fib."

"Are you comfortable?"

"Very much so, and very happy. Any plans for to-night?"

"No, nothing special—I want only to relax."

"You should; you have worked too steadily on the book. And do you remember where you mentioned about the old French Quarter teeming with romance?"

"Yes, I do."

"Well, since it's raining and you are relaxing, won't you please tell me about one of those romances?"

"You're so damned sweet Honey, I could not possibly refuse you anything."

"It is easy for me to be that way with you, Emile; you are the only man on earth I would humble myself to."

"Why?"

"Because you reciprocate with such kindness; and oh, now that I've learned to express those affectionate sentiments, I shouldn't want to be otherwise for I know I should lose you."

"That would happen. You know, Grace, a Northerner once

said to me, 'Emile, you Creoles think much more of your women than we do, but you exact a price.'

" 'In what way?' I asked him.

" 'Well, you handle them with kid gloves and you place them on a pedestal as God's greatest creation, but you demand obedience and humility in return—I wonder whether it's worth it'."

"And what was your answer?"

"To the effect that our women demand constant and lasting affection, as did their mothers who realized that to prolong the courtship after marriage they would have to continue to be their sweet, humble selves. Girls and boys living in such an environment, I further explained, absorbed this ideal of living and knew no other."

"I could have answered him as to the price we pay."

"What would you have said?"

"Well, that I would pay that price a hundred fold. In fact, I have been reared in a thoroughly different environment; and since I've known you and have acted as I've seen Jeanne act towards Paul, and Belle towards Jean, I have for the first time in my life felt thoroughly feminine. How would you describe this kind of life?"

"Well, one never hears a woman boast that she henpecks her husband, even though there are many, for the reason that she realizes it is wrong. If one should ask her why she henpecks, she would first deny it and would, if forced to give an answer, say that she did not know; and Grace, she really wouldn't know, for the reason is in the subconscious mind."

"I don't exactly understand the subconscious mind. Can you explain it so—er—er—possibly give me an example?"

"Well, let's see—yes, here is a true example. One of my friends was working at his trade a distance from the city. He informed his employer on Saturday that he would resign unless an increase in his wages was forthcoming by the following Tuesday on account of the distance he was forced to travel. On Sunday morning he was in exceptionally high spirits; and when I asked the reason, he explained his conversation with his employer, and added, 'Emile, truthfully, I haven't the faintest inkling as to what my employer's decision will be so that I cannot tell you whether the fact that my wages may be increased, or that I may be idle to enjoy myself is responsible for my happiness.'

"You see, his subconscious mind caused him to be happy; but he didn't know why. Personally, I would believe that although his conscious mind did not know it, either decision by his employer would have been welcome to him."

"Oh! I see. That is the reason why at times I feel somewhat depressed; and when I wonder why, I often suddenly remember an unpleasant thought that I had many hours before."

"That is exactly an occurrence of the subconscious mind. Let me explain further for it is necessary that you thoroughly understand this subject to appreciate the beautiful love story you're about to hear."

"A woman endeavors without really knowing why to break a man to where he will take orders from her. If and when she succeeds, she again, not knowing the reason why, loses not only all respect for him, but also whatever love or affection she may have for him. This reaction is caused by nature, that is, woman subconsciously demands that the father of her children be a man of courage, one capable of ruling a home, since woman herself, again subconsciously, doesn't feel that she is the equal of man in making momentous decisions. This, of course, is an inheritance from the stone age when women who mated with inferior men had inferior protection with usually the loss of their childless lives; therefore it was only natural that those who had children were those that endeavored to 'break' their men, and failing, accepted them as their mates."

"My, it is simple when it's explained. In other words, a woman's choice is actuated by her subconscious mind. But tell me, shouldn't this inheritance diminish with each generation?"

"Only slowly, for remember that man inherits from his mother two breast which are definitely useless to him as woman inherit from her father a certain male organ, both of which have been handed down from generation to generation for thousands of years. Now, since those are parts of the human body, so also is the brain with its subconscious desires."

"And have you actually witnessed a woman endeavoring subconsciously to break a man?"

"Certainly, hundreds of times."

"And if the woman fails?"

"Then comes love—not because her conscious mind realizes that she cannot rule the man, but because her subconscious mind is satisfied with him as a mate. And Grace, that is the reason why scientists claim women are more sensible in chosing their mates, for the men choose strictly for appearance as is evidenced by the females using cosmetics, powder, etc., while handsomeness of the male is definitely of second importance to the female, her subconscious acceptance or, as some name it, her sixth sense acceptance being of first importance."

"Then, would you say that love is a product of, or rather the acceptance of the subconscious mind?"

"Definitely, all true love is of that mind; proof of what I say can be found in the life of anyone who has loved and forgotten. For instance, let anyone think back to the time he loved someone to actual distraction, and learned later not to love that person. Should he see the party of his former affection, he wondered why he loved her, not being able to understand what attraction caused the former affection, finding no reason whatsoever. In other words, the conscious mind cannot see what the subconscious mind accepts or will accept as a mate."

"I understand, but I'm afraid we've digressed. I asked you to explain so that I could understand the Creole ideal of living, that is, concerning the actions of the men towards the women and vice versa."

"Well, since you now understand the principal of the action of the subconscious mind, you can understand why members of the human race prefer the exact opposite, and the more they are separated, the more one appeals to the other. Let me put it this way: 'Blonds prefer brunettes; tall men prefer short women; thin men prefer heavy women; and in like reasoning, the more a woman is feminine, the more masculine she prefers her man. Of course, by feminine I mean gentle and dependent."

"In other words, Emile, a one-hundred per-cent masculine man prefers a one-hundred-per-cent feminine woman."

"Yes, that is right—the one-hundred-per-cent man would care less for a seventy-five-per-cent feminine woman and not at all for a masculine woman; and, of course, the same is true of the really feminine woman. Now, humility is definitely a feminine trait; and if we find it in a man, we call him a sissy. So that the more a woman is humble, the more she inculcates in her man masculinity, which lies in his subconscious mind, definitely not the conscious; he experiences a satisfaction that leads him to treasure the woman; and not knowing why, or accepting the reasoning of the conscious mind that she is 'sweet', he desires to hold her, to kiss her, and to tell her flattering things. So the Creole men, if I may repeat, demand humility; and the women, domination. They continue their love and affection after marriage, for it is not as I've heard elsewhere, 'the signal of business' or, a case of 'Love flies out of the window after marriage'."

"In other words, courtship continues after marriage."

"That is exactly what happens."

"And how long does it continue?"

"Through life. But, Grace, my limbs are aching a bit, suppose we go to bed."

"Now Honey, you sit at the head of the bed with a pillow behind you."

"Like this?"

"Yes. And now I shall lie on my back across the bed with my head resting in your arms—like this."

"That is odd, my holding you, but I imagine it is new to all newlyweds. However, I rather like you in this position."

"I am enjoying it too for it is very restful; and I have but to look up to enjoy seeing a beautiful face."

"May I kiss you?"

"Surely, sweet, help . . ."

"But Emile, I don't . . . seem to want . . . to stop."

"Well, you had better or I can't tell you the story of that beautiful romance."

"Alright, begin—but when I stop to ask, 'what comes next', may I just kiss you once? You know, you are a terrible temptation lying there."

"Yes, I know you kissing bug. But you know Sweet I enjoy those shapely lips of yours."

"Darling, you do say the nicest things—begin."

CHAPTER II

LAFITTE THE PIRATE

"Well, Grace, we shall have to go back to the year 1814. It was then eleven years since the tri-color of France had been lowered in Jackson Square and the Stars and Stripes raised there; and although the population resented the transfer, the Creoles accustomed themselves to the fact that they were citizens of the U. S. A.; but they continued to live as they had formerly done.

"Among them was a man who operated a blacksmith shop as a ruse, being in reality what some called a buccaneer, while others termed him a pirate."

"A real pirate?"

"Yes, a real pirate; and his blacksmith shop stands on the corner of Bourbon and St. Philip Streets; it's a picturesque building, and it has large cypress posts between the bricks; they were placed there so as to offset the inevitable sinking of the building in the water-soaked earth. In this building, on the second floor, the pirate, Jean Lafitte, often entertained his friends. One day he sat there conversing seriously with a sailor. 'Jean, I tell you, the English fleet is in the Gulf.'

" 'But what can they do? Our fort protects the river.'

" 'Yes, but aboard that fleet is an army.'

" 'What?'

" 'Yes, an army; and if I'm not mistaken, they will try to take New Orleans.'

" 'And from where are they receiving their supplies?'

" 'Mainly from England, but other ships deliver their freight to Mexico and from there it is delivered to the fleet; and Jean, the 'Southern Star,' a French ship, is bound with full cargo for Mexico.'

" 'That's odd—a French ship bound for Mexico!'

" 'That is what I think.'

" 'And you say the name is 'The Southern Star?'

" 'Yes.'

" 'When did you last see her?'

" 'Yesterday; now she should be near the mouth of the river.'

" 'Will you come with me?'

" 'No piracy, Jean!'

" 'No, I promise.'

"And, Grace, the two men left the blacksmith shop and, mounting their horses, headed for the river. Once across, they continued towards the swamps. There, among the cypress trees, were tied dozens of pirogues; and a few feet away was a band of men, a motley crowd, playing cards. Each, when he lost, swore at the top of his voice. Jean Lafitte and his guest reached these men, who, at his command rose, entered their boats, and followed their chief. 'Something serious is afoot, Josef,' one said.

" 'Yes, I've never seen him so serious.'

" 'Nor have I. Maybe, Josef, the monotony will be broken.' And so continued the conversation as they travelled westerly in the bayou for many miles; then south to a strong lodge or fort, where hundreds of men awaited them. Lafitte drew up, still in mid-stream, and asked, 'Where is Dominique?'

" 'Eating,' came the reply.

" 'Call him.' A man then rushed into the lodge and emerged with another, one that any antagonist would respect. 'What's up, Jean?'

" 'Leave eighteen men here. You and the remainder follow me.' So saying, Lafitte sent his pirogue southward along the beautiful bayou, followed now by hundreds of small boats with two men in each. Dominique You, Lafitte's first lieutenant, paddled quickly and, reaching Lafitte's boat, tied them together saying, 'Jean, what is wrong?'

" 'Plenty, Dominique. The British are preparing to invade our beautiful city.'

" 'Jean, you don't mean that!'

" 'I do. We will seize all ships delivering supplies to Mexico.'

" 'To Mexico?'

" 'Yes, for ships from other countries are delivering their cargoes there, not realizing that those supplies will help the British.'

" 'Damn it!' And, in silence they paddled past alligators and snakes, down, down the winding stream until they reached a bay where four large ships lay anchored. About them hundreds of porpoises sported in the green sea water, their bodies seeming to form large serpents. Lafitte and his men practically lived among them; so they paid no attention to them, paddling directly to the boats. The men aboard, realizing that something of a serious nature had happened, jammed the bulwarks; some dived overboard and swam towards Lafitte and Dominique You, their naked bodies gliding through the water as gracefully as those of the porpoises. Returning to their ships, the men separated, each proceeding towards his particular vessel. On board, everything was in order; the cutlasses were in their places; and the guns, ready for firing. Lafitte immediately gave orders to unfurl the sails. Then, with his ship as flagship, they sailed out of the peaceful harbor, bent, as the crew was told, to capture the 'Southern Star'. Lafitte also explained the reason; and each man, realizing the condition New Orleans would be in under the British, swore that the 'Southern Star' would not escape. The chase was on—and Lafitte, after steering directly south for leagues, divided his boats in a way that they were eight leagues apart, the total distance being twenty leagues, and then hoisted a signal which denoted a shift to direct east."

"Those four boats, Emile, twenty miles apart and sailing east with their sails extended must have been a beautiful sight."

"They were, especially to the men in the crow's nest, who, with their powerful glasses scanned the horizon in the hope that they would be the first to sight their victim, as Lafitte had offered a special prize of five hundred dollars.

"They had traveled for hours when they sailed into muddy water which they knew was south of the Mississippi River. Lafitte was about to veer farther to the south when a voice from the crow's nest bellowed, 'Sail to port, sail to port.'

"The weather was beautiful, as a strong west wind was blowing against the heavy canvas sails while overhead soared hundreds of pelicans and gulls. Now and then, small fish seemed literally to push themselves through the water into the air in order to save their lives from bigger fish. Lafitte ordered his fleet to continue on the same course and at the same distance, for, if they steered all the boats in the direction of their victim, they would excite suspicion, and probably the 'Southern Star' would escape. All the men hid so that when the skipper of the 'Southern Star' trained his glasses on the pirate fleet, he concluded that they were fishing vessels, especially when seins hung from every ship, a natural camouflage to all boats in that trade. The men in the crow's nests having slid down the ropes, hand under hand, reported to their captains that the 'Southern Star' had many guns. The crews, on being informed of this fact, rolled up their sleeves, while their faces plainly revealed the satisfaction they felt at the idea of a fight. And, Grace, while Lafitte's boats traveled swiftly, the 'Southern Star' had to tack due to the west wind. Again Lafitte gave orders, this time veering all his ships to head towards a point he knew where the enemy would be when they would meet. On they sailed, all converging to that one point when the captain of the 'Southern Star', becoming suspicious, changed his course and veering south, sought to escape. Lafitte then changed his order to 'give chase'. Everyone was excited, for here was a captain that was not docile, and they well knew that when a skipper decided to flee he would, on being overhauled, fight.

"The pirate's flag had been hoisted; and Lafitte ordered his three other boats to reduce their canvas so that his alone would engage the enemy for, Grace, although Lafitte was called a pirate by some, he was a gentleman and would not take advantage of a foe. Naturally, he wanted to intercept that ship; so he reasoned that if he were in danger, the other ships would close in with all canvas to the wind. His ship, one captured from the Spaniards on a previous raid, was faster than the 'Southern Star'; and the latter's captain realized that he would be overhauled and that his rival was no ordinary pilot, but one that would permit the other fellow a fighting chance. Sharply turning his ship he headed directly for Lafitte because, as he thought, the possibility of wounding or killing the leader of the band might cause disorder which might permit his escape.

"The captain, a French nobleman, was tall, somewhat slender, clean shaven, with blond hair and sharp blue eyes, eyes that had now narrowed as if in sympathy with his tightly closed lips that ordinarily attracted many women. He loved a fight; and as the ship neared, his keen eyes began to sparkle, and his thin stern lips changed slowly into a smile, at the same time showing teeth that were forced together:

"As the two ships came toward each other the veteran Lafitte, realizing that the 'Southern Star' might get by his larger ship and sink the smaller ones, decided to cross his bow and at the same time give the Frenchman a broadside while he would be at a disadvantage and could not use his guns. He didn't reckon with the man, for the captain of the 'Southern Star' expected this move and immediately swung his ship around and ordered a broadside. Whether it was luck or marksmanship, we shall never know, Grace; but he struck Lafitte's main mast; the timber with its heavy sails fell to the deck, entangling the other lines so that the spars would not answer to their ropes. In this condition, Lafitte's ship would have been at the mercy of the 'Southern Star'; but, since Lafitte had acted as a gentleman by not permitting his fleet to crush his antagonist, the Frenchman also reciprocated like a gentleman; so, getting out of range, he steered his boat directly into the other three boats. Dominique You, realizing what had happened, ordered two boats to maneuver so that the 'Southern Star' would be between them; then they might come close enough to make fast to the ship and board her. He also ordered the third boat to rescue Lafitte and, of course, be his flagship. While this ship completed its mission, the captain, realizing that he was trapped, decided to ram Dominique You's ship, and, in turning, again whether through luck or marksmanship, he struck You's mast; and it, like that of the flagship, crumbled to the deck.

"It was now too late to change his course, so, veering as best he could, the Frechman side-swiped You's ship; and that pirate, taking advantage of the vessels touching each other, ordered his men to prepare to use the grapling hooks. Hundreds of them were ready. So, when the ships met, the hooks were attached; and almost immediately You's men with their cutlasses boarded the 'Southern Star'. The captain, realizing what had happened, ordered his men to fight, and drawing his pistol, fired with telling effect; and would have again won had not Lafitte's second ship made fast to his other side. Its men poured into his ship, making him realize that further resistance meant death to his crew and himself. For himself he would have fought until death, but to have his crew murdered was certainly not the tradition of a Frechman. So the brave man surrendered to Lafitte after crippling the pirate's two larger boats."

"Emile, he became the prisoner of a mean pirate?"

"No, Grace, for Lafitte was not mean; on the contrary, he was a gentleman who recognized gallantry and bravery; so much so that when the captain was brought before him in his lodge, the pirate welcomed him, not as a defeated warrior, but as a brother, since he was a Frenchman. The pirate invited him and his crew to partake of their dinner, serving them their finest foods and wines, and also introducing many delicious dishes which were new to the Frenchmen. However, I'm ahead of my story."

CHAPTER III

ANTOINE

" 'No, captain, I have no desire for your sword.'

" 'But this is irregular.'

" 'Not when Frenchmen meet Frenchmen.'

" 'But you have stolen my ship.'

" 'You are wrong. But first permit me to introduce myself, I am Jean Lafitte. May I ask your name?'

" 'Antoine Floret.'

" 'Floret, Floret—let me think; I know that name. Oh! yes, surely I do, Captain Eugene Floret.'

" 'He is my father.'

" 'His son! Oh, yes, now I see the resemblance; and, Antoine, I now know why your ship was so perfectly maneuvered, and from whom you inherited your courage and bravery.'

" 'Then you knew my father? I hope he did not feel towards you as I do.'

" 'Knew him? He was the only captain that beat me while he sailed a ship for Spain. Later we met in New Orleans; and when he realized his mission, like all true Frenchmen, he forgave me, and we became the best of friends.'

" 'My father is more magnanimous than I am.'

" 'I refuse to believe that, and—'

" 'Will you please inform me as to what disposal you will make of my men?'

" 'Gladly.' And, Grace, walking to a large door that led to the mess hall, he opened it wide and said, 'Captain, come and see for yourself.'

" 'Lafitte, I don't understand you. First, you confiscate my ship; then you feast my men. Or maybe it is the death feast. Tell me, are you friend or foe?'

" 'I assure you, Antoine, I am your friend.'

" 'I don't understand!'

" 'Of course you don't. But tell me, did you not pass the British armada when you passed south of Alabama? '

" 'I do not. But before I answer another question, kiindly explain why you attacked my ship, a French ship flying a French flag.'

" 'Antoine, are you not aware of the fact that the United States and Great Britain are at war?'

" 'Now, yes, but I definitely know that your country and England will sign a Treaty of Peace by the latter part of this month.'

" 'The English may attack before then or after, since it will take weeks for the news to reach their fleet.'

" 'That may be true; but France is not concerned, and her flag should be respected.'

" 'Antoine, listen well to what I have to say. First, I have adopted New Orleans as my home and the United States of America as my country. Second, I, like you, was born a Frenchman, and again, like you, I would fight any but my adopted country to uphold the honor of the tricolor. Don't interrupt, please, let me finish. I have not seen your papers, but I know you were enroute to Mexico. There you were to discharge your cargo—a cargo that was destined for the British fleet. As a Frenchman, knowing that the English will attack my French city, my New Orleans, my hundreds of friends, I attacked you. Now just what would you have done under the same circumstances?'

" 'If such were the truth, I would have acted as you've done; but I don't believe the English will attack.'

" 'Man, I don't want to get angry with you, but please believe me, for—'

" 'What proof have you?'

" 'Proof?'

" 'Yes, you wouldn't expect me to believe you under the circumstances.'

" 'Yes, maybe you're right. Tell me, would you recognize the English name of Nicholls, Lieutenant Colonel Nicholls.'

" 'Yes, I know him personally.'

" 'Would you recognize his signature?'

" 'Definitely.'

" 'Then, mon ami—I call you that for I know you will be my friend—read this document!' And, Grace, he read where the British announced themselves friends of the Creoles and were ready to liberate them from the United States. But they did not state under which flag New Orleans would be; so Antoine realized the perfidy of the sender.

"'Mr. Lafitte, I would question this document had I not recognized Edward Nicholl's signature, but that does not mean an attack.'

"'Antoine, here is another, and please notice that it is addressed to me, or the "Commandant at Barataria". I found those documents when I returned from the city.'

"And he read where the British—"

"Emile, please read me the exact document?"

"I will have to move."

"Please, Emile."

"All right, sweet, but I will want to be in the same position.

Now kiss me first and then I will read."

"There, now read; but that document is brown with age."

"Yes, it is. Now listen, it begins with:

"'Mr. Lafitte, or Commandant of Barataria:

"'Sir—

"'I have arrived in the Floridas for the purpose of annoying the only enemy Great Britain has in the world, as France and England are now friends. I call on you with your brave followers to enter into the service of Great Britian in which you shall have the rank of captain; lands will be given to you all in proportion to your respective ranks on a peace-making basis, and I invite you on the following terms:

"'Your property shall be guaranteed to you and your persons protected; in return for which I ask you to cease all hostilities against Spain or the Allies of Great Britain. Your ships and vessels are to be placed under the orders of the commanding officer of this station until the Commander-in-Chief's pleasure is known; but I guarantee their fair value at all events. I herewith enclose you a copy of my proclamation to the inhabitants of Louisiana, which will, I trust, point out to you the honorable intentions of my government. You may be a useful assistant to me in forwarding them; therefore, if you accept, lose no time. The bearer of

this, Captain McWilliams, will satisfy you on any other point
you may be anxious to learn about, as will Captain Lockyer of
the Sophia, who brings it to you. We have a powerful reinforce-
ment on its way here, and I hope to cut out some other work for
the American than oppressing the inhabitants of Louisiana. Be
expeditious in your resolves and rely on the verity of

"Your very obedient servant,

" 'Edward Nicholls.' "

"Thanks, Emile. Was Antoine convinced?"

"Well, as Antoine read, his large hands alternately closed and
opened until near the end when they remained tightly closed,
forming two large fists. Lafitte, watching closely, also noticed
that the arteries in his neck swelled almost to the bursting point,
while his face was red with rage. When he lifted his head, his
expressive blue eyes revealed the emotion within his breast; he
rose saying, 'Lafitte, if I wasn't positive of that signature, I would
say that it is a forgery, for it is unbelievable.'

" 'I am glad you realize its authenticity and its importance to
my people; I swear by all that is holy that the English General
Packenham will not take my city. You, Antoine, can help me
as you will also help other Frenchmen by fighting by their side
to preserve their women, for they, the British, are crying,
'Beauty and Booty'; and man, if you are a true Frenchman, you
. . . will . . . fight.'

" 'You mean that they will harm French women?'

" 'Exactly.'

" 'My God, Lafitte, I'll—tell me, what do you propose doing?'

" 'I now see that you are a true Frenchman—talk of harming
women and your blood boils. But to answer your question—I
know that Jackson is recruiting an army; and since my men are
natural fighters and second to none in bravery, I'll call on him in
person and offer our aid; and unless he is an ass, I am certain he
will accept it.'

" 'Who is Jackson?'

" 'The American general in charge of the city's defense.'

" 'But, if I understand my father correctly, there is a price on
your head.'

" 'Yes, there are placards about the city by Governor Claiborne
offering a reward of five hundred dollars for my capture. You

know what I did when I saw those placards, Antoine? Well I printed some of my own and offered fifteen hundred dollars for the arrest of the Governor.'

"And, Grace, both men laughed. However, when both had become quiet, Antoine asked, 'But wouldn't someone recognize you and cause your arrest?'

" 'Oh, everyone recognizes me; and I walk the streets of my city as you would, since all the people like me.'

" 'Like you?'

" 'Yes, for more reasons than one. You see, I bring them goods and wares at much lower prices since they are not compelled to pay me duty. I get them free by being a privateer. Further, I smuggle in slaves; and, Antoine, I do this without any compunction whatsoever, since the Americans have forbidden the entrance of slaves, and you will soon learn how dependent the Creoles are on them.'

" 'And you walk directly into the city with the merchandise and slaves?'

" 'No, the people all meet at a rendezvous in the swamps, and they are not the rabble, since there are no really poor persons in the city, but rather the clean-cut Creoles, including the priests.'

" 'I understand. But when Jackson sees you, won't he have you placed in irons?'

" 'Again I say, unless he is an ass, he will welcome my aid.'

" 'And if he doesn't?'

" 'Then, such a fool I can easily outwit.'

" 'I'll grant you that. But when will you see him?'

" 'When he reaches the city, which should be in a day or so.'

" 'Will he know you?'

" 'Who in America does not?'

" 'I didn't know that. But tell me, may I go with you.'

" 'I am sorry, but I must answer in the negative, for it will be necessary that I play a lone hand. I am going to the city tonight and will be glad to have your company. Incidentally, there will be one of the annual balls tonight; and I may be able to have my lawyer gain entrance for you, although you will not be able to attend as a captain, for you would be questioned about your ship.'

" 'But, Lafitte, why not return my ship.'

" 'On one condition only.'

" 'And what may that be?'

" 'That you order your men to sail it up the Mississippi to New Orleans.'

" 'That was my intention for, since the British intend fighting the Creoles, and especially since they intend to harm the women, I will be responsible for that ship reaching its new destination even though I realize the penalty of my being charged with piracy; and, Lafitte, mon ami, I will visit the city with you.' "

CHAPTER IV.

PETITE

"It had rained in the city that day, but the night was beautiful; every star shone as if in competition with the full moon whose rays cast weird shadows on the brick mansions and banquettes. Now and then, from all the streets, young Creoles, the girls accompanied by their mothers as chaperons, made their way to a central point—the grand ballroom. In some instances, female slaves accompanied their masters and mistresses carrying large pitchers and towels in one hand and shoes and stockings in the other.

"Although Creoles were dressed in the finest of suits and gowns, many having been imported from Paris, they were barefoot, since it had rained. To wear their shoes and stockings would have meant to enter the ballroom with them soiled. You see, Grace, until a few years ago the banquettes, or sidewalks as you call them, were always muddy after a rain. However, when these people reached their destination, they repaired to a room set aside for the purpose; there the women sat while the slaves washed their feet and put on their shoes and stockings. Of course, a room was also provided for the men; for no man saw his fiancé's feet until they were married."

"My, they were modest!"

"Too much so."

"What happened next?"

"Impatient little honey!"

"I like the way you said that."

"Why?"

"Because it seems to flow from your heart."

"Thanks. However, among the many families that would attend that ball was one named Champlain. It consisted of, in in addition to the parents, four girls and two boys. All of the children resembled the parents more or less, except one girl, who, all agreed, had inherited not only the appearance of her grandfather, but also his daring and cunning. This Louise, or

'Petite' as she was nicknamed, was charming. Besides, she had also a distinctive voice, for it was rich and throaty, seeming to be a compromise between the voice of a man and that of a woman.

"I don't exactly understand."

"Well, the only other way I can possibly describe it is to say it sounded like a feminine voices that seemed to emanate from deep down in the throat."

"Was it pleasing?"

"Very much so, for whenever she spoke her voice attracted people; so they immediately turned to look at her. In fact, she was always chosen to read or recite at the Ursuline Convent where she received her splendid education because, as the superioress explained to her mother, Petite's voice was not only pleasing, but also impressive as it changed when she read of sorrow or happiness; and her eyes, too, expressed every emotion."

"What color were they?"

"Dark brown, with long lashes and a mischievous expression. She was a real imp, Grace, not knowing a serious moment; in fact, it was generally acknowledged that there was never a dull moment when Petite was around."

"That sounds interesting. Do you know about some of her pranks?"

"Well, let's see—Oh! yes, I remember one, the wedding night, of her elder sister. After the ceremony, and at the height of the dancing, she pleaded illness and induced the groom's brother, Maurice, supposedly to accompany her home. Hardly had they left the hall when she confided to him a plan 'to have some fun'. They then stole over to the newlyweds' new home, and Petite unlocked the the door and Maurice lit the candles.

"Petite had taken a brush from the slave, and securing a scissors from her sister's sewing cabinet, she gave them to Maurice with instructions to cut the hair of the brush into millions of small particles, and to spread those particles on the sheet. She then poured a sizeable quantity of sedelitz powder into the night glass."

"But, didn't the newlyweds go on a honeymoon?"

"No, they retired to their new home; and, Grace, the custom

in the Vieux Carre is for the bride to remain in retirement for
fifteen days."

"You mean that that was the reason we remained at Belle's
home for fifteen days?"

"Yes."

"But I did not leave Belle and Jean."

"That is correct. You see, honey, they knew the Northern
custom was a honeymoon and regarded our stay as one. Since
they also knew the Creole custom, they expected our stay to
be for that length of time, knowing that I would not permit you
to leave the house nor to meet my friends in New Orleans until
that time had elapsed if we had returned to the city. In other
words, they feared you might resent being kept a prisoner; or if
I permitted you to go and come as usual, I should naturally have
been embarrassed before the neighbors."

"Oh! I see. But what did happen to the couple?"

"Well, when they returned that night and retired the cut hair
adhered to their skin which caused itching and the sedelitz powder effervesced when the night glass was used. In short, the
bride remained concealed for sixteen days."

"Emile, that must have been comical."

"Not to the newlyweds, for they remained angry with Petite
for over two weeks, knowing that her love for mischief had
prompted the deed. They would have remained angry with her
longer, but one could not—. Let me tell you their exact conversation on her first visit to their home."

"Please do."

"Well when Petite entered on the sixteenth day, she asked,
'Still angry?'

" 'Yes,' was the curt reply. Petite began to laugh, realizing
the reason why they would not answer the bell until the sixteenth
day instead of the fifteenth, and laughed until they began to
laugh with her; then she knew she was forgiven."

"She is interesting. Please tell me more about her."

"Well, to begin with, let me explain that she was the youngest
child; and like most last children, she was spoiled not only by
her parents, but also by her brother and sisters. This spoiling,
if you'll permit me to continue to use that expression, led her

to do many things that were not permitted other Creole girls."

"For instance?"

"Well, when she was ten years old, she begged her brothers to permit her to accompany them on a duck hunt. They had a small gauge gun that they used for hunting rabbits and took it along, too. They placed Petite in the center of the pirogue, a light hollowed-out log boat which they poled and paddled over the prairies, and placed her in a blind."

"A blind?"

"Yes, Grace, a blind. Oh! I forgot that word is new to you. You see, in the fall the men around here pole and paddle; that is, they push their pirogues over shallow water with a pole when the boat barely touches the bottom of the prairies and paddle where the water is deep, to small islands in the prairies and swamps, islands that might be only large enough to accompany one person. On these they build, with the surrounding dried grasses and weeds, what the French call camouflage, that is, places where one can be completely concealed and yet have full view of the surrounding water. Duck and other water fowl swoop down to feed around these places, never seeing the hunter. So they are called blinds; and into one of them Petite went, warmly clad, with a shotgun and ammunition, while her brothers occupied other blinds within earshot of hers. When the hunt was over, which was about eleven o'clock, imagine their surprise to find floating Mallard and Teal ducks and some geese equal in number to their kill. From that time, Petite went whenever she wished to, taking one of the slave girls named Phoebe, who knew the swamps, as she had accompanied other slaves in the trapping season for muskrats. Petite traveled the prairies and swamps far and wide hunting, in addition to ducks, squirrels, doves, and occasionally deer. By the time she was eighteen years old she knew the prairies and swamps as one knows a book."

"That was odd for a woman!"

"Yes, especially for a Creole, for her parents frowned on such masculine sports; but when they remonstrated, Petite only laughed and ended by kissing away the objection."

"I can understand that. She must have been sweet."

"Grace, she was not only sweet, but also impulsive and extremely gay at all times. Whether she was at work or play, she was always on the run, her chestnut brown curls tossed from side to side. Her gaiety charmed the men, for the girls of this community were very sedate."

CHAPTER V

SLAVE PSYCHOLOGY

"The ballroom was a beautiful large hall lighted with hundreds of colored flambeaus that cast a soft subdued light on the highly waxed cypress floor. On the walls and suspended from the pale blue ceiling that was covered with stars exactly as they appear in the night sky the committee had draped red, white, and blue bunting in addition to the flag of the United States and the tri-color of France. To the rear and in the center was the bandstand, built in a semicircle and also decorated with flags and bunting, while on its raised floor stood the music stands, each lighted by two extra thick candles that would burn until the wee hours of morning. Every window was open, permitting the fragrance of many flowers to enter from the surrounding patio where all varieties of beautiful sub-tropical blossoms were in bloom.

"The entrance was through two large doors, where, on this particular night, masses of young men congregated in and outside of the ballroom; they were bedecked in their finest, each waiting for a favorite girl—possibly one that was too young 'to receive company,' or again possibly one that had not consented to receive that particular young man as a 'beau'.

"Of course, many unmarried couples also entered, followed by the girls' parents and their younger offspring, that is, those between the ages of fourteen and sixteen. Those that lived at a distance, who were without carriages, were accompanied by slaves with pitchers and other essentials, as I've told you. The building had a side entrance for them where the young men purposely avoided the ladies so as not to embarrass them."

"Usually, Emile, one would expect the young men to be 'just there. "

"Not with these people, for, as I've told you, they were taught to respect women as God's greatest creation."

"An example of Creole culture?"

"That's right. However, through this side door strode Petite

and her mother. Sitting down, Petite extended both feet; and
the faithful slave washed them and carefully put on her stockings and shoes, ending by saying, 'Miss Petite, I hopes yo enjoy
yoself.'

" 'I will, Phoebe. I usually do.'

" 'I knows, for I seed Marster Joe, Marster Emile, Marster
Georges—tell me, honey, which do yo likes?'

" 'I like all of them.'

" 'Don't yo likes one better then the rest?'

" 'No, no one in particular.'

" 'But, Miss Petite, dere must be a best one.'

" 'Phoebe, they are all sweet and all good dancers; but I would
not care for any of them as a beau.'

" 'Yo not in luv, honey?'

" 'No.'

" 'But ev'ry girl at yo age is in luv.'

" 'Yes, I know, and I often wonder why I'm not.'

" 'I knows why.'

" 'Phoebe, you've been snooping.'

" 'No-o-mam—I ain't been snooping—I swears it. But I knows
how I got my nigger.'

" 'You mean Sam?'

" 'Yes'm.'

" 'How did you get him?'

" 'By letting all the other wenches make over him. Den he gits
disgustipated an bees my man.'

" 'You mean, since the boys shower me with their attention, I
lose interest?'

" 'Dey does more den showers yo. All yo hears is, "Yes, Miss
Petite, and I gets it fo yo, Miss Petite," and that is disgust—'

" 'Now, don't you say disgustipating. The word is disgusting.'

" 'Yes, but "disgustipating" am a bigger word an' means more
disgusting. But, Miss Petite, one day some man gonner say, "No,
Petite," and "Do dis, Petite," and den, sudden like, yo'll bees in

luv, and when yo falls, honey, yo am gonner fall heavy.'

"'I believe you're right, Phoebe, for not one offers any resistance, and that is disgustipat—, there, you've got me using that word.'"

CHAPTER VI

The Ball

" Grace, as I can feel you are tired of holding me, we'll reverse ourselves; that is, you lie on your back, and let your head rest in my arms. See, I'll sit up and you—that's it, rest your head right here and stretch out. "

"My, this is comfortable; and, darling, I can look right up into your eyes—but tell me, just what causes you to be so affectionate in this position?"

"Don't you enjoy my kisses?"

"Surely I do. See, I place my arms up over your head and press you closer—. But won't you explain why this position causes such a reaction?"

"Well, my beautiful sweetheart, when I hold you like this, I feel and know you are mine, and mine only. Like a miser with his precious gold, my love, my subconscious selfishness causes me to hold you and recognize you as the most precious thing in the world. And, Grace darling, what more could a man want?"

"Emile, . . . if you continue . . . I know I'll not hear . . . the rest of the story; and, darling, there is a time for everything."

"I don't reconcile that phrase with love, little sweetheart; when I hold you like this and look down at your lovely lips, partly apart, I would—"

"Emile, please, the story. But, first tell me who sponsored the dances?"

"Well, the young men butchers, fish dealers, vegetable dealers, and others of the French Market—a joyous band who called themselves the 'French Market Buzzards.' "

"Buzzards?"

"Yes, a name any fun-seeking clan would choose; but each and every man and woman had to be known or vouched for by one that was known to the committee."

"They were all good people?"

"Yes, so much so that they were one of the few organizations that the law permitted to have a ball without the customary police attendant being present to insure order. However, it was nearly eight-thirty and the musicians were tuning their instruments when Petite and her mother, having emerged from the side room into the street, entered through the large doors followed by the young men Phoebe had mentioned and others. Petite was a picture with her dark eyes flashing in anticipation of the excitement of the evening. She wore, for the first time, a beautiful brocaded silk gown that was sent to her from Paris by an admiring old sea captain. A neighbor's slave hairdresser had combed and set her dark curls. As the woman excelled in this art, Petite looked lovely. Admiringly the men, meticulously garbed, had gathered around her, each eager to write his name opposite a dance named in the program.

In Petite's case, her program was always filled before the music began; but, as in all cases where one is very popular, quarrels were inevitable since some of the men, especially those who cared for her, unwittingly chose more than their share of dances; so Petite, on this night, realizing that this was the most popular dance of the year, told them that she would not produce her program but would dance with those of her choosing as the ball progressed. Just as she completed her conversation, an elderly gentleman approached and said, 'Good evening, my friends, do you young men object to my conversing with Petite alone?'

" 'Not at all, not at all,' they chorused reluctantly as they stepped aside. The gentleman then gently took Petite by the arm and slowly walked to a secluded corner. He said, 'Petite, you are more beautiful tonight.'

" 'From you, too, Mr. Gaymes, I hear of my appearance!'

" 'But aren't those words music to your ears?'

" 'You know the old French saying that too much sugar spoils the pie?'

" 'Yes, I know and understand; but when the right man enters your happy life, then it will be—'

" 'Music, love, everything to my heart. But tell me, you being a lawyer and a man of the world, why, Oh, why can't I love as other girls do? Surely those men are everything a girl should want—handsome in their well-chosen attire and certainly not wanting in their manners. Phoebe is of the opinion they are all over-attentive.'

" 'Petite, I've often thought of that, for others who are not nearly so popular as you meet and mate while you, so full of fun and gaiety, remain unconquerable. Oh, well, I suppose time will tell. However, I'm here tonight on a mission for Lafitte.'

" 'And how is he, the old salt?'

" 'Just fine. He asked me to secure an invitation to this ball for a young friend of his, a sea captain from France, who for the first time is visiting our city. He asked that I contact you and make known his desire that you take this young man in charge; and, Petite, he said to me, "Gaymes, I am choosing Petite against my better judgment." '

" 'Why, I wonder against his better judgment?'

" 'Because he, like myself, realizes that all young men that come in contact with you learn to care before the evening is over.'

" 'Again, Mr. Gaymes, too much sugar in the pie.'

" 'But, is it not the truth?'

" 'I er—er, look, Jacques, the committeeman, is walking to-wards us and—'

" 'Good evening, Petite. Good evening, Mr. Gaymes. This gentleman has asked that I direct him to you.'

" 'Thank you, Jacques. And, Antoine, I see you are on time.'

" 'Yes, although I feared borrowing a suit from your friend would make me late. But I see you have company, will you excuse me—'

" 'Not at all, for I want to present to you Miss Petite Champlain; and, Petite, may I present Mr. Antoine Floret?'

" 'I am certainly glad to know any friend of Lafitte's and, as a committee of one, I welcome you to the ball.'

" 'Thank you, Miss Champlain.'

" 'And, Mr. Floret, it is Mr. Lafitte's desire that I'm to see that you enjoy yourself.'

" 'He has certainly shown his friendship towards me by select-ing you.'

" 'Now, don't you begin to compliment me, for, if you do, I'll insist on your dancing every dance with me.'

" 'You are sweet, you are beautiful, you are—' And they both laughed as the strains of a beautiful waltz reached their ears.

" 'May I?' he asked softly, holding out both arms.

" 'With pleasure, Mr. Floret,' And off they glided as though made for each other; and round and round they went, first to the right and then to the left, oblivious of everyone else. To Petite, tonight the musicians seemed to play with their very souls, while Antoine realized what Mr. Gaymes had meant when he said, 'Antoine, if you are lucky enough to dance with Petite tonight, you will experience, let me call it, an inward pleasure, a happiness that will reach your very soul.'

"Around and around they danced, neither speaking, but instead, moving in perfect rhythm as if in a dream. Some of the dancers, noticing their movements stopped to watch, as did the elderly people who were sitting on chairs that surrounded the walls; and these people noted, as did others, that the music had ended and yet, those two were dancing, and only stopped when the aplause for an encore started; then again they moved into position as naturally as though they had danced together dozens of times."

" 'Miss Champlain, may I compliment you on—'

" 'You may not.'

" 'I insist on saying that you dance divinely; and, further, I also insist that you keep your word to dance every one with me.'

"Insist, Grace—that one little word started something that was to influence their lives, for it was new to Petite that a man insisted on anything from her; and she said, 'I like the way you phrased that sentence.'

" 'Why?'

" 'Because, in addition to being over complimentary, the young men usually beg for dances; and, Mr. Floret, it bores me.'

" 'I can understand that, and I can also understand why they flock around you.'

" 'Be careful, you are treading on dangerous ground.'

" 'Dangerous ground! I dare call you beautiful—sweet—and say that your voice is charming.'

"And, as Phoebe predicted, those words had a different meaning now for Petite; for while he dared, the others wouldn't, if for no other reason than etiquette, they remaining silent or changing the subject. However, that dance being over, Petite said

'Mr. Floret, I should like to acquiesce in your desire for every dance, but—'

" 'No buts, Miss Champlain.'

" 'I understand you are a sea captain.'

" 'That is right.'

" 'And that as one, you expect discipline and obedience?'

" 'I'm afraid so.'

" 'And you would expect that same unquestioning obedience from a girl?'

" 'Miss Champlain, I'm not going to be false and tell you I would not although I have a premonition I may lose the friendship of what promises to be the most interesting girl I've ever met; but to tell you that I could be different would be dishonorable, and surely I wouldn't want to be that to you.'

"Again, Grace his words awakened in her a new respect, for she knew definitely that Antoine, although acknowledging her charm, did not know her as did the young Creoles who worshipped at her feet. He was different, decidedly so; for instance, when the band again began to play, he took her in his arms and waltzed away. Another young man would have asked her permission, but he did not, for she had told him that if he persisted in complimenting her she would insist on his dancing every dance with her. This was all new to Petite; and every now and then, while dancing, she slyly looked up into his face.

"Why was he different? True, he was older than her usual male associates, those boys who, when in company with girls, were always on their guard lest they do the wrong thing, while Antoine seemed to act his own, true, plain natural self. And it was natural that he'd do so since he had met and fought under the world's most intellectual human being, the illustrious Napoleon. And through him he often visited the French court where he met and conversed with the Empress Josephine and her ladies. Yes, his mannerism bespoke of a subconscious unpretended confidence, a confidence that was extremely appealing to Petite, to say the least. While dancing, she said, 'Mr. Floret, you are different.'

" 'I hope to your satisfaction.'

" 'I—I—don't know.'

" 'Please try to understand.'

" 'I—I—think I do.'

" 'Now that the dance is over, let's not wait for the encore, but let's go where it is quiet.'

" 'All right, to the patio. Give me your hand and I'll lead.' And as he followed he thought of how Petite reminded him of his small country home, Villefloret, a village named in honor of one of his grandparents in sunny southern France on the Loire River; a village he had left when he was fourteen years of age to study soldiery, and one he had never seen since.

"And everything here seemed to transport him back to that little town. The small sunny city of New Orleans on the Mississippi River with its one Catholic Church; the country dance with the same musical renditions that had just reached this side of the wide Atlantic; the people, practically all of peasant stock from which he arose; and Petite, just a natural, healthy, unassuming, pleasant country girl; a queen among her people. A queen, and yet not disdainful and haughty like the ladies of the intriguing court.

"And, Grace, although they had danced together for four dances and many more encores, the touch of their hands seemed to cause something to pass between them, something similar to the new thing they were talking about called electricity."

"In what way?"

"Well, let me explain it this way: Petite had intended sitting under the taper light as was always her custom, but the touch of his hand awakened in her a desire to be with him alone—a desire that the subconscious mind had summed up, but that the conscious mind could not fathom. In other words, she unconsciously led him past her favorite seat to one in a dark recess, one surrounded by flowers that would have been unknown to Antoine had not their aroma permeated the air, especially the tuberoses.

" 'My, it smells sweet here—'

" 'Sweet? Oh, yes. And Mr. Floret here is the bench.'

" 'Thanks, but please let us not separate our hands.'

" 'It is a pleasure to you, too?'

" 'Yes, but er—do you really experience the same pleasure?'

" 'I think so, for, to be candid, I am enjoying holding your hand.'

" 'My, that is sweet of you. Tell me, are you always that candid?'

" 'I've never before had occasion to be.'

" 'Then I shall bargain with you.'

" 'What for?'

" 'For candidness and truth.'

" 'For candidness yes, but as for truth—well, a gentleman usually accepts the word of a lady.'

" 'You are squeezing my hand; so I know that you do not intend that as a rebuff.'

" 'No, I certainly didn't. But what do you wish to bargain for?'

" 'Well, I've known you less than two hours—is that correct?'

" 'Yes.'

" 'And yet I feel as though I've met you before, somewhere in my past life.'

" 'Maybe I resemble some girl you knew.'

" 'No, I've never met anyone like you, and yet—'

" 'Maybe I can answer, for I have the same feeling.'

" 'You have?'

" 'Yes; and I believe, again being candid, that it is possible that we've always had an inward desire to meet someone just like ourselves.'

" 'That's the answer, Petite—Oh! I'm sorry. I am so excited, I forgot to say Miss.'

" 'That is all right, for I, too, had a desire for a bargain and had intended asking that we call each other by our first names. However, you, too, are of the opinion we had an inward desire to meet someone just like ourselves?

" 'Yes. For instance, at Versailles I met and was able to study many of the ladies. One, Emily by name, was as beautiful as you are, but she was so hollow.'

" 'Antoine, if you speak of my appearance again, I'll remove my hand.'

" 'Please, Petite, I'm sincere. And Georgette was as unassum-

ing and candid as you, but she was not as sweet and free from
care; insteady, always complaining.'

" 'And?'

" 'And Clothilde had your beautifully shaped lips and the same
very expressive eyes, but she was not near as friendly, being
rather haughty.'

" 'Antoine, at last you've reached one of my bad points, expressive eyes. You should have said mischievous eyes, for I do
some of the most outlandish things.'

" 'Well, that may be a fault, but to me I find in you, good or
bad, everything I've admired in others. And I believe you, too,
have possibly seen, again good or bad, those same requisites in
me.'

" 'Yes, Antoine, I believe your reasoning to be absolutely true,
for I see collectively, candidly speaking, everything I've admired
singularly in others. Mentioning the word "candid" reminds me
you wanted to bargain with me.'

" 'Yes, I do. You see, I have written many novels, and always
kept my characters in doubt of each other's affection; that is,
instead of being candid, I felt that doubt causes interest and that
interest when one is in love increases the affection. Although I
now realize how brutal that type of courtship is; nevertheless,
"keep him in doubt" or "keep her in suspense" are bywords with
those who are supposed to be wise in the art of how to make
love.'

" 'And do you think that that might cause a reaction?'

" 'Definitely, but it is a false or forced love; and, like all things
that are not natural, that is, which are against nature, it will end
in failure. This is one reason, and I might say the principal
reason, why so many marriages go on the rocks. Now, realizing
this and considering the way we feel towards each other, and I
am judging your heart by mine, I should like this romance, for I
believe our feeling to be the beginning of one, to be one
devoid of all doubt and jealousy. To do this would mean that
solemnly we shall have to promise to be candid, that is, to reveal
to each other our exact feelings; for lovers are in ectasy when
the loved one says "I love you" or "I've missed you." To tell
you now, Petite, that in less than four hours I truthfully feel
that I love you is certain to make something tingle inside of
you.'

" 'You are judging me by yourself, Antoine?'

" 'Yes. Now I solemnly promise that I will at all times be perfectly candid with you. May I hope to hear you also repeat those words?'

" 'Yes, with pleasure. I solemnly promise to be perfectly candid with you.'

" 'Petite, I feel a terrible urge to hold you close to my heart and to kiss you, but I know it would be wrong since we have known each other for so short a time. But tell me that you reciprocate the feeling.'

" 'I do.'

" 'My, but it's wonderful to hear that you would like to be kissed my me.'

" 'This is proof of what you've said about being candid. But listen, they are beginning the Pot Pourrie. Shall we dance it?'

" 'I should prefer remaining here with you, and I believe you, too, have the same desire.'

" 'Yes, I should; but now that it is getting somewhat chilly I see no harm in nestling closer in your arms.'

" 'But, honey, don't you thing we should visit your mother?'

" 'Yes, you're right, for she may be hunting for me now.'

THE SONG OF PETITE

Petites' a pretty Creole girl, who in the Square resides,
The sweetest lass that ever lived, who fills all heart desires.
For the joyousness that eminates from out that cute sweet form,
Causes all the lads to dream of love, their hearts burst into song,
    for

        Petite, Oh! how I love you,
        As does every other man!
        And I, as they, will give you
        All the pleasure that we can.
        Please choose among us one,
        That happy he can be,
        While the rest of us will envy him
        The love he's won from thee.

As she dances and she prances, to the music in their heart,
They beg of her and plead with her, her love to them impart,
As they promise and they swear to be, her very humble slave,
And its Petite this and Petite that, and on and on they rave, for

CHAPTER VII

THE SONG OF PETITE

" 'Mother, this is Mr. Antoine Floret.'

" 'I'm happy to know you, Mr. Floret.'

" 'It's a pleasure to know you, Madame.'

" 'And how long have you been in our city?'

" 'I just arrived today.'

" 'Well, I hope your stay will be a pleasant one.'

" 'Thank you, but I've decided to remain here.'

" 'Oh, then, you came to live here?'

" 'To be truthful, I did not come with that intention; but I've just recently come to this decision.'

" 'Well, you must call on us at your earliest convenience?'

" 'Tomorrow?'

" 'Surely, if you wish. And Petite, the United States Secret Service Agent, was inquiring for you.'

" 'I expected that; but, Mother, Antoine and I am returning to the patio.'

"Hand in hand they picked their way through the crowded ballroom, and returned to their former seat. This time Petite nestled in Antoine's arms and although they didn't kiss, their faces very often touched and as often they remained together until some parts of conversation caused them to move."

"For instance?"

"Well, in one case the band had begun playing a very catchy tune and Antoine had remarked hearing it in France.'

" 'Yes,' said Petite, 'it is very popular here. In fact, one of my acquaintances wrote a parody of the chorus about me. And,

Antoine, will you promise not to believe me vain if I sing it for you?'

"'I promise. Now start for here's the chorus.'

> "'Petite, Oh! how I love you,
> As does every other man!
> And I, as they, will give you
> All the pleasure that we can.
> Please choose among us one,
> That happy he can be,
> While the rest of us will envy him
> The love he's won from thee.'

"'Petite, honey, your voice is beautiful, I love it.'

"'And I'm angry.'

"'You're what?'

"'I said, I'm angry. Antoine, I expected you to be jealous and ask me the name of the writer.'

"'Not tonight, for I will permit nothing, not one single, solitary thing to dislodge this ecstasy of holding and loving you; an emotion I never knew existed. And, honey, since we are now so close I've decided to tell you about my being in New Orleans for, for me to hide the truth from you would cause me to feel like a cad for the rest of my life.'"

CHAPTER VIII

The Engagement

"It was a beautiful evening. The southern wind that came from the green gulf was now blowing almost directly against the symmetrical façade of the St. Louis Cathedral and, dividing, found its way through the two alleys. Crossing Royal Street, it again united at Orleans Street; and passing through the iron-lace work was once more on its way entering old carriage entrances and patios and absorbing there the fragrance of many lovely flowers. And then over the roof tops it went; and back again to the street and through the windows into the brick homes it passed to complete its mission by indirectly reminding the occupants that God made those flowers grow and caused the wind to carry their fragrance to remind mankind to give thanks for the many blessings He had bestowed upon them.

"This, Grace, was exactly what Antoine experienced as he followed the same route, and he thanked God for his happiness—that He had led him to Petite. His heart began to beat faster the more he thought of her. Over the wind rose his notes. He gayly whistled the tune of a new song, one he had succeeded in learning that day. On reaching the chorus he sang:

" 'Petite, Oh, how I love you,
 As does every other man!
 And I, as they, will give you
 All the pleasure that we can,
 Please choose among us one
 That happy he can be,
 While the rest of us will envy him
 The love he's won from thee.'

"And he sang as one does when marching to music and paid no attention whatsoever to those he passed who looked after him and shook their heads, saying 'Drinking or in love.'

"Reaching Petite's home in this mood, he joyously used the

knocker, rapping it six times to the tune of the song. Glancing about, he noticed that the carriage entrance was closed; and the thought that Petite and her family might be out chilled his heart. Just then the large, solid walnut door swung open on its hand forged, heavy hinges; and Phoebe, the slave maid he had seen the night before, said, 'Come in Massa Antoine.'

" 'You know my name?'

" 'Yes, Massa, fo we's heard yo name all day.'

" 'All day?'

" 'Yes, der misses will tells yo about it.'

" 'How do you know?'

" 'Because she done tole me. Now, follow me.'

"And through the candle-lit hall Phoebe led him up a winding stair to the second floor to the parlor which faced the beautiful patio. As he entered, Petite greeted him. With extended hands she grasped his hand and led him to her father, saying, 'Father, this is Antoine.'

"After a scrutinizing glance, Mr. Champlain replied, 'Antoine, it's a pleasure to know you, for I've heard your name mentioned dozens of times today.'

" 'Well, Mr. Champlain, if you had been near me I assure you you would have heard a certain lady's name also mentioned dozens of times.'

" 'No doubt, for Petite, like all dutiful daughters, told her mother and me everything that had happened last night, and I was particularly interested in the pact of candidness. Will you mind if I also am perfectly candid?'

" 'No, Mr. Champlain, I would prefer it.'

" 'Then, Antoine, your appearance impresses me favorably; but, as all dutiful fathers, it is necessary that I know more about you.'

" 'I'll be happy to tell you of myself; but first I should like to ask if you have any objection to the nobility.'

" 'No, not to those who work.'

" 'Well, I work; I am the son of Count Floret.'

" 'Eugene Floret?'

" 'Yes, he's my father.'

" 'Well, well, I feel that I know you, for Lafitte presented Count

Floret to me, and Eugene became our fast friend. Tell me, did he give you a letter to Lafitte or me?'

" 'No, for he didn't know that I should be here. Let me explain that I am the captain of the French ship 'Southern Star,' carrying supplies of guns, ammunition, food, etc., and that my destination was Mexico. On arriving in the Gulf of Mexico I learned that in Mexico my cargo would be reloaded onto British ships for the use of the soldiers under Packenham, who I personally know intends to invade this city. You, good people, can imagine my consternation and rage when I realized that my ship, flying the French flag, was aiding the British to defeat the French of this city.'

"Petite, feeling proud of Antoine, said, 'Tell them what you did.'

" 'You know, Petite?'

" 'Yes, father.'

" 'Why did you not tell us today?'

" 'Because I knew that Antoine was visiting us tonight, and that he would tell you if he wished you to know, for, as he explained to me last night, diverting his ship was a serious international act.'

" 'Oh, I see! Antoine, you diverted your ship?'

" 'Yes, sir. After I had definite proof of what I've told you— well, to make a long story short, my ship is being piloted up the Mississippi at present. I came by fast boat.'

" 'Regardless of consequences?'

" 'Yes, regardless of consequences. And I am at the command of the local authorities, having been a captain in the French army under Napoleon; and, Mr. Champlain, anyone attacking a Frenchman attacks me.'

" 'Well said, my lad, well said,' answered Mr. Champlain; and with that, he rose and extended his hand.

"Petite beamed with pride, and was so elated that she exclaimed, 'Antoine, I shall never forget that phrase.'

" 'Thanks, Petite. And now, Mr. Champlain, may I explain something that concerns my heart?'

" 'Certainly.'

" 'Last night, as you know, I met Petite at the ball. Unbelievable as it may seem, I fell violently in love with her; and an affection exists between us that I hope and pray may ripen into deep devotion. With your kind permission, I am extremely desirous to visit her with that in mind.'

"Mr. Champlain turned towards Petite, who, nervously anticipating a favorable reply, sat on the edge of the love seat, and asked, 'Petite, does Antoine's request meet with your approval?'

" 'Very much so, Father.'

" 'Then, Antoine, our home is at your disposal.'

"Rising, Antoine blurted, 'Many, many thanks; and, Mr. Champlain, I'll assure you that you will never regret your decision.'

"Before he had again taken his seat, Petite smiled, saying, 'Antoine, come and sit with me—the sofa is more comfortable.'

"Antoine, remembering their agreement of candidness, realized that she, too, was eager that they be near each other. During the conversation that followed they discussed the defense of New Orleans. Antoine related how that very afternoon he had talked with one of the Creole soldiers concerning his offer to help. The man had told him that if he did not succeed with the local authorities he could join Lafitte, who, he understood, would fight with all his men on the French side. Then he asked about Lafitte.

" 'The Federal authorities call him a pirate. But we know him as a buccaneer and like him very much. You see,' continued Mr. Champlain, 'he brings us slaves we sorely need for our growing plantation.'

" 'Oh, I see; and for this reason you care for him.'

" 'Oh, no, not only for this, but mainly because a needy person can always rely upon him for help—so much so that I honestly believe when he brings wares near the city one-third of them is given to the poor. In fact, he is known here as The Robinhood of the Sea.'

" 'And since the United States regards him as a pirate, the government officials are searching for him?'

" 'Yes, they are, and have placed placards around offering five hundred dollars for his apprehension; but we like him so much that on his visits he walks around the city as you do and no one molests him.'

" 'Then, Mr. Champlain, you would consider him a good man?'

" 'Definitely; and, Antoine, I was telling my wife this morning, that if the city is saved, it will be at least partly through the efforts of Lafitte. But to associate with him would be to be classed as a pirate by the Federal Government, with its consequent punishment.'

" 'You mean hanging?'

" 'Yes.'

"At the word 'hanging,' Grace, the blood left Petite's face, for she had been told the entire truth the night before, which included an account of the sea battle, for Antoine felt that she should know. What could she do? Maybe, if they went walking, she might be able to advise him. With that in mind, she said 'Father, will you and mother accompany us on a walk?'

" 'Yes, I think so. It is only nine o'clock; and, instead of tomorrow morning, tonight I shall place my order for provisions at the French Market.'

"Immediately Petite reached for Antoine's hand and half led him through the candle-lit house, followed by her mother and father. I said house, but it was a brick mansion built in seventeen eighty-eight, after the disastrous fire that had razed practically the entire Vieux Carre, making five thousand homeless. They walked towards the river on narrow Ursuline Street. Mr. and Mrs. Champlain questioned Antoine concerning France while Petite was silent, so much so that she puzzled Antoine, who gently squeezed her hand; to his amazement she immediately reciprocated. He then realized that something of a serious nature was on her mind. Reaching Chartres and Ursuline Streets, he asked her, 'Petite, what is that old building?'

" 'It's the Ursuline Convent.'

" 'Where you said you received your education?'

" 'Yes; and every night at this hour the Mother Superior is in her room checking papers while the other rooms are dark, for the nuns are asleep.'

" 'I was wondering why that one room is illuminated. How old is the building?'

" 'It took seven years to build it, and it was finished in 1734; it is the second oldest building in the Mississippi Valley. And, Antoine, all of the lumber is cypress and is held together by dovetailing and pegs.'

" 'In France we use square nails made on an anvil.'

" 'We do also; but nails were unknown in those days. However, we are now at the market. Let us remain on the banquette while mother and father give the order.'

"Hardly were her parents out of earshot when Antoine softly said, 'Petite, you are perturbed, and I'm surprised your parents do not see it.'

" 'They realize it, for they know me like a book; but I'm sure they believe the cause is my affection for you. You see I've never cared for anyone before.'

" 'I see. But tell me, why are you worried?'

" 'Because if the United States Marshal should arrest you, you will be hanged.'

" 'Nonsense, sweet, for my boat will soon be docking, and the fact that it was diverted by Lafitte with my approval would, of a certainty, be proof of my loyalty to the Creoles and indirectly to the United States.'

" 'Yes, that would make a difference, wouldn't it?'

" 'Surely. Now smooth that troubled brow; and, sweetheart—I believe I am privileged to call you that—it is a pleasure to know how much you have learned to care; and believe me, sweet, my every thought, whether awake or asleep, is of you.'

" 'Asleep, too?'

" 'Yes, for I dreamed a beautiful picture, one I wish I had time to tell.'

" 'Of me?'

" 'Yes, of you and—'

" 'But, Antoine, we shall be alone for about ten minutes longer. Please tell me about it.'

" 'Well, little sweet, you and I were sitting on the love-seat conversing in tow tones while mother's hands were rapidly moving, crocheting; her thoughts seemed miles away. Your father, having excused himself, was busy at the mahogany secretary with his records of the plantation. While we were conversing, your glance would drop to my lips as mine also did to yours. Presently, you puckered up your beautiful lips; in our conversation, which is as vivid now as when I dreamed it, I said, not changing my tone so as not to attract attention, that I would love to, referring to kissing your lips. And you answered you would, too. Then I asked how, and you shrugged your shoulder, mean-

ing you didn't know. Then, I said and stopped, glancing at our
chaperons, your parents, to see whether they were listening, that
there must be a way. Again you shrugged your shoulder and
I squeezed your little white hand. Just then, there was some
excitement outside, and this part of my dream is a bit hazy. I
believe it was a fire; so all in your home left to see. You and I,
realizing we were alone, remained seated; and then I reached
over and drew you into my arms, kissing you, sweet, with such
delight that I am constantly over and over re-living that dream,
and—'

" 'And what, Antoine?'

" 'And when you threw your arms around my neck and placed
your lips against mine, my joy knew no bounds, and I called
you darling.'

" 'Antoine, I'm supposed to be candid?'

" 'Yes, we've both agreed to that.'

" 'Then, in real life that dream would be heavenly.'

" 'Petite, when you are as honest as that, you make it hard for
me.'

" 'How?'

" 'God, girl, I get such a desire to hold you, to love and kiss
you, that I'm afraid that I shall not be responsible.'

" 'Then, by my explaining how the minutes seemed as hours,
and that the hours seemed as days until you came tonight, perhaps I might convince you . . .'

" 'Today then was the longest day in your life, too?'

" 'Yes ideed, but after dinner I retired to my room and lying
in my bed flat on my back I closed my eyes and recalled all of
the wonderful incidents of last night. The more I reminisced,
the more I realized how much I do love you; and, Antoine,
maybe I shouldn't admit it, but I was sorry that I could not
recall your having kissed me.'

" 'And how I did long to do that.'

" 'Maybe tonight; maybe now.'

" 'I'd love to say yes; but, Petite, my darling, it wouldn't be
fair to your parents.'

" 'I know, but the desire is so great that it hurts, Antoine, to
where—'

" 'Stop! Now listen to me. The hunger I read through your

eyes is also in my breast. Please, don't look at me that way for—
listen, darling, if I were to lose you now, I would have no desire
whatsoever to live. My live would be empty and full of torture. Do you also feel that way?'

" 'Definitely.'

" 'Then, tonight, I will—' And, Grace, just then Petite's parents
returned; and they started homeward through the narrow, dimly
lighted streets, passing first Chartres Street, then Royal, and
finally reaching their home on Bourbon Street; neither Petite
nor Antoine spoke, but she knew that he had reached a decision
and was determined to put it into effect that night. Reaching
home, they entered; and when Mr. Champlain was about to
excuse himself, Antoine asked, 'Mr. Champlain, will you and Mrs.
Champlain enter the parlor with us? I have something to ask
Petite and should like your presence.'

" 'Already?'

" 'I'm afraid so, for neither she nor I can go on—; but please
come with me.' And Grace, they entered the spacious, white,
walled parlor; and Antoine, walking over to Petite, placed both
hands on her narrow waist and said, 'Petite, my darling, you
have known me only a little more than twenty-four hours. During that time not one minute have you been out of my mind
and not one minute have I been from yours, as you've so humbly admitted. Tonight I've wanted to kiss you—only honor prevented. You too, darling, have again humbly admitted you felt
the same desire. I am a gentleman, my love, and—'

" 'I believe you.'

" 'Then, will you be my wife?'

" 'Gladly.'

"And, Grace, she unconsciously made a slight gesture as if to
move closer to him when he said, 'Wait, sweet, please wait, for I
am now asking your parents for their approval.'

"And, Emile, did they give it?"

"I just love to torment you."

"Why?"

"For, when you are in that mood, you have the sweetest expression about your little mouth. However, let us return to Mr.
Champlain's parlor. Petite, not hearing her parents' approval,

left Antoine, and addressing her father, said: 'Father, please, your answer.'

" 'But, Petite, my child, this is all so sudden I can't hardly reconcile myself to the fact that your great love for each other has grown so out of bounds in a little over twenty-four hours. What may I expect in forty-eight or seventy-two hours?'

"Antoine answered, 'Mr. Champlain, whether it will be seventy-two hours, or seventy-two days, or seventy-two years, I will always honor and respect Petite.'

" 'Not only that, Father, for I realize that you know little of Antoine. But if you could have seen how successfully he fought his emotions tonight to hold me and kiss me, all because he said it wouldn't be fair to my parents, you wouldn't feel as you do. Listen, Father,' she continued, her voice growing deeper, 'I know Antoine is a gentleman, and I am ready to stake my honor with him. Say yes, please; and during our engagement, prove for yourself the truth of what I say.'

"Grace, Mrs. Champlain, like the big-hearted woman that she was, said to Mr. Champlain, 'Henri, remember our engagement— how we curtailed it because of our love and how that love continues to this very day and—'

" 'Yes, I remember, Henriette—Antoine, I'm certainly sure you are a gentleman; it is nothing personal that I have against you. I also recognize the love you both have for each other, for tonight while I was at my secretary, before we left for the market, I heard you and Petite use the exact expressions that my wife and I used during our courtship and recognized the desire. Now, don't blush, my son, for those things are only natural. There is only one reason why I do not consent, and that reason is your possible association with Lafitte. Remember, if you are captured, the penalty is inevitable, and might ruin Petite's life. However, I realize that my refusal would also have that same effect; so, Antoine, promise me that you will be careful; and as a son I will expect you to report to me the steps that you take.'

" 'I promise; I swear by everything that's holy!'

" 'Then I give my sanction to your engagement, and may God bless you.'

"Antoine stood before Mr. Champlain, bewildered and dazed; his heart beat like a trip hammer, as if endeavoring to force

added blood to the brain in an effort to normalize it—a brain
that had become confused. Suddenly, he heard the words gently
murmured, 'Antoine, my beloved.'

"Regaining his senses and forgetting entirely to thank Mr.
Champlain, he grasped Petite in his arms and kissed her, one,
two, three times; then he said, 'Darling,' while Mr. and Mrs.
Champlain looked on with approval. He continues to kiss her,
four, five, six times, and then reverently he prayed, 'My God,
that Thou shouldst have led me to her, the sweetest of Thy sweet
creatures. I promise Thee, my God, to cherish her and I pledge
my life to her happiness.'"

"Emile, that is beautiful."

"Yes; and when her parents witnessed that scene, they realized
that there was no need for a chaperon and discreetly withdrew
from the room."

"Do you know what happened in the parlor after her parents
had left?"

"Yes, her diary reveals everything, but—"

"Emile, no buts—you see, I'm beginning to—now don't laugh
for—"

"For what?"

"Well,—Oh, you know how I love romance, and please, don't
tease me."

"All right, honey, I'll tell you. You see, according to her
diary they remained in that embrace for what she guessed to be
about five minutes after her parents had left. She further states
that she was the first to discover that they were alone and said,
'We are alone, darling, and er—er—'

" 'And what?'

" 'Certainly, my dream—come to the sofa. Now I shall sit at
this end and you—why, you know exactly the position—'

" 'Yes, one I've pictured myself in ever since I've known you.'

" 'My, doesn't it seem as though it was years?'

" 'Yes, but Antoine, my darling, what a wonderful pleasure it
is to lie in your arms. Kiss me please, and don't, oh darling,
don't ever let me go.'

" 'My loved one, you shall never be free from me—I'll be your
slave through life, and—'

" 'But you don't know I am to be your slave—ever to obey, ever to be humble, my lord and master.' "

"Emile, what happened then?"

"Well, Grace, such humility, with Antoine as with every man, touched a chord, one that man has inherited through the ages—the protection of his loved one. That chord still responds today, as it did years and years ago—lord, master, protector, and lover! This emotion, and the reaction of his subconscious mind guided his every act, his every word; and Petite accepted and absorbed them as her inheritance, as God intended her to do. She was from that time a woman in mind and soul as well as in body.

"Hours and hours they enjoyed the joy that no mind can possibly pen or described. They lived in a world of their own, not seeing or knowing such material things as chairs, walls, cities, or countries. Time meant nothing to them, for nothing, regardless of consequence, ever entered their minds. She was his and he was hers . . . nothing else mattered.

"And, Grace, they were only disturbed once and that when the candle burned out and had to be replaced by another. It was six o'clock when the slave maid, who, hearing voices in the parlor, entered and confusedly said, 'Miss Petite, yo been up all night?'

" 'All night, Phoebe? What time is it?'

" 'Six o'clock.'

" 'My, it seemed but a half hour. And, Antoine, did it seem the same to you?'

" 'Yes, but what will your father say?'

" 'Nothing, for I'll explain everything; and, darling, please stay for breakfast.'

" 'I'd love to, sweetheart; but I am to meet Lafitte's men by seven o'clock. If you will assure me that your father will not scold you, I'll leave now.'

" 'Father will understand. But, Antoine darling, what dangerous mission do you now contemplate? Please, please, be careful. Oh, Antoine, I cannot, I will not let you go. No—'

" 'Listen well to what I'm going to tell you. To leave you now is to leave everything that is precious and important to me in this large world of ours, except honor.'

" 'Except honor?'

" 'Yes, for I gave my word to Lafitte to meet him at his lodge at Bayou Barataria, and his men await me. Let me assure you, my sweet, the thought of you will govern my every movement. I swear, darling, to hasten to you as soon as I can; and I know it is needless to tell you to think of me.'

" 'Oh, Antoine, promise me that you will be careful.'

" 'I promise, and please tell your father that I go to meet Lafitte. Now kiss me—and au revoir.' "

CHAPTER IX

THROUGH THE SWAMPS AT NIGHT

" 'Petite, has your fiancé gone?'

" 'Yes, father, about an hour ago.'

" 'And both of you remained awake all night?'

" 'Yes, and it was the shortest night I've known.'

" 'You two are certainly in love; your first experience, I believe.'

" 'His first, too; and, father, he is sweet.'

" 'Well, I saw he was a gentleman.'

" 'In every respect; he is most considerate.'

" 'And why didn't he accept your invitation to breakfast?'

" 'Because he had to meet Lafitte today. Father, how did you know I had invited him to breakfast?'

" 'Because, in addition to your desiring him to remain near you, your training has been such as to make you a good hostess. And, Petite, how do you feel, now that he has gone? I see you are worried.'

" 'Yes, I am terribly worried. Fear, something new to me, has gripped my heart. Oh, father, if anything should happen to him'—

" 'Now—now—don't cry—why I'm ashamed of you—after all my teaching. Don't you remember how I've explained that out of one hundred times that people worry, ninety-nine times have been definitely proved needless?'

" 'I know, but with so much at stake—well, I just can't take it.'

"And, Grace, she rested her head on her father's shoulder and sobbed bitterly while he tried to console her. Finally, when she became more composed, Mr. Champlain said, 'Petite, you know the power of prayer?'

" 'Yes, Father.'

" 'Then if I were you I should do as Antoine would want you to under the circumstances.'

" 'And what would that be?'

" 'Go to your room first to pray and then to sleep. In the

meantime, I will visit Lafitte's blacksmith shop and order one
of his men to see that Antoine is protected at all costs.'

"And, Grace, with that in mind, she climbed the mahogany
stairs and entered her room. She walked to the bureau and
lighted the two candles under hurricane globes on either side
of the mirror. Looking into the glass, she whispered, 'Coward!'
more to bolster her morale than to criticize herself. When she
had changed her clothes, she knelt on her prie-dieu; and after
saying her usual bedtime prayer, she asked God to protect Antoine and bring him home safely. Then after hours of meditating
—sometimes smiling, sometimes frowning—she fell into a very
troubled sleep. Hour after hour, her faithful slave maid, Phoebe,
watched over her, while Petite turned, twisted, murmured, and
uttered unintelligible words, the result of a very troubled mind.

"You know, Emile, her happiness of the night before with the
subsequent worry reminds me of a phrase of an old philosopher:
'Why be happy today; tomorrow will be troublesome.'

"Yes, I've read that, too; but my life has been the reverse—I
might say, 'Why be sorrowful today; tomorrow will bring happiness.' And when one actually schools oneself along this line,
one lives a much happier life, for, as Mr. Champlain had taught
Petite, ninety-nine times out of a hundred worry is unnecessary."

"I see. This is the reason why you have an optimistic outlook."

"Exactly. Try it. However, to return to Petite—towards
evening her father returned, and finding her still sleeping explained to her mother that Antoine had left with Lafitte's men;
that he was regarded as an accomplice, and since he was unknown in the city, he was further looked upon as a spy. So he
had decided to go to the Governor's home, for, as he understood,
the United States officials were preparing to leave by nightfall
to capture Antoine, choosing that time in the hope that Lafitte's
men would be off guard."

"Emile, that was a very serious situation."

"Yes, very serious; especially when one considers that it might
take over a month for the 'Southern Star' to reach the city. The
authorities might consider his explanation of diverting that ship
merely a ruse."

"What happened next?"

"Well, towards six o'clock that evening Phoebe heard moans; and rushing to the bed, she was frightened when she looked at Petite. On her forehead were large beads of perspiration while every muscle in her sweet face was taut as if she were in intensive pain. Again she moaned and began to sob and ended with a shriek. Phoebe loved her mistress; so when she saw her strange condition, she leaped to the bed and shook her, saying, 'Wake up, Miss Petite, wake up, wake up, for yo is dreamin'.'

"Petite opened her eyes, stared at Phoebe, and told her, 'No—no—no.'

" 'Miss Petite, yo is dreamin'.'

"Then Petite, regaining consciousness, sat up abruptly and said, 'Thank God, thank God, it is only a dream; but—'

"And, Grace, leaping from the bed, she raced down the winding stairs, shouting, 'Father, father!'

"Her mother hearing her rushed to meet her and, noticing that she was shaking from head to foot, said, 'Petite, please compose yourself.'

" 'But, Mother, I've had a terrible dream.'

" 'You've had a dream?'

" 'Yes, I saw him hanging—oh, Mother, what shall I do? Please help me.'

" 'But, Petite, your father has explained to you many times that a dream is only an unfinished thought, and I'm surprised at you.'

" 'But, Mother, it was so real—the large cypress tree, the rope—good God!'

" 'Petite, if you compose yourself I want to tell you something important.'

" 'About Antoine?'

" 'Yes.'

" 'Please, mother, please—Oh, my God, I know he is in trouble; I can see it by your—Mother, what is it?'

" 'Your father returned when you were sleeping, and told me that Antoine is regarded as a pirate and spy. Now, Petite, sit down,' she continued as she noticed that Petite was tottering. 'Now, that is better. Listen, honey, your father told me to tell you not to do anything rash; I mean, not to do anything that might cause the United States authorities to regard you as an accomplice. As it is, President Madison knows that we Creoles resented the Stars and Stripes when Louisiana was sold by France, and they would naturally construe any move made by anyone of us as leading a change of governments. An accomplice would be a dangerous—'

" 'Accomplice, Mother, accomplice! What care I if I am an accomplice if he hangs? Hangs'—she repeated, and then continued, 'then let them hang me, too.' She then yelled, 'Phoebe.'

"The slave came running, calling, 'Yes'm, yes'm.'

" 'Come with me. We're going to Lafitte's lodge.'

" 'But, Petite, I command you, as your mother, not to go.'

" 'Mother, do you think he would hesitate if I were in trouble? No, he would defy the world to save me; and I love him just as much as he loves me and—and—I will warn him. And Mother, should we escape to France, please don't worry about me.'

"Grace, leaving her mother dumbfounded, she raced back to her room, changed her clothes, and, accompanied by Phoebe, left her home and headed for the river."

"My, she was brave."

"In addition to being naturally brave, she had the great incentive, as I've told you before, one that braves every danger, surmounts all obstacles, large or small, and fights for the loved one—"

"Love?"

"Yes, love. On reaching the river, she found their pirogue among the many oyster luggers, whose owners graciously made way for her. Some even offered to cross her. Refusing their help, she placed Phoebe in the fore end of the hollowed out log with a freeboard of only two inches; and to the astonishment of the men, she stepped aboard like a veteran and paddled across the wide, muddy river with its numberless ever-swirling eddies. One oyster luggerman leaped into his skiff and followed her, for he knew the river was about sixty feet deep and that the current in the center flowed at the rate of about five miles an hour. But, Grace, he did not know Petite, for although her small boat was often caught in eddies and spun like a top, and although the river was filled with drift wood, which she knew would overturn the small craft if it struck the boat, she maneuvered the pirogue safely across that turbulent expanse. Then began the

,arduous task of lifting the boat or rather dragging it to the swamps. Once safely over, she placed the oars to one end and, instead, poled her craft over the swamp which was lighted by a full moon; the rays filtered through the overhanging moss that clung to the century-old cypress trees—moss that moved and swung with the passing of every breath of air, causing grotesque shadows to fall and waver on the unfriendly bottom, where malaria and yellow-fever mosquitoes lurked, and water moccasins and rattlesnakes dwelt. Overhead, in the trees, large black buzzards waited patiently for the morrow when they would search for the prey. Thousands of living things were hiding in the dismal swamp—things that waited to bite and kill or to lie apparently dead to avoid being killed.

"Through all this silent waste, Petite poled, knowing full well its dangers, yet resolute and determined; now and then she passed around small islands where muskarts teemed, and death-dealing black widow spiders wove their webs among the tall grasses. Phoebe was in the rear, seated directly on the bottom; she was almost white with fear, for to her ghosts were real things, and the shadows seemed like ghosts; yet she murmured not a word, realizing that her mistress was ill at heart and it was her duty to obey.

"Presently, she ventured, 'Miss Petite, look, de bayou.'

" 'Yes—thank God—the bayou.'

" 'Ah thanks God too, but tells me, which way yo is goin'?'

" 'I don't know—I've never been this far before; I've only heard of it.'

" 'Den we is los?'

" 'Oh, no, Phoebe, for I will paddle to the open where I can see over the trees and find Etoile Polaire.'

" 'Etoile Polaire?'

" 'Yes, the North Star. Oh, high up there is the Great Dipper, or Ursa Major, with its pointers, and the guardian stars; but the trees hide the North Star. However, Phoebe, in this direction is north; so we shall paddle this way or to the west; and, Phoebe, you don't have to crouch so low now—the worst is over.'

" 'Not wit dose big mouf alligators—look, ain't dat some on de bank?'

" 'Yes, but they are asleep and—'

" 'Miss Petite, why is dere no trees in de bayous?'

" 'Because a bayou is a river that drains a swamp, that is, after rainfalls.'

" 'Oh, I sees! Den de bayou am deep?'

" 'Yes, at some places as much as twenty feet.'

" 'Miss Petite, is dat a light? Look, tru de trees.'

" 'Yes, it is and just around the bend.'

"And Grace, paddling softly Petite hugged the opposite shore in an effort to pass unseen, for she knew not whether the light belonged to friend or foe. However, the sharp ears of the sentry had heard the swish of the water; and peering intently, he had seen a moving object and called 'Who are you?'

"Petite's heart leaped with joy for his accent was unmistakably French; so she answered him, steering her boat in his direction, 'Petite Champlain.'

" 'Mon Dieu, girl, what are you doing in the bayou tonight?'

" 'I'm headed for Lafitte's lodge.'

" Why?'

" 'To warn the Frenchman.'

" 'Something serious?'

" 'Very much so.'

" 'Then, be on your way. I wish I could go with you, but I must remain at my post. And Petite, Pelican is the password for tonight; you see we have some new men that don't know you.'

" 'Thanks, thanks very much,' she called softly as she again dipped the paddle dexteriously into the water, turning the pirogue again westward through the beautiful winding bayou where the trees on both sides reached half way across forming a continual arch. Looking up, she felt as though she were in a cave, whose ceiling was draped with beautiful greyish green moss that had the appearance of stalactites and was reflected in the water by the faint rays of the moon filtering through the giant oaks. She would have appreciated this picture had not her mission been so serious.

"Only the dipping of the paddle was heard as Petite deftly rowed her boat under that canopy. Finally she reached a small tributary where a covey of black geese were spending the night. The shores were marked with thousands of tunnel-like holes formed by muskrats, leading from their subterranean homes to the water. The reeds, grown high, were gently fanned by the mild south wind which penetrated even this jungle, swishing softly through them as if sighing and as softly drawing a sigh from Petite, who through sheer exhaustion had laid her paddle in the boat and permitted her pirogue to drift.

" 'Led me try ter paddle, Miss Petite.'

" 'No, thanks, Phoebe. Handling a pirogue takes lots of practice. It looks easy when one is experienced,' Petite answered as they neared a curve and she again paddled to avoid going into shore. Just then, they were startled by a clear call in French, which rang through the wilderness, 'Who are you?'

"Before Petite could compose herself, Phoebe, through fear, yelled 'Pelican, Pelican!'

"As the sentry realized what had happened, for he recognized the accent to be that of a superstitious slave, he laughed loud and long, only stopping when Petite asked whether she might proceed.

" 'Be on your way—I've heard enough.'

" 'Thanks, but tell me, how far are we from the lodge?'

" 'A good twenty miles.'

" 'My God.'

" 'Where are you from?'

" 'The city.'

" 'Well, you've traveled over fifteen miles. It must be important.'

" 'It is.'

" 'Care for water or food?'

" 'Water? Oh yes, please. I hadn't noticed until you mentioned water how very dry my throat is.'

" 'Paddle to the shore. That's it. Here now, drink. Give some to your slave. There. Now, do you feel better?'

" 'Yes, thanks.'

" 'Do you care to rest?'

" 'No, I must be on my way.' And again she courageously sent the paddle into the water with renewed strength, and from that time, she was challenged at every mile with 'Who are you?'

" 'Petite,' came the answer.

" 'Password?'

" 'Pelican.'

" 'Be on your way,' was the order followed now by a howl that was heard by the next sentry. At three o'clock in the morning, she sighted the sleepy little village of Barataria, a village sparsely peopled mainly by Indians and a few Acadians, those true French Patriots who had been taken from Canada by the English and put ashore on the eastern seaboard. Gradually they had made their way through the wilderness to the French territory of Louisiana.

"Reaching the village, and to the south when she met another bayou, she paddled for about a mile when, completely exhausted, she reached the lodge."

"Describe it, Emile."

"Well, at a point on the bayou stood four huge oak trees that were hundreds of years old before LaSalle sailed down the Mississippi to its mouth to claim all of this territory for France. Under those gnarled trees that supported millions of strands of moss, or 'Spanish Beard,' as it was then called, the Indians had, by first using clam shells, made a hill on which they later built a village. In 1765, when New Orleans was leveled by a fierce gulf storm, the same storm wrecked that village, and the Indians abandoned the site. It was only natural that Lafitte would choose it later for his colony.

"Felling large gum or willow trees from the higher lands, the pirate and his men floated them from the upper bayou to the hill and built what seemed to be a large log cabin to the casual observer. Inside they placed massive cypress posts upright as pilings at all corners, extending from twelve feet down in the earth to the very top of the structure; there were eighteen in all, and they used them for the purpose of making the lodge storm-proof, a method still employed today, Grace, by many bayou builders. The roof was covered with brown terra cotta tiles which had been taken from a Spanish ship. The brown color quickly changed to green, caused by the growth of this subtropical climate of lichens and other moisture-requiring plants. The windows and doors were of solid ship-siding and battened together. Around the building extended a large porch covered only by the huge branches of the aged oaks. Surrounding this lodge on the grounds facing the bayou, were cannon of various sizes, each covered with a specially fitted tarpaulin or canvas that had been at one time the sail or a ship; and at the base of the guns, neatly piled, were solid cannon balls. Buried in the ground, near each gun, were large earthen jars, that had formerly left Spain filled with olive oil. Into these jars, the pirates poured gunpowder, carefully covering the tops with heavily oiled canvas.

"Entering the building, to the left, was Lafitte's private room. It contained a bed, a large ship heater, a desk, chairs and built-in closets. To the right were the barracks where the pirates kept their muskets neatly stacked around the room. They reloaded their guns each week to insure fresh powder, while across the center hung, from irons, carefully laced hammocks. This room was purposely placed near the entrance so that at a signal the men could quickly reach the bayou."

"He was clever, Emile."

"Yes, Grace, and that fact is being realized more and more each day. However, behind this room was the galley, fitted with their best cook stove and copper and iron utensils, while the knives, spoons, forks, china, and glass bore many names, the initials or crests of captured ships. To the rear of Lafitte's room was the large dining room or mess hall as they called it, with its mahogany table fitted as it had come from the officers' quarters of a Spanish battleship. In a jamboree the buccaneers had long before wrecked the chairs which had accompanied the table, and had replaced them with home-made benches. To the rear of this building was a powder magazine made of earth and ingeniously walled with tile. The ground surrounding the lodge had been carefully landscaped with plants from Spain.

"Petite gazed at the beautiful moonlit scene as she neared the lodge. The sentry, having heard the howling signal, expected friends, but seeing only women whom he believed to be men in disguise, and at that time of the morning, deemed it best to notify the men; and with this thought in mind, he fired his gun. Immediately the place was peopled. Like disturbed ants, they rushed for their guns and then ran towards the waterfront.

"Petite immediately held her paddle, but Phoebe, again white with fear, yelled at the top of her shrilly voice, 'Pelican—pelican —pelican.'

"A short, stout man reached the water's edge. He quickly decided that French would be understood by a friend; so he asked, 'Who are you?' in French.

"And Petite answered, also in French, 'It is I, Petite, Dominique.'

"'Mon Dieu, Petite,' he said, now using his broken English, 'paddle to dis cove.'

"Obeying, she steered the pirogue to where Dominique drew it to solid land and gently helped her to her feet.

"'Petite, mon amie, what brings you here at this hour?'

"'Is he safe, I mean Antoine? Oh, is he safe?'

"'Did you not receive my note?'

"'No, but—'

"'I send you note last night saying he was safe and for you not to worry.'

"'Thanks, thanks, Dominique. But where is he?'

"'Gone to the island with Lafitte. My, girl, you are wet; and this chilly air will give you pneumonia. Come,' he started to say. But Petite reeled, and Dominique sensing what was happening, grabbed her just as she fainted. In his powerful arms he carried her to Lafitte's room and gently placed her on the pirate's bed, and ordered Josef to 'fire dat stove until it is raid— raid, you hear me.'

"Then he ordered Phoebe to remove Petite's wet clothes and place her under the cover. Phoebe, limping from being in one position for hours, gently removed her mistress' shoes and stockings and was about to unhook the hooks and eyes of the dress when Petite opened her eyes and said, 'Phoebe, you faithful one.'

"'Yes'm, Miss Petitie. And I seed yo is smilin'.'

"'Yes, I'm happy, for Antoine is safe and—and—let me help undress. My!—I can't use my arms; they are useless!'

"'Now, yo rest, Miss Petite; and ah'll undress yo. Turn ober, an' lets me unlace yo corest. Yo know, Miss Petite, yo're sure got it bad.'

"'I know and love it.'

" 'Now, git under de cover,—dere—now, please, Miss Petite, go de sleep.'

" 'Not until I see Mr. Dominique You. Where is he?'

" 'In de kitchen, drinkin' coffee. Yo wants him?'

" 'Yes.'

"In a minute Phoebe returned followed by Dominique, who asked, 'Petite, you want me?'

" 'Yes, and let us talk in French. Now, sit down and tell me, do you know that the United States Federal men are after Antoine?'

" 'Yes, as a pirate and spy.'

" 'How do you know that?'

" 'Why, Petite, you know the affection the Creoles have for us —why shame on you!'

" 'Oh! I see. And that is the reason why Antoine is not here?'

" 'No, for no enemies of ours would dare attack us here, for we know every nook and cranny; but Antoine has gone to Barataria to drill our men so that they will fight the British. Now, go to sleep, for I see that you're very much fatigued; and Petite, you are brave and courageous; and I heard him say to Lafitte that in New Orleans he had met a beautiful girl. And Lafitte asked her name, forgetting that he had suggested that Mr. Gaymes introduce Antoine to you. So Antoine told him Petite. And Lafitte told him to say no more, for he could see that Antoine was in love. And Antoine told him that you and he already become engaged.

" 'And Lafitte stated that he could scarcely believe him; and told Antoine that he had tried to court her without success.

" 'Then he reminded Antoine that he must not think of love, but only of saving New Orleans and you and his friends. He also remided him of the English slogan, 'Beauty and Booty'; and Antoine became very angry and swore—actually swore—he would kill anyone who harmed one hair of your head.

" 'So Lafitte told him to go with him for they had plenty to do. And, Petite, off they went, to make soldiers out of sailors, to fight for la Nouvelle Orléans. Now, promise me that you will sleep; and I'll promise, on your awakening, to have a pleasant surprise for you.'

"Closing her eyes, as if obeying Antoine, she fell into a deep sleep, Phoebe, her faithful mulatto slave, resting at her feet."

"And, Emile, all loved her. But tell me, how did they know her?"

"You forget, Grace, that in this small community, all knew one another from infancy; and since Lafitte's men were always in and out of the city, entering as fishermen, they must have come in contact with her at one time or another, either being introduced by an acquaintance or, as in many cases, dancing with her at the balls."

"Oh, I see! And what happened next?"

"Well, towards ten o'clock in the morning, she awakened and, realizing where she was, shuddered at the thought of having come through the dismal swamp at night. Many a day, while hunting, she had seen snakes slinking ahead of her and on occasions, while sitting for a rest, had discovered at a short distance, a pair of greenish eyes staring directly into hers."

"I again say, 'She was brave.' "

"Yes; but I've explained before, love knows and recognizes no hazards. However, scanning the room and its log furnishings, she noticed a letter placed within easy reach, one that should have been on its way to her home. Reaching for it, she looked at the envelope. On it was written one word, a word properly used that causes lovers an unexplainable joyous sensation—the word—"

" 'Darling.' See, Emile, I recognize it."

"Yes, I see you have. But, sweet, you're beginning to feel heavy; so suppose we change positions."

"Gladly, dear, for my back is beginning to ache."

"Well, suppose I lie on my back and prop up my head like this, and you rest your head on my chest—not the back of your head, but face me; that's it; now rest on your side—there, are you comfortable?"

"Yes, but I can't see you."

"All right, change to whatever position you like."

"Darling, I hate to be a fussy cat, but I must look at you. Emile, I'm afraid I love you too much."

"Grace, are you joking? For if you're not, I want you to retract that 'loving too much'."

"I wasn't joking, and I take it back. Now, lie on your back, full length. That's it, and I shall lie in such a way by your side as to look directly into your eyes and—"

"To where you have only to drop your head for our lips to meet. You little vixen, that is what you wanted."

"Yes, darling, so here goes,—"

"Now that you have come up for air, shall I continue the story?"

"Please tell me about the letter."

"Well, when she realized it was meant for her, and that no one but Antoine would dare address her as darling, she tore the envelope open, and unfolding the paper, read, and—and Grace, if you continue to drop your head and kiss like that, you will probably never hear the end of the story."

"Why?"

"Because, I am only human."

"I'll bet you wouldn't put this into a story if you would write one."

"The hell I wouldn't."

"You mean, you would be that candid?"

"That is the only way the French or their extraction know how to write."

"I see—now for the letter."

"It started, 'My dear little sweetheart, how my life has changed —what a difference it makes to love—and to be loved. I am writing in a pirogue, directed by a brawny man and am surrounded by at least fifty others; where they came from, I do not know, nor do I know when they met us, for I was staring straight ahead, seeing only you. God, darling, what a continual sensation. I had always believed love to be like one starving who, after eating, was satisfied. But it is not, for the hunger of love is insatiable—there is always that constant hunger or desire to be near you. I'm beginning to fear it for I find myself lonely, although I am surrounded by men, and, too, I find myself asking, shall I have to go through life dissatisfied with myself, with the world, unless you are with me? Fear; imagine a soldier and sailor of France using that word; and yet, love to me is new and different from ordinary thoughts; for while everything else on this beautiful earth of ours attracts in proportion to its nearness, the further I get from you, the stronger seems the attraction,

being possibly a selfish, subconscious feeling of going further
away from what I treasure more than life itself.

"'In other words, sweet, I don't belong to myself any more, but
rather to an urge, one that leaves me minus will power; and as
I travel, so does that urge force itself on me with definite growing intensity mile after mile, ever stronger, stronger, stronger to
return to you. My darling, will there be a limit, or, will I, in
desperation, before I reach my destination, race back to you?
You see why I fear? My thoughts and motives are all actuated
by an unseen force that is so powerful that I am scarcely able to
control it. Of course, I realize its cause—a little five-foot-two
bundle of sweetness; and yet, I am going away from it, but I will
return. And, my sweet, when I do, I will hold you forever as
mine—mine, what a thrilling thought!

"'Now I find myself meditating, thinking how I should treat
one so precious—. I promise, sweetheart, to dedicate my life,
my entire life, to keeping you happy in appreciation of the love
you so lavishly bestowed upon me last night.

"'I could write forever; but as I'm nearing the lodge, I shall
close this letter by kissing it, knowing that you, too, will do the
same. Darling, believe me when I say I will be forever yours,
Antoine.'

"It's beautiful, Emile. But what is that book you are reading from?"

"Petite's diary."

"May I see it?"

"No, Grace, for I've given my word not to permit anyone to
read it."

"But you are reading it?"

"Only certain parts."

"Oh, I see! Then, by all means, keep your word. You know
I wouldn't want you to change for the world."

"That is a compliment, especially from one's wife."

"I mean it."

"I know you do—. Kissing me again, Grace?"

"I love it."

"I love it, too, but let me continue the story."

"Please do."

"Well, Petite having been informed that a courier had been

dispatched immediately upon her arrival to her home to inform her parents that she had arrived safely, decided to remain at the lodge, for at least she then would be nearer to Antoine, even though they were separated by miles. Upon being informed of her decision, Dominique You gave an order and another courier headed downstream, towards Barataria."

"It is surprising that she did not go herself."

"One of the men suggested it, but Dominique explained and Petite realized that Lafitte's orders were always religiously obeyed. Even though he, Lafitte, might have consented, as all believed he would have done if he had been there, they agreed it was best for her to remain, as no women visited them."

CHAPTER X

Love Song Telegraph

" 'François, let me at least help peel the potatoes.'

" 'Miss Petite, if you don't gat out quisine, I'll tell the Baron dat you tried to mak love to me.'

" 'And who is the Baron?' Petite asked smilingly, as if she didn't know.

" 'Captain Antoine.'

" 'What?'

" 'Oh! you did not know? Now, I'm in trouble again. Please, Miss Petite, don't tell dat I told you. And, don't let dat mak no difference, for he lov you; mon Dieu, how he lov you!'

" 'Yes, I know; and, François, I love him.'

" 'We know. Did you not brav the swamps an' prairies for to warn him?'

" 'Yes, and I'd do it again.'

" 'And, Miss Petite, if you promise to keep secret, I'll tell you another.'

" 'I promise.'

" 'Well, Dominique sent Josef to Antoine to tell him dat you are here.'

"Just then Dominique entered and Petite said, 'Dominique.' And, Grace, she placed her arms around the pirate's neck and kissed him.

" 'What for you kiss me, Petite?'

" 'Just because I like you.'

" 'François, you been talkin' again. You, François, some day I will keel you.'

" 'No, you won't, Dominique. You know, good news should not be withheld, especially from a lady.'

" 'Then François know more about ladies than I do? But I guess he do. I fight.'

" 'Yes, Dominique, you are not only known for your bravery, but also for your being able to accomplish the impossible. Do you know what Antoine said of you all?'

" 'No, what he say?'

" 'He said, speaking to father, "Mr. Champlain, if New Orleans is to be defended successfully, it will be through Lafitte and his men." '

" 'And he did not say Captain Dominique You?'

" 'No, but as Lafitte's lieutenant, he also meant you.'

" 'I'll show dem double-crossing Breetish.'

" 'God help them, eh captain?'

" 'They weel need it.'

" 'But tell me, will Antoine come this afternoon? Is he near? May I go to him? Oh, Dominique, I love him, hear me, I love him.'

" 'We know dat, Petite; but remember, soldiers got to be trained; and if he don' come, well, he will put patriotism above love.'

" 'Above love? Why, Captain, nothing is above love.'

. " 'I don't know. You see, I am not ladies' man; and I always lose wit dem. But stay wit us. Me and all my men want dat you stay with us. Will you?'

" 'For a day or two. And now I shall wander around.'

"So, Grace, she left the building accompanied by Phoebe. On reaching the outside, she noticed that the lodge was built like a fort and that it was set in a grove of beautiful oak and cypress trees. In front was the bayou where lay rows and rows of pirogues of various sizes; there were probably over two hundred. Walking to the rear, she saw a large corral where the pirates kept deer; some had been trapped and others had been bred in the enclosure; their large round eyes watched her suspiciously. The young that had been born there and were tame, leisurely walked toward the wire to receive a piece of lettuce Petite temptingly waved at them.

"Leaving there she followed a footpath that led to a bend in the bayou where the men had ingeniously constructed, with fallen trees and nets, a place to keep live fish. Along the shores were hundreds of floating lattice boxes which permitted the water to flow through and in which were live crabs or what they termed 'busters'. That is, crabs that would soon shed their shells and become what is known as soft shell crabs, one of the Creoles' best prized delicacies.

"Looking across the queer boxes, she noticed that the water was covered with wild ducks and geese, their various colors blending with the reeds and hyacinths—birds that had left the frozen North, as they had done for years and years, to fly to this beautiful sanctuary. Farther down was a flock of native birds—poules-d'eau, or water chickens, their gleaming black feathers reflecting the brilliant rays of the sun.

"Walking aimlessly, Petite soon found herself in a dense wood where overhead in the trees the mocking birds vied with one another in beautiful song which came from quivering throats to attract their mates. A male cardinal, whose gay red feathers caught her eye at once, was busily singing in a willow tree while blue birds on the ground tossed dried leaves around in search of insects for their young. At her feet were thousands of violets, shyly poking their little heads from under dark green leaves, while here and there copper-colored irises invited grayish brown humming birds to sip nectar from their deep yellow throats. And, Grace, in the midst of all this beauty Petite, with love in her heart, knowing Antoine was safe and her parents assured of her whereabouts, felt such keen happiness that she too, like the birds, burst into song, singing 'My Creole Belle.' Her rich voice echoed back and forth; all the world seemed in tune; the axman's ax fell in rhythm, while François, although a distance away, beat the whipping cream, each stroke striking as the notes reached him.

> " 'All coons are prancing
> Singing and dancing
> Go wild with glee,
> I'm as happy as happy can be,
> Fill my heart with ectasy.
> All over the nation
> A celebration
> Surely will be
> 'Cause married I'm going to be, today.
>
> My Creole Belle,
> I love so well,
> Around my heart,
> She's cast a spell.

> When stars do shine,
> I calls her mine,
> My dusky baby,
> My Creole Belle.'

"When she began the chorus, the men accompanied her; and as the words echoed through the swamps and down the winding bayou, it was picked up by various of Lafitte's men traveling back and forth with supplies until it—"

"Emile, may I interrupt?"

"Certainly, sweet."

"Can sound be heard quite a distance in the swamps?"

"Yes, over a mile; and when that sound is the most popular of tunes, it is quickly recognized. However, at that time Antoine was busy marching and training his men; that is, they were marching, saying as they stepped, one—two—three—four—and then, again, one—two—three—four. Soon one of these sailors faintly heard a familiar tune in the distance and, substituting its words for the numerals, began singing, My—for one, Cre—for two, ole—for three, Belle—for four, and I—love—so—well—again for one, two three, and four. And, Grace, all the men with him joined in until the entire band was singing the song. Antoine looked on in amazement for there were his men marching better in song than with numbers; and Lafitte, looking on, walked quickly over to him.

" 'Antoine, that song traveled down the bayou from the lodge.'

" 'I see. Lafitte, it certainly inspired the men. But man, why are you smiling?'

" 'Because, mon ami, love songs are never sung out here. Only buccanneer songs are heard.'

" 'Lafitte, your smile has grown broader. What have you up your sleeve?'

" 'Antoine a woman started that song at the lodge not over an hour ago.'

" 'In one hour it traveled fifty miles? But say, you told me there were no women at the lodge?'

" 'Listen, Antoine, do I have to strike you with a blugeon to make you see light?'

" 'You mean that—Oh, no—no, Lafitte. It can't be, for she would have had to travel at night.'

" 'Nevertheless, I'll wager with you one hundred pesos that it's Petite. Antoine, I see that you don't know her. Wait, here comes one of my elderly men. Gustav. Oh, Gustav!'

" 'Yes, sir.'

" 'Would you know how that song that the men are singing started here?'

" 'Yes, sir—down the bayou.'

" 'And would you say a man or woman started it at the lodge?'

" 'A woman, sir.'

" 'And who do you guess it to be?'

" 'Petite.'

" 'Will you wager?'

" 'Yes, sir.'

" 'Why?'

" 'Because Petite is the only woman from the city that would know or brave the swamps.'

" 'Now, Antoine,—'

" 'Lafitte, I must go to her.'

" 'You forget you gave me your word. Remember, war before love.'

" 'Damn it. I'm sorry that I ever learned honor. But, Lafitte, you are laughing—I think you are teasing me.'

" 'Be on your way, mon ami; and I will place André in charge. Incidentally, I, too, will have to leave, for I must be in New Orleans by six o'clock.' "

CHAPTER XI

THE DUEL

"And, Emile, what about Petite?"

"Well, Grace, she was extremely happy. When she had finished singing, she again read Antoine's letter and repeated, 'What a continual sensation,' he says, and I too feel the sensation continues as he wrote it does. 'God, how wonderful Thou are that Thou hast caused him to come to me and fill me with this strange happiness! No wonder Thou art called Father.' And, Grace, she would have continued her thanks had not the bronze boat bell announced that dinner was ready, for François was striking it repeatedly and repeatedly its gong echoed back and forth. It was then that Petite realized that she had not eaten for thirty hours; and, taking Phoebe by the hand, she ran across the woods, her brown wavy hair tossing from side to side. As she reached the lodge, Dominique met her, leading her to the head of the table—the place always reserved for Lafitte.

"'Now, Petite, ma chère, I want for you should say grace.'

"Rising, while the men remained seated with bowed heads, she thanked the Supreme Being for the bounteous food that was spread before them, ending by saying, 'Our Father, protect these men, for they are good and true.'"

"And you say all of the men cared for her?"

"I don't think I should be exaggerating if I stated that every man present at that dinner would have risked his life for her safety."

"I see—what happened next?"

"After dinner, which was at twelve o'clock, they played games. When they grew tired of them, the men gave Petite a gun and then beat the bushes in order to force the rabbits to come out within her range. This continued until the shadows of the large trees lengthened, indicating the approach of evening when, if possible, Antoine might return.

"With this in mind, Petite walked down the bayou towards the Gulf of Mexico in hope of meeting him and wishing at every turn she might see his lone pirogue. As time passed, her hope waned; so almost at dusk she retraced her steps. It wasn't long before darkness overtook her when she was only half way back. Dominique, missing her, sent men to hunt for her in the direction from which Captain Antoine would come.

"In the meantime, Petite heard the paddling of a pirogue oar; and as it came near, her heart began to beat rapidly. Scanning the starlit water, she at last saw the boat gliding around the bend with its lone occupant leisurely stroking the water. As Petite was sure it was Antoine, she called, 'Antoine, Antoine.' The man, hearing her and recognizing the name, headed toward shore. Petite then realized her mistake. Though she knew Lafitte's men, she feared this one might be a stranger; so she asked, 'Who are you?'

"The answer came in perfect English, but with an accent that was new to her, 'I am James.'

" 'I don't know you. Be on your way,' replied Petite.

" 'I don't know you either, but any friend of Antoine's is an enemy of mine.'

"And, Grace, with that he leaped ashore and grabbed Petite, who screamed at the top of her voice. Her scream reverberated through the woods and swamp. Dominique's men heard it, as did also one other in a racing piroque. The men needed no further urging, for all rushed to the scene—some on land and one on the water. They reached Petite at the same time. As you have probably guessed, the one on the water was Antoine; and when he leaped ashore, the man James, who had tried to attack Petite, drew his sword while Petite leaped towards Antoine, who gently pushed her behind him. With sword in hand and by the light of torches, he eyed her would-be attacker with a hatred that fairly blazed from his eyes.

" 'Step aside, men,' he said as Lafitte's men started towards James, 'this is my affair.'

"And with that, their swords met, and Antoine spoke two words to his antagonist—'Till death.'

"One of Dominique's men who had hunted for Petite quickly leaned towards her and said, 'Miss Petite, let me kill him, for I have powder and ball!'

"'No, don't,' was her simple answer, for, as much as she loved Antoine, she wanted fairness.

"Just then a scream was heard. Petite turning saw Antoine remove a handkerchief from his pocket and wipe his sword, and then he said aloud, 'By God, I said I would kill anyone who harmed her.'

"'Beautiful swordsmanship, Captain,' said one of the men.

"'Thanks, but where is Petite?'

"'Here, sir. She has fainted dead away.'

"'Petite, Petite, my darling.'

"'Here, Captain, is some water.'

"Suddenly she said, 'Antoine, did you really kill him?'

"'No,' said someone, 'for I hear moaning. Shall I finish him?'

"'No, no,' Petitie replied. 'Take him to the lodge.'

"'By Gar, Captain, you are wan lucky man.'

"'I know it, Dominique, and I—'

"'And I am lucky, too.'

"'Yes, Petite, you too, are wan lucky girl to have man risk life for you.'

"'How is he? Is he dead?'

"'No, he weel live—but he mus' hang, for he is wan British spy. He say dat he know you, Captain.'

"'Yes, I know him and have known he was an English spy for years; and that is why I forced him to leave Barataria. Now, Dominique, if you will excuse us, I should like to be alone with my fiancé.

"'Oh, I see. Well, be gone to Lafitte's room.' And they left, Grace, followed by Phoebe.

"When they had closed the door, Petite walked up to Antoine with raised hand and uplifted face; her hair had fallen to her back. He looked at her, started to reprimand her, stopped, and taking her in his arms, kissed her with all the fervor that was in that heart of his. Moving his lips and still holding her tight, he looked directly into her eyes and said, 'Petite, darling, I want a promise from you—and I want you to give it to me on your word of honor.'

"'Sweetheart, I'll promise you anything.'

" 'I want you to promise that you will never follow me through the swamps again.'

" 'Even if you are in danger?'

" 'Yes.'

" 'But Antoine—'

" 'Petite!'

" 'I promise on my word of honor never to follow you through the swamps.' "

"Emile, I'm sure he loved her even better for those words."

"I see that you have learned how man appreciates humility in the woman he loves."

"Yes, I've noticed when I'm sweet, as you call it, how you hold me more tenderly, as it were, and that your kisses are, shall I say, more sincere. But tell me, what did they do next?"

"Well, Phoebe being in the room as chaperon, Antoine made Petite rest by lying on the bed while he sat by her side and kissing her again, said, 'Petite, you took some dreadful chances.'

" 'But I know the swamps and bayous.'

" 'Not at night.'

" 'No, not at night. But aren't you glad to have me here?'

" 'Glad does not even partly describe it.'

" 'I know, for I am extremely happy, and I know you are, too. And, Antoine darling, now I realize how much you do love me.'

" 'You do?'

" 'Yes, for I saw your eyes when you had your sworn in hand; and, darling, please tell me that you will never look at me with that expression.'

" 'I promise. But tell me, was it that fightful?'

" 'I don't know that I should call it frightful, but you looked as though you would tear that man apart, limb from limb.'

" 'That was exactly as I felt; and, sweet, that is the way I shall always feel towards anyone that harms or tries to harm you—I mean that.'

" 'I know it, and that was the reason why I said now I know the depth of your love.'

"Just then, Grace, a knock sounded on the door, and Antoine answered with, 'Entré.' The door swung open on its creaky hinges and in walked Mr. Champlain.

" 'Father,' cried Petite, starting to rise, when Mr. Champlain answered, 'You remain there, you bad girl,' and walked toward Antoine with outstretched hand, saying, 'My boy, Dominique has related everything, and I am proud of you.'

" 'Thanks, Mr. Champlain.'

" 'Antoine, would you object to calling me father?'

" 'Not at all—I would really find it a pleasure.'

" 'That's fine. But tell me, what do you think of this little—'

" 'That, father, is love.'

" 'But poor reasoning.'

" 'Father, when love enters, reasoning goes. I know for I have the same symptoms.'

" 'And you were here?'

" 'No, I was with Lafitte, training the men.'

" 'Then how did you know she was here?'

" 'Well, she sang "My Creole Belle", and others along the bayou heard and sang it, too, and in that way we heard it. Lafitte was certain it was Petite.'

" 'But, darling, Dominique sent a message.'

" 'Oh yes, I believe someone paddling did say something as I passed him. You see, father, how preoccupied I was.'

" 'Yes, I see—but what am I going to do with this girl? First, she braves the swamps for her lover and then, miles away, delivers a message to him through song.'

" 'Fifty miles, to be exact; and Lafitte assured me that not one hour had elapsed between the time Petite sang and the time we heard it there.'

" 'I see; but, Antoine, I shudder every time I think of last night. Do you know what could have happened to her?'

" 'Yes, she could have been swallowed up out there as though she had never existed And tell me, why are you here?'

" 'I came to take her back home. If I had known you were here, I would have spared myself the trip, for I believe she will obey only two people in this world.'

" 'If she disobeyed me, I would place her across my lap and spank her.'

" 'That, my sweet, would be a pleasure.'

" 'You little vixen. And suppose your father spanked?'

" 'His hand would be heavy; but, Father, it has been many

years since you lifted your hand against me.'

" 'Yes, Petite, it has been—but you are returning home with me in the morning.'

" 'But Dominique has invited me to stay as long—'

" 'Petite!' said Antoine.

" 'But—'

" 'Petite!'

" 'All right, darling, I will return; but I do so want to be near you.'

" 'I know, for don't I long to be with you every minute we are parted. But, little darling,' he continued, holding her face with both hands, forgetting that Mr. Champlain was present, 'I have my part to play in defending you and all of the other women in New Orleans; and to be truthful, I should be at Grand Isle now. However, I have found a man who has received some military training; and in a few days he will be able to relieve me.'

" 'It shall be as you will.'

" 'Darling.'

" 'But, Antoine,' she said as fear entered her mind, and she fixed her dark expressive eyes on her fiancé, 'what about the Federal men—my God, darling, don't—'

" 'Petite, don't act that way, please. Listen, by that time Lafitte will have contacted Jackson; and the man would be a fool to refuse his offer. Do you understand, I shall be free to walk the streets of New Orleans.'

" 'Thank God.'

" 'Now, you should sleep—'

" 'Please, Antoine, don't make me—'

" 'I won't, sweet.'

" 'Kiss me again—and again. Oh, Father, I love him so.

" 'Yes, I know, you needn't tell me after my scare of last night. And you, my son, with your sword—I believe you are evenly matched. Dominique told me that his men swear that they saw sparks shooting from your eyes.'

" 'That could have been, for God knows that I have never experienced such hatred—and I hope I never shall again.'

" 'Well, son, I'll let you two alone for I am tired and shall retire. Goodnight.'

"And, with that, they were left alone with Phoebe, who

promptly fell asleep. The first thing Antoine said was, 'Little sweet, it sounds so dictatorial for me to force you to do things, but please, not for me, but for your own sake, please obey without any insisting.'

" 'Darling, it is love that makes me want to rebel.'

" 'Yes, I know; but take, for instance, last night—it could have been disastrous.'

" 'I understand. Now that I have relaxed, let us walk outside, in the beautiful moonlight.'

"And arm in arm they walked on the bank of the bayou, where the reflection of the huge moss-covered trees, illuminated by the soft beams of the full moon, cast grotesque shadows which seemed to dance on the water with every slight movement made by the breeze.

"They remained outdoors, confessing all of their emotions to each other until well past midnight when, as they turned to enter the lodge, they heard in the distance the sound of paddles striking the water.

" 'Listen, sweet. Doesn't that sound like paddles striking the water?'

" 'Yes, it does.'

" 'Let's wait to see—'

" 'Antoine, it's the sound of many paddles.'

" 'Then I will call the sentry.'

"And, Grace, he called the attention of the sentry to the sound, saying, 'Sentry, do you hear the paddles of pirogues?'

" 'Yes, I've been hearing them; but they are friends.'

" 'How do you know?'

" 'For two reasons. First, those paddles are moving in rhythm —only our band of men are so adept. Second, two shots would have been fired, one ten miles up the bayou and the other at five miles, if they were not.'

" 'You mean, one can hear at that distance?'

" 'Not at that distance as the bayou winds, but as the crow flies. In other words, five miles up the winding bayou are only two miles by air.'

" 'Oh, I see. But they must be near.'

" 'About a half mile.'

" 'Then, we shall wait.'

" 'As you wish, Captain.'

"And Grace, they sat on the bank of the bayou, listening to the sound that drew nearer and nearer until, emerging around the bend, was a flotilla—as we later found out, consisting of seventy-two boats, manned by over one hundred men heavily armed with Lafitte leading them. The pirogues in formation glided over the peaceful moonlit bayou, every strike from the brawny, half-robed, sun-tanned men sending them nearer and nearer, until one by one they fell in line; then, with powerful thrusts the pirates sent their light craft up on the sloping clay shore. Lafitte, first to land, greeted Petite and Antoine, removing his large black sombrero. With a graceful sweep of his arm, he gallantly bowed, and said with a large smile which revealed his beautiful white teeth, 'Good morning, my good friends.'

" 'Good morning,' echoed Petite and Antoine.

"Then Lafitte continued, 'Petite, I heard about your adventure last night. Let me compliment you on your initiative. And you, Antoine, can now visit the city at will, for I spoke to Jackson today, and we reached an agreement.'

" 'Jean Lafitte, I could kiss you.'

" 'Don't Petite, for one kiss would fan an ember that has long remained dormant in my heart—Antoine, have you transferred your command to André?'

" 'No, I haven't and will not for a few days.'

" 'But he has had military training.'

" 'Not enough to suit me. You know, Lafitte, we have much at stake.'

" 'Yes, especially you. However, if you believe it important enough to separate yourself from that sweet one, it must be necessary.'

"And, Grace, it was very important for the sailors to be properly trained if they were to make good soldiers."

"I see. What happened next?"

"Well, as the men landed they raced to the lodge and awakened those who were asleep, crying, 'We are now free men.' "

"Meaning what, Emile?"

"Well, they explained that since they had been pardoned, they, too, could have sweethearts and marry; for we must remember that those men were just as human as other men and in their subconscious minds was the desire to mate and have homes of their own. So, when the entire clan realized the significance of Lafitte's agreement with General Jackson, pandemonium reigned, for there was 'grog and more grog'. Petite and Antoine also joined in the celebration, as did Mr. Champlain. It was, indeed, a merry crowd; and Lafitte, who at all times demanded discipline, for once permitted them free rein.

"However, at daybreak, or rather sun-up, they started—Mr. Champlain in a single pirogue; Petite an Phoebe in a large one, for Dominique had sent one of the men to paddle for them; and Antoine in his racer, a tricky craft. Petite's boat was in midstream waiting for Antoine's. Lining the shore and shouting all sorts of good wishes stood the happy buccaneers. Antoine, having completed his conversation with Lafitte, dipped his paddle ever so lightly; and in two strokes his small racer was lying alongside of Petite's large craft. All of a sudden all became quiet, their eyes fixed on the two boats. Antoine's racer with only one inch of free-board did not permit his leaning over, so that it was Petite, who, bending over him, placed her lips on his. The men ashore applauded; those wearing hats tossed them into the air, for they had witnessed what was uppermost in their hearts—the love of a brave man for a beautiful woman.

"Grace, you understand Jackson's strategy? To pardon them would be first to enroll them as brave fighters; and second, their being able to make their homes in the city was an added incentive to save New Orleans."

"He surely had good judgment,—it was truly wonderful for those men—"

"Yes, it was, for—but wait, I'm ahead of my story."

CHAPTER XII

HALLUCINATION

"Emile, may I kiss you?"

"Certainly. It has been sometime since you did."

"But, you admonished me before."

"Why?"

"Because I overdid it; but I could not help it."

"Yes, I know. But if you will just be patient—wait until I finish the . . ."

"Sweet, what would you have done with someone less affectionate?"

"I should have remained a bachelor."

"I'm glad you didn't."

"And so am I."

"And why do you and I feel towards each other as we do?"

"Because of suggestive psychology."

"Meaning what?"

"Meaning that as we continue the story of the two lovers, it suggests to us subconsciously a desire to have the same pleasure they are experiencing. You see we, Grace, are inherently selfish since we desire that which others possess. In other words, we desire the same pleasure and excitement they have, and that is the reason why we desire to express our love for each other more tonight than usual."

"But I love to kiss you every night."

"And I feel the same way towards you, but will you admit that tonight our desire is stronger than it is on other nights?"

"Yes, I do. Oh, I see. And what can we do to counteract this?"

"Rest your face on my chest as I first suggested."

"Then you knew what our reaction would be?"

"Yes."

"Well, I'll do as you say. Now, is this the position you wanted me in?"

"Yes. Now, don't you feel more comfortable?"

"Yes, more comfortable, but not so romantic."

"That is exactly what we are trying to avoid until I complete the story."

"I see. Now continue and relate everything that happened next."

"Well, Lafitte, Dominique You, and Antoine had their men in perfect shape, physically and mentally, when on the twenty-seventh of December, eighteen hundred and fourteen, Jackson called them. General Packenham, probably England's bravest soldier, had arrived two days before as commander-in-chief of the British forces. Jackson now realized that he had a capable opponent; so he placed the hardy band of pirates where the greatest strength was needed. Remember, Grace, sailor-soldiers wore no uniforms—in fact, some were only in trunks. One can imagine how Packenham and his men laughed when they saw this clan. Little did he realize that it was they who would—but, again, I'm ahead of my story."

"How do you think those men felt towards the British?"

"Admiration for their beautiful uniforms, but contempt for their fighting; for buccaneers were second to none in handling cannon and guns, as only the brave chose their vocation."

"Oh, I see. And about the battle?"

"Not so quick, sweet. You see, there were skirmishes—some large and some small. On January the seventh, eighteen hundred and fifteen, Antoine, worn and haggard, entered Petite's home.

" 'Oh, Antoine darling, it's wonderful to hold you again. Please, when this is over, if God sees fits to let you live through the battle, I pray that you may never have to leave me again.'

" 'Right, darling But did you sleep last night?'

" 'No, I couldn't; I simply couldn't when I thought of you and the other brave men fighting—'

" 'Petite, a major battle looms now, and I believe it will be on the morrow. It is necessary that I rest today; so Dominique sent me home, for I've handled my cannon for sixty consecutive hours. I am worn to such an extent as to be useless unless I can get some sleep. When I'm with you, I seem to get what one might call second wind. If I listened to my heart, I would do naught. else but hold you, kiss you, my sweet. But, if I'm to do my share tomorrow, I must rest. Please, let me lie on the sofa.'

" 'No, Antoine—lie in my bed.'

" 'As you say.'

" 'Let's go upstairs . . . now into my room. Sweet, let me re-move your boots.'

" 'No, please, I'll do that myself.'

" 'It's too late, see, I have them off. Now for your shirt—there. Do you want to be alone?'

" 'Yes, if you're going to sleep; no, if you're not.'

" 'I will not, now, for I want you to rest your head in my lap, like this; that's it. And now, darling, I'll kiss you, and while I run my hand through your hair, I want you to close your eyes and sleep—'

"In fewer than three minutes Petite noticed that he was sound asleep and gently said, 'Now, my sweet, that you're asleep, I'll move your head thus and place it on the pillow. Antoine, my darling, this may be our last day together; so I'll watch over you. Oh, darling, my eyes burn so—I can hardly keep them open—' Slowly her eyes closed. Her head rested against his pillow.

"And, Grace, they slept from eight in the morning until six that afternoon, when Mr. Champlain awakened them on his return from the front.

" 'Anything new, Father?' asked Antoine.

" 'No, except Jackson intends attacking at daybreak.'

" 'Good.'

" 'Good, Antoine?'

" 'Yes, for our men are at fever heat and ready to give all they have; and, Father, those devils actually outshot the trained ar-tillerymen of the British, silencing them every time they started to fire.'

" 'I understand that they are Jackson's most valuable men.'

" 'They are; and, well, you know what happened when Dom-inique complained to Jackson that his men were receiving wet powder?'

" 'No, what?'

" 'Well Jackson said to his orderly, "Let Lafitte's men be the last to receive wet powder." '

" 'That speaks for itself. And, Antoine, I understand that you leaped over the parapet and rescued one of the "devils" who had fallen and upon whom British fire was concentrated. I understand it was almost sure death. You must have had a special interest in his rescue?'

" 'Well, one of the other boys would have done it; but when I realized that it was André, who has four daughters, and there he was, an old man fighting for them, I, for the first time since I've met Petite, forgot her and helped him. Tell me where did you hear about it? One would imagine fighting the Redcoats would be more important than relating such incidents.'

" 'Well, when Jackson was talking to his orderly, he said, "Gentlemen, we cannot lose this battle with such men as Antoine Floret, who leaped over the parapet and saved one of his comrades." Antoine, I could feel my chest expand.'

" 'Thanks, Father; and, Petite, forgive me for forgetting you, darling, for that moment.'

" 'Yes, but I fear for your life.'

" 'Listen, sweet—get my dagger out of my coat pocket. Now, I give it to you. Should we lose tomorrow, you are to plunge this blade its full length into the heart of any Britisher that attacks you. Kill him. kill him, you hear—'

" 'Now, sweet, please calm yourself. That's better. Now, listen to me. Should the battle be lost, I will plunge this dagger, which shall remain from today in my belt, into my own heart—'

" 'Petite—'

" 'Please, don't interrupt. I definitely know that no Redcoat will pass you while you're alive. Should I see one, I shall know that you gave your all; and since life will be useless to me then, I shall do as I said. I know that your heart grieves to leave me just as I suffer to see you go; but, Antoine, my darling, my very breath of life, go; and I'll visit the Cathedral and pray the night through for you.'

" 'Darling, let us descend the stair together. See, there's mother down there.'

" 'Mother, where are you going?'

" 'To Madame Porée.'

" 'Why?'

" 'Because all of the women are gathering there for the night since the men are at the front. You, too, Petite, must come.' "

"Emile, did she go?"

"Yes, with hundreds of others. You see, fearing bodily harm from the British soldiers, many like Petite had daggers, and all of them felt there was safety in numbers. When Petite arrived, she noticed that the women had rosaries and were praying. Remembering her promise to Antoine, she stole away from Madame Porée's home at Dumaine and Royal Streets, and walked quickly through the heavy traffic of men and guns going down Chartres Street, to the Cathedral which was kept open that night for the devout. Kneeling before the beautiful Belgian altar, she prayed with the devotion that comes from a pure heart.

"Petite remained for hours on her knees, telling God that, although they ached as though cut with a knife, it was her way of proving to Him the hell she would willingly go through if Antoine would return to her safely—safely she repeated. Just then she was disturbed by someone kneeling next to her, and turning, she saw old lady Denégre with her grandson, who had been shot through the cheek; and evidently a friend of his with a bandage around his neck, while his arm rested in a sling.

"Just then the Cathedral bells began pealing, for young Bayone's body was enroute to the church preparatory to burial. He had been shot through the heart. It was only then that Petite fully realized war meant casualties—meant death!

"For the first time she realized that by this time Antoine might have been wounded—he might be bleeding to death. And what with his absolute scorn of fear as he so aptly displayed in defense of his ship and with his sword, and lately his leaping the parapet to save André's life in the face of British fire, why she was certain he would die on that battlefield. Fear possessed her to such an extent that she was sure he was bleeding on the Chalmette battlefield, asking for her while she remained in the city, protected by him while he—no, she would not stay—impulsiveness had replaced sound reasoning, and, jumping to her feet, she ran through the center aisle. The slaves in the gallery seemed saying to her, 'Hurry, Petite—rush to him.'

"Reaching the street, Petite hailed a carriage filled with men, determined men, each with his gun—no guns were alike; and she told them that her wounded lover was calling for her. Grace, she actually believed it herself. They made room for her and away went the carriage over dirt roads—faster, ever faster, passing Fort St. Charles, then Esplanade Avenue. The horses foamed at the mouth as the driver continually urged them on— on to the battlefield. The carriage rumbled over bridges which covered canals that drained the evil-smelling swamp. It joined the many conveyances going to Chalmette, for there were farm wagons, closed and open milk wagons, carts, sulkies—in fact, any and everything on wheels that could be drawn by horses.

"In the wake of this mad rush snakes lay writhing in the road as wheels and more wheels passed over them; turtles that had tried to cross and were caught in the center of the road, with their shells cracked by horses' roofs, lay helpless; crayfish, moving in droves to where there was more water, were crushed, causing the wheels to slide into ruts that the driver strove to avoid.

"Petite, inside the rolling carriage, was tossed first against the side and then against a soldier; she was black and blue from her bruises. This was war, and women were not intended to be on blood-stained battlefields. 'On, on,' she kept urging, impervious to her aches and pain.

"Finally they reached the third line—a line that Jackson planned should the first and second fall, never once realizing the splendid fighters Lafitte's men would prove to be.

"'Which line, Mam'zelle?'

"'The battle line! Hurry, the battle line.'

"On they rolled, passing the second line when one of a matched pair of roan horses dropped dead on the road. The carriage veered to one side, and the door sprung open. Petite was thrown into the weeds. Rising quickly, forgetting her pain, she raced along the road to the battlefront and Antoine. Nearing the line, she saw a man on horseback and called to him. Above the din her voice carried; and the horse started towards her.

"'Please, oh please, where are Lafitte's men stationed?'

" 'Why?'

" 'Because I must see Antoine Floret.'

" 'Here, give me your hand; that's it; now spring up—. You've made it. Now hold onto me.'

" 'May I ask your name?'

" 'Yes, I'm Jackson.'

" 'The General?'

" 'Yes.'

" 'And you know Antoine?'

" 'Yes. Is it for you that he is fighting?'

" 'I—I don't know. Why?'

" 'Because no man would fight as he does without some exceptionally great incentive. But here we are—Whoa. There he is, Miss, directing the replacing of that cannon. I'll call him for you. 'Antoine, I have a visitor for you.'

" 'Petite!'

" 'Antoine! Oh, darling, darling—you are smiling when I thought you would be angry with me.'

" 'I'm smiling because I knew you would come.'

" 'You knew?'

" 'Yes, you forget, little sweet, that I now know you.'

" 'But—'

" 'Petite, you braved the swamps at night when you thought I was in danger. What would be more natural than for you to come here when you knew, definitely knew that more danger threatened me.'

" 'Antoine, darling, I saw you lying on the field wounded, asking for me. Nothing, darling, nothing this side of hell could have held me. I am here now, and I swear I'll comply with your orders.'

" 'And suppose I order you back home?'

" 'I'll go; but please, don't do that.'

" 'I won't. But tell me, will you sleep tonight?'

" 'No.'

" 'Then, my orders are for you to remain with me until daybreak, when you will proceed to the second line. Should this front fall; and, darling, it may, since we are outnumbered four to one, and since we are facing trained soldiers—soldiers fresh from the Battle of Waterloo—while our men, except Lafitte's, know nothing of war, then you are to proceed to the third line. After that, you will act as you see fit, because—'

" 'Yes, I know, because you will be dead.'

" 'I swear, sweet, that no Redcoat will cross this section alive.'

" 'I know that. Oh, look at Dominique and Lafitte. They see us.'

" 'Why, Petite, what are you doing here?'

" 'I saw Antoine lying wounded; so I hailed a carriage, and here I am, Lafitte.'

" 'But did you, Antoine, explain to her it will be dangerous and—'

" 'He has, and I'll obey his orders.'

CHAPTER XIII

THE BATTLE

" 'Now, darling, you sit here where I can see you, for I must be with my men.'

" 'As you say.'

"And, Grace, she sat there watching his every movement and listening to his orders to the men. Every minute she admired him more and more, especially when Dominique, internationally known as a real soldier, said, 'Antoine, your men are perfectly trained.'

" 'Thanks, Dominique.'

" 'And why are you placing those cannons at an angle?'

" 'Because I'm determined that no Britisher shall pass through that center.'

" 'Oh, I see. Your training in France has not been forgotten. Antoine, I now see a look of—shall I call it determination or—'

" 'Dominique, I'll kill, you hear, I'll kill—'

" 'I know, I know. We all will; this is war, and we are defending our city.'

" 'It may be war to you, and it may be your city; but to me, it is not defense of my country, but defense of women.'

" 'One in particular?'

" 'Yes, and all in general. You know, Dominique, as I love Petite, others love other women.'

" 'I have one, too.'

" 'I know.'

" 'You know who she is?'

" 'Yes.'

" 'And do you criticize me?'

" 'No, for even though Marie Villars is a quadroon, she is sweet and worth fighting for. Remember, I know that she became a mother for you and—'

" 'Captain Antoine, where do you want this cannon?'

" 'Over there, to the right, covering that wooded section.'

" 'But, captain, that will be dangerous for from the trees they can spot the cannoneer.'

" 'I know. I'll man that one.'

" 'But, captain—'

" 'Joseph, it is my order.'

" 'Yes, sir.'

"And throughout the night, Petite looked and listened and wondered—wondered, Grace, whether Antoine would be alive after the battle. And a new fear gripped her heart; so, leaving her seat, she ran to Antoine and said, 'Antoine, my darling, intuition tells me that your determination is getting the better of your judgment—darling, darling, I can't bear that. I can't.'

"Placing both arms about her as if to protect her, he replied, 'Please, my sweet, calm yourself; and I'll promise to be careful. That's better; and, Petite, it is now daybreak, and I am ordering you back to the second line. See, Jackson is moving from place to place, giving orders; and firing will soon start. Now, darling, I kiss you—again—and again. Now, go.' "

"And, Emile, did she go?"

"Yes, but as soon as the boom of the cannon could be heard, she left the second line and ran, ran until she was barely behind Antoine, who was pumping balls as fast as one could throw them, never once stopping to wipe the perspiration that was falling on his hot cannon and turning into steam. She knelt amid balls and shots that fell all about her, and prayed, never permitting her gaze to leave Antoine.'

"My she was brave."

"Yes, she was the only woman on that battlefield."

"What happened next?"

"A brave British lieutenant with his followers had gained the parapet and was about to climb when Antoine spied him; and, since it was necessary to fire from the exposed side, he, rather than order a man to that dangerous position, took the gun from Josef. Then ordering him to man the cannon, Antoine leaped over and began firing. Petite saw this; and, rising, she rushed forward and started to climb over to reach him. In that short moment, she saw him aim and pull the trigger; and as the bullet struck its target, she heard Antoine say, 'This one will not harm you, Petite.'

"Suddenly one of the men grabbed her and forced her down just as a bullet struck the top, showering dust about them. Listening in a crouching position, she again heard him say, 'This one will not harm you, Petite.'

"Then his gun was silent; and Dominique You, missing him, asked Josef where he was, and Josef explained quickly what had happened. With a curse, Grace, and in full view of Petite, who was petrified with fear, brave as she was, Dominique leaped over to Antoine. In a flash, with the British balls striking about him, he again climbed and leaped to safety, bearing Antoine in his short, stout arms. Petite, white as a ghost, rushed to them, for, from Antoine's left side blood was slowly oozing—his life blood! Jackson, seeing Dominique's feat from a distance, rode up; and Petite, recognizing him, called 'General.'

" 'Yes, Miss.'

" 'Please, oh! please, get a doctor—Antoine is wounded.'

"Calling to his orderly, the general sent him immediately for a doctor. Petite, placing her small lace handkerchief over the wound, leaned over and whispered in Antoine's ear. After the doctor had administered first aid, Lafitte gave orders to have Antoine carried away . . . Petite was at his side. So neither heard the word 'Victory.' "

CHAPTER XIV

Ask For My Forgiveness

"Victory! Everyone in the small city was jubilant. All the women, except one, had removed the small daggers from their belts and then flocked to the St. Louis Cathedral to attend mass that would be continual. As they passed, slaves threw open heavily barred windows and doors. In one building, nuns in black and white, noiselessly moved to and fro to help the doctor; and later, to assist the priest who was administering the last sacrament. Or perhaps a minister offered spiritual consolation to one who just two hours before had worn a redcoat, for red coats, homespun shirts, Indian blankets, Creole robes, Negroes' overalls—all lay under the many beds that stood in the large room which was very simply furnished and had a bare floor. Against the wall, between two windows, was fastened a large life-sized crucifix that the good priests of the Cathedral had lent the nuns. For years it had stood at the entrance. Beds of every description—singles and doubles, mahogany and walnut, and pieces from beautiful hand-carved bedroom suites were placed almost side by side. Grace, this was the improvised hospital.

"In one corner lay a man between life and death; and beside him sat the one person who was allowed there, and her lips were in constant motion as her small white fingers moved from bead to bead on her rosary of gold and pearl—beads given her on her first communion day. Her eyes moved from the quick motion of his chest to the calmness of his face, and she thought how determined that face looked when he said, 'That one will not harm you, Petite.'

"She lowered her hand to her belt and nervously fingered the piece of cold steel there. Then, for the first time, tears filled her eyes, and slowly coursed downward until they reached her small, sad mouth, saddened for the first time in her life. She was about to place her head in her hands to hide her uncontrollable sobbing when she noticed someone was motioning to her. Turing her head, she saw a man beckoning her to come to him. Dropping her gaze, she noticed a red coat under his bed. Her glance returned to Antoine, who had made no change. Then silently, she slipped from the chair, the rosary still in her hands, and noiselessly moved over to the British soldier. Grace, there was no hatred in her heart; but, instead, tenderness. As she reached his bed, he asked, 'Please, give me some water. Please, oh please, don't hate me!'

" 'I don't.'

" 'You should.'

" 'Why?'

" 'It was I who shot him, and I now ask God to take me, but to let him live—to let him live, you hear me—'

" 'Yes, I hear. Calm yourself.'

" 'You ask me to calm myself when your fiancé lies at death's door—and you are in tears—but that's war. Now, will you get me water?'

" 'But it may be against the doctor's order.'

" 'It is; but in my leaving, maybe God will hear my prayer and save him.'

" 'You feel you owe me much.'

" 'Yes, more than—'

" 'Then lie down and rest. See I am not nervous. I, too, have prayed and I feel sure He has heard my prayer. Now be quiet, for here comes Father Mideau; and see, he has stopped at the Indian.'

"With that she turned and walked over to Antoine; she had been watching him while she was talking to the Britisher. Antoine was still breathing rapidly. A nun approached and took his wrist; she counted while the large French watch ticked away the precious minutes.

" 'Please, Sister Agnes, will he—will he live?'

" 'No one knows, Petite. Brace up child, and don't cry. God knows best.'

"Outside the two guards saluted as a tall thin man entered. Stopping here and there and giving encouragement to those who were conscious, he eventually reached Petite's chair. From the rear he placed both wrinkled hands on her solt white shoulders. Looking up, she saw the General.

" 'Petite, he cannot leave you when you have such devotion. See, his lips are moving. Listen, child—'Petite, Petite'—no, child, don't move; he is in a coma; his subconscious mind is active.' "

Grace had long since risen to a sitting position and had been breathlessly absorbing every word that Emile uttered. Slowly, her small hands opened and closed, and she started to say, "Did he die?", but checked herself and instead asked, "Emile, may I kiss you?"

"Surely, sweet."

Placing both hands to the sides of his face, she kissed him and pleadingly demanded, "Emile, please, did he die? Oh, Emile, don't hesitate—I must know. Did he die?"

Just then, the front door bell rang, and Emile asked, "Hasn't it rung four times?"

"Maybe it did, but—"

"Now, Grace, be patient, for just one minute."

"There's the bell again, Emile; two—three—four; yes, four times. And, Emile, here are your slippers," as he hurried to the front door, candle in hand.

Grace, now alone, began wondering about Emile's excitement when she heard through the drapes, 'Why, Petite! My God, girl, I'm happy to see you. Let me hug you, and, Antoine, you are looking fine!"

Grace rubbed her eyes and reached for her hand mirror; peering in it, she muttered, "Am I dreaming? Did I hear right?"

Then listening again, she heard Emile say, "Petite, you are as beautiful as ever; and if I did not know your age, I should think you are in your twenties; and you, Antoine, you old—"

Emile stopped dead short, for he had noticed that Antoine was staring at the open drapes; and, following his gaze, he saw Grace standing there with open mouth and staring eyes. In a flash, Emile realized Antoine's reaction since he had not heard of his marriage, and Petite's, for she too was staring.

"Grace, come here."

At his words she came out of her daze, and realizing that she was in her gown, she quickly drew the drapes together and was about to retreat when she heard, "Grace, I want you here, just as you are."

Slowly, the drapes were again parted. Blushing, Grace entered and rushed to Emile, placing both arms about him and hiding her face. Emile instantly placed his arms about her. Facing Petite and Antoine, he said, "Folks, I have had a beautiful romance since I saw you last, and I want you to meet the only girl who has ever given me a desire to say 'I do.' Grace, Petite and Antione, and Grace."

Petite rushed to her and, taking her from Emile's arms, hugged her and led her to the sofa where they both sat down; and Petite, placing both hands on Grace's shoulders, turned her to where the candle light shone on her face and said in her rich, deep voice after kissing her, "Emile, if I were a man, I too would have said, 'I do.' Grace, you are truly beautiful; you're so soft and sweet too. And remember this, we shall love you as we do Emile."

"Thanks, but are you the Petite who followed Antoine through the swamps, who was with him at the Battle of New Orleans, who—"

"Yes, Grace, the same." And in a whisper, she continued, "And I love him as much today as I did then."

"But, Petite, why whisper? I thought you two had an agreement to tell everything to each other."

"Oh! Emile has told you our romance?"

"Yes, Petite, I have; in fact, I've just completed relating it to Grace."

"Antoine is edging his way over here to look at you, Grace. Antoine, take my place on the sofa while I talk to Emile."

"Grace, I am happy to see that Emile has fared so well."

"But I have fared well, too."

"More so than you will ever know. But tell me all about yourself. From your accent I can tell you are from the North; and yet, when Emile ordered you to enter, you immediately obeyed.

I thought only girls from this section were obedient to their husbands."

"Now, I am one of you people; and in answer to your question, I want you to know that I consider myself lucky to learn your Creole ideal of living, and I love it."

"Antoine."

"Yes, Petite."

"Emile insists that we sleep here tonight."

"But, sweet, our things are on the boat, unpacked. You see, Emile, when we reached the city, we immmediately came to you. We just couldn't wait until morning."

"I see. But in the armoire in the room that belonged to Belle's mother you will find everything that you need."

Grace and Antoine rose, and they bade each other "Goodnight"; Petite and Antoine, with their arms around each other's waist, and with a lighted candle, ascended the mahogany winding stair, while Grace stole to her bed, later followed by Emile, who had escorted his guests to their room.

"Emile, you big brute, lean over me."

"Say please."

"Please!"

"Not in that tone, honey."

"Please."

"Now, that's better. Tell me, what is wrong—as if I don't know."

Ignoring the last remark, Grace said, "You didn't hint, not even once, of their being alive."

"I know, honey."

"Well, since they love each other to so great an extent, I should like to know what happened on their wedding night. See, I will sit on my legs and—"

"Well, that I can't tell you, for they gave me their diary over three years ago, and I am in honor bound not to reveal certain of its contents. Now, my little sweet, it is after midnight; so I will slip under the cover, like this; and resting my weary head on the down-filled pillow, close my tired eyes, and proceed to sleep."

Grace looked at Emile, who appeared to be serious; and her large eyes narrowed, and her pretty lips drew tight, and formed only two lines; while her small hands formed two small fists.

She raised them, still looking at Emile, who realized physchologically the effect the story had had on her and without opening his eyes, having too often experienced her impulsive actions, said, in his low bass voice that Grace respected and admired,

"Grace, don't you dare;" and he then burst into laughter. With both hands against his face, she said, "You big teasing brute,—ask for my forgiveness or—"

FINIS

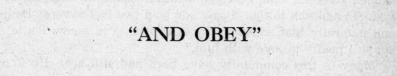

"AND OBEY"

CHAPTER I

Emile and Grace — Petite and Antoine

"Good morning Petite. My, let me hug you to see if you are really not a dream."

"No, not a dream, but Petite in person. And where is Emile?"

"Oh, he leaves early for the plantation to plan the work for the day for the slaves; but he is usually back for breakfast. Now, tell me where is Antoine?"

"I've just wakened him, having dressed first so as to be alone with you for a while. You see, we love Emile so much that we wish to know more of you, for we want to love you as well."

"Petite, I've loved you two before I knew you, for Emile recounted your romance to me last night; well, the two characters suddenly became real; now you can understand my affection for you. In addition to that, I saw how you two feel towards Emile and naturally that added to my affection. You know, Petite, I am still madly in love with him."

"Many in this community have been and still are. He is so good-natured and, shall I say, full of fun."

"Full of fun is putting it mildly—let me tell you what happened this morning."

"I thought you were going to say last night."

"Why?"

"Because we heard him laughing heartily, and Antoine said, 'Same old Emile—up to some of his tricks.'"

"He was; but let me tell you what happened this morning."

"Wait, here comes Antoine; half-dressed, I bet, to see you."

"Morning folks, I—"

"Antoine, your suspenders are hanging."

"Oh, they are? My error."

"But, Grace was about to tell me of a prank Emile played on her this morning."

"That isn't surprising, please tell it."

"Well, as you know, we retired late last night."

"Yes, we know; Emile was still laughing when we went to sleep."

"Well, this morning I awakened somewhat groggy; and, as is my habit, I threw my right arm over him, my left resting on the bed at my side. 'Emile,' I said, not opening my eyes, 'I had a beautiful dream last night.' I could have sworn that I had heard him say, 'Huh,' so I continued telling all of my dream, from the very beginning to the end, talking about fifteen minutes. When I finished, with my eyes still closed for the room was dark, I asked him how he liked it. Not hearing an answer, I repeated my question, this time squeezing him to force him to talk. Imagine my surprise, when he offed me no resistance; but I felt something flatten and it was the pillow Emile had ingeniously placed to replace his body. I pushed the thing away in anger; but, after reflecting, I began to laugh."

"It was laughable, Grace. I suppose you are getting accustomed to him by now?"

"I never shall. Listen, I'll tell you why you heard him laughing before you retired. As you know, he related to me your romance last night—how you two petted, caressed, and loved each other. For four hours I listened to his realistic account of your love-making; and as he progressed, we became more and more affectionate; in fact, towards the end we became passionate, and I had a great desire to be loved. And, after meeting you two, and realizing the pleasures you've had, why, my desire soared to the high heavens."

"We can understand that."

"Well, do you know what the big brute did?"

"What?"

"Well, when he came to bed, he half lay and half sat on his pillow, and blinking his eyes, he said, 'Now I will slip under the cover like this; and resting my weary head on the down-filled pillow, close my tired eyes, and proceed to sleep.' There I sat, on the bed with both legs folded under me, staring directly at that calm face, void of even the faintest smile, and apparently completely in earnest."

"I know you were angry."

"Angry is not the proper word—I was boiling."

"What did you do?"

"I don't know what my expression was, but I was damn mad; and closing my hands to fists, I raised them, when he said still with his eyes closed in that low commanding bass voice of his, 'Grace, don't you dare.' And then you heard him laugh."

They laughed, and Petite said, "Grace, I know you love that low bass voice of his."

"Love it? I adore it, especially when he issues a command—"

"And don't you love those commands? I do."

"Love them? I wish he were here now. But I hear his footsteps."

"Your wish is granted, my sweet, for I could smell that fried chicken one-half mile away and urged the horse to faster speed."

Rushing, she grabbed Emile's head with both hands and, drawing his face downward, kissed him so hard that the imprint remained on their lips."

"My, that is beautiful," said Petite.

"But you don't know that I have competition."

"How, Emile?"

"A lowly, inanimate, down-filled bag—a pillow."

Laughing heartily, Emile led them to the dining-room where Marie, the slave maid, had prepared a delicious breakfast.

"Antoine, and you, too, Petite, I'm elated over the way you are enjoying that food."

"Emile," answered Antoine, "two years ago we left the French Quarter and the Creole food; and we have made a trip around the world, returning only last night. We have visited practically every country of any significance and every large city; nowhere, you hear me, did we eat food as we Creoles cook it here. Did we, Petite?"

"In answer, I can only say that this is the first appetizing meal I've had since we left," answered Petite as she sank her beautiful teeth into the leg of a young pullet.

"We have one thing more here than you've found anywhere else in the world."

"What is that, Emile?"

In all seriousness, Emile answered, "We have acquired in the Quarter since you left a beautiful girl, whose heart is as large as her body; tears collecting in her large eyes when one describes one's sadness; and her blue eyes smile when one describes one's gladness."

Grace glanced at him out of the corner of her eye for, even though he was speaking in all seriousness, she had begun to realize his humor.

"We should like to meet her, Emile."

"Well, Petite, you'll be sorry."

"Why?"

"Because she will dog you until you relate to her—" and he stopped for he saw Grace looking directly into his eyes, both her hands resting on the white embroidered cloth. In her right hand resting on the table was a knife projecting into the air, while in her left was the fork in the same position. This was one of the few times that Emile could not suppress a smile. Grace reopened the conversation, saying mockingly as she held her head to one side, "Continue, my love."

Petite and Antoine, sensing that it was another of Emile's jokes, asked, "And who is this beautiful girl?"

Emile, rising, slowly walked around the table, while Grace followed him with her eyes, until he was directly behind her. In a flash he reached over her shoulder and playfully grasped both her hands, placing the side of his face against hers and repeated, "Because she will dog you until you relate to her a romance of the Vieux Carre."

"All laughed as Grace bent her head backward, and Emile kissed her. As he released her, his hands slowly traveled up both of her arms until they reached her white shoulders, and then to the underpart of her face; he stood erect and caressed her while he earnestly said to Petite and Antoine, "All jokes aside, folks, this is the sweetest thing I've ever known; she's ever ready to be petted and caressed and kissed. See how instinctively she moved her head backward so that I might pet her."

"Yes, I saw that; in fact, last night Antoine and I found her very attractive when she entered at your command in her nightgown and ran to you, placing both arms around you, while hiding her face. 'Petite,' Antoine said to me, 'I'll wager that we'll find Grace exceptionally sweet and one hundred per cent feminine.' So you see, Emile, what you're telling us is no news."

"I knew you would like her; but I still insist you are in for a rude awakening if you know a romance."

"Why, that will be wonderful, for I've long wanted to relate to someone the story of Jeanette and John. Do you remember that story?"

"How could I ever forget it when it concerned my next best friend, John."

"And who was John?" eagerly asked Grace.

"You see, Petite, how little it takes to interest her when one just hints at romance."

"Our relating it will certainly be a pleasure with so attentive a listener; and now, Grace darling, John was the Britisher who shot Antoine in the Battle of New Orleans, and who prayed God to take his life, while he was lying wounded in the hospital, and save Antoine's."

"Oh, yes, I remember. So you, Antoine, and John became fast friends?"

"He was second only to Emile."

"And when shall I hear the story?"

"Today, if we can encroach on your kindness. But we must first get some things from our baggage on the ship."

"Your baggage is here, except the trunk."

"Emile, are you joking?"

"Hell no, I picked it up as I returned from the plantation. You two don't think I would let you stay on the ship until you opened your house."

"I don't know what to say, except that I should have expected it. You see, Antoine and I being away two years have learned not to expect such courtesy."

"But, Petite, you haven't forgotten any of the story?"

"Very little, Grace, if any. And if I did, Antoine, with his wonderful memory, will substitute."

CHAPTER II

A Kiss in the Hospital

"Emile, now that we've finished breakfast, what are your plans for today?"

"To accompany you, Antoine, to see all of your friends. As the barouche is now ready, let us leave the women folk to themselves."

With that the men entered the vehicle, and Emile, taking the reins guided the horses slowly out of the driveway into the street. The slave maid, having tidied Grace's bedroom, entered the dining room to remove the dishes.

"Grace," said Petite, "I should like to see your bedroom."
"Come, for in there you will find the most comfort." And

taking her by the hand, Grace led her through the white hall into her bedroom.

"My, it is large and Oh, how beautiful—blue and gold—why who chose those beautiful pictures?"

"I started to say I, but really, I don't definitely know."
"I don't understand."

"Make yourself comfortable on the chaise lounge—that's it, and now I'll explain. You see, we had only been married one month when one morning I waked from a nightmare in which I saw Emile severely wounded. Upon realizing it was a dream, I was so overjoyed that I leaned over him and awakened him with kisses; first, on his lips, then on his face, and finally on his neck. He grabbed me and petted and caressed me until my love for him seemed to surge, to take me into another sphere. He was quick to see this, and raising my shoulder to where he could look directly into my eyes, he said, 'Darling, I want you to dress immediately and go to Holmes's Store, and there I want you to choose a score of pictures showing lovers in affectionate poses. Now, he continued, 'do hurry.'"

"I yet don't understanding."

"Well, you see, I was in a mood of extreme affection, and before
that affection could be satisfied, as he later exlained to me, he
rushed me for the pictures. The fact that every one that sees
them admires them is proof of his judgment."

"Oh, I see. I was wondering how any one person could so perfectly choose such a number of pictures with love for a subject.
See, even the features on the faces show clearly the ecstasy that
the lovers are experiencing. And, Grace, everything—this down-
filled chaise lounge, that tufted rocker, that can comfortably hold
Emile with you on his lap; that large French Psyche mirror that
reflects one in various positions—everything is conducive to love.
If Antoine were here, I would make him lie beside me and I
would love him. Oh, Grace, this room is enchanting. I can understand now how you felt surrounded by this beauty, especially
after your lover Emile had related to you a very romantic
story."

"He knew it, too, and that is the reason he teased me by slipping
under the cover last night—the brute!"

"Emile will never change with his good humor and kindness.
Now, Grace, are you ready for the story?"

"Petite, I'm always ready for a story of the French Quarter.
Those romances are so different from anything I've ever heard
or read, and yet they're true."

"Well, this one to you will sound unbelievable; but to the Creole, well, she would instantly understand. To start, I shall have
to begin when Antoine was lying at death's door in the improvised hospital after the Battle of New Orleans. From the morning of January eighth to the next morning I had remained at
his bedside, my prayer beads constantly moving. How many
times I said those beads the good Lord only knows. At eight-
fifteen that morning, tired, worn, and baggard, in addition to
the constant gnawing at my heart, for I realized Antoine's condition, and never letting my gaze leave him an instant, watching
the rhythmic motion of his chest and his closed eyes, I happened
to see his eyelid quiver. 'Antoine,' I said in a soft whisper,
slowly rising so as not to disturb him, trembling from head to
foot—my knees were about to buckle. He heard me; and making

a supreme effort, he opened his eyes wide. I realized that he was out of his coma, and then a terrible fear took possession of me. What if I did something wrong in my anxiety to help him? What if he tried to move from his longing to touch me, to place his arms around me? I was shaking, as I said, with the palms of my quivering hands almost touching his shoulders, as though to hold him down, 'Antoine, darling, don't move—for God's sake don't move.' Then I continued, 'It's good to see your eyes open again.'

"And, Grace, without turning, I called softly, but loud enough for the nun to hear me, 'Sister Agnes, come quickly; come quickly.' And as I heard her footsteps from the other end of the room, and still staring directly into Antoine's dark blue eyes, I said, 'Darling, how I would like to kiss you, but I must not, sweet; I must not because I might hurt you. Don't smile, darling, please don't smile—it might hurt.'

"And then the nun, followed by Dr. Contreau, interrupted me. Stepping nearer towards the head of the bed, I watched while the doctor fingered his pulse and carefully examined his ugly wound. Finally, placing both hands on my shaky knees in an effort to steady them, my glance wandered from Antoine to the doctor, who was watching me, and with a smile, he shook his head—up and down. That, Grace, was the last I knew for that day; for I was told afterwards I had fainted, and that I was placed next to Antoine completely out. I was also told that if it had not been for the sister, Antoine would have risen while the doctor lifted me from the hard cypress floor. However, at two-thirty the next morning, as I afterward learned, I could faintly hear, as if from a great distance, 'Petite, darling, please wake up.'

"I wanted, oh, so much, to close my ears, if that were possible; and yet, I found myself straining them in an effort the better to hear; and then the words became more distinct, and I could feel something squeezing my hand. I tried to open my heavy eyelids, but couldn't; I tried to move my body, with the same result. Just then I heard a command, and it made my body tremble from head to foot. It was from Antoine; and I had heard distinctly, 'Petite, it's my order that you open your eyes.' I now knew that it was he who was holding my hand, and with every ounce of energy in my body I forced, Grace, actually forced my eyelids apart. Staring at the ceiling, I heard the words, just above a whisper, 'Thank God.'

"Again I recognized the voice—it was Antoine's and that was the only impulse I needed. In what I thought was a superhuman effort, I writhed until I became fully conscious.

" 'Antoine,' I said, lying perfectly still on my back, for I was afraid to move, as I might hurt him.

" 'Petite darling,' was his whispered reply, again feebly squeezing my hand.

" 'May I move?' I asked.

" 'Slowly, to your left," he answered.

"I did just that, Grace, ever so gently, and continued until I had turned completely over, resting on my both arms, my face just above his. He looked searchingly into my eyes as if to see if I were ill. I smiled to reassure him and, Grace, when he smiled in return, tears quickly collected in my eyes and fell to his cheeks. His eyes closed and his lips became compressed, as if he wanted to stifle his emotion. Suddenly, out of nowhere came the words, 'Kiss him.' I say out of nowhere because we were in a world all our own, not caring when nor where we were. I obeyed. Slowly I permitted my head to drop to where our lips barely touched, and kept them there; then I noticed that his eyes were again opening, and I could feel his lips relax under mine. And then, with possibly all of the strength that remained in that battle-scarred body of his, he raised his head quickly compressing his lips to mine, and then dropped hard to the pillow, his eyes now only half open.

" 'Darling,' I whispered, 'don't ever do that again, or I will never kiss you.' His lips moved, as if to say, 'I won't,' and his eyes closed and he relaxed. Again out of nowhere came the words, 'Let him sleep.' This time I looked to the side of the bed, and there stood the doctor. Before I could utter a word, he said, 'He is recovering, but must have more sleep. He remained awake last night waiting for you to regain consciousness. Now let him rest.'

"Then I arose, ever so gently. Upon regaining my feet, imagine my astonishment when I saw at least a score of convalescing sol-

diers wide awake; all had been spectators. One in particular motioned to me. After finding my shoes, and with a glance towards
Antoine, I went to him. He made no effort to hide his emotions,
for both eyes were moist.

" 'Petite,' he said and continued, 'may I call you that?'

" 'Surely, John,' I answered.

" 'Well, Petite, I am happy. Oh! ever so happy that he will recover. To think that it would have been I who would have
blasted such an affectionate devotion—' And with that, John
dropped his head into his hands and sobbed convulsively.

" 'John,' I said, 'please don't,' for his sincerity had touched me
deeply. However, he having had very little rest that night and
knowing that John was not seriously wounded, I asked him,
'John, would you care to talk to me or would you prefer returning to sleep?'

" 'Petite, like Antoine, I haven't slept since you fainted; but I
would prefer, more than anything on earth, to talk with you.'

" 'That is quite a compliment, but tell me who you are.'

" 'My name is John Lancaster, and I am from Lancastershire,
England; and if you will promise to keep a secret—'

" 'I promise.'

" 'Well, I am the son of the Earl of Lancaster.'

" 'I see. And, John, I will keep your secret, for I know the
nobility here is frowned upon because they are drones—they live
on the State.'

" 'Thanks, but aside from being the beautiful sweetheart of
Antoine, who are you—? I mean—Oh! what do I mean?'

" 'I am—'

" 'No, not you, but what I want to know is if you have any
sisters?'

" 'Yes, three.'

" 'All married?'

" 'No, one married.'

" 'Good!'

" 'What did you say?'

" 'Oh, Petite, forgive me, but—may I see them?'

" 'Surely.'

" 'When?'

" 'Well, they're visiting Antoine this afternoon.'

" 'And you will bring them to me?'

" 'I'll be happy to.'

" 'You know, Petite, I am sure I'll like them—at least one.'

" 'How old are you, John?'

" 'Twenty-two.'

" 'Well, one of my sisters is twenty, and I'm sure she will like you.'

" 'Please, what is she like?'

" 'Well, she is a typical Creole girl, a bit taller than I, weighs about one hundred and twenty pounds, and is very fair, with lips shaped like mine and much larger eyes than mine; and in general she's very pretty; now, if you don't want her to see you in a sleepy condition, you had better sleep.'

" 'I would like to create a good impression.'

" 'You will. Now go to sleep.'

" 'Good night.' And with that, Grace, this lad closed his eyes, and I returned to Antoine. Seating myself by his side, I noticed that the movement of his chest was somewhat slower, and my eyes then rested on his lips. The more I looked, the more came the urge to touch them ever so gently. That urge became so great that I felt myself rising, and was about to lower my head when I heard, 'Not now, Petite.' Falling back in the chair, I turned and saw John resting on his elbows, and he repeated, shaking his head, 'Not now, Petite.' "

CHAPTER III

JOHN AND JEANETTE

"On January tenth, the sun rose at seven fifty-seven. I know the time for through the window of the hospital I saw the large, orange-colored orb emerge out of nowhere. The nuns were noiselessly moving to and fro, handing a tray here and there. Light chicken broth was served to those less fortunate, that is, those with serious wounds; for instance, Antoine. I had aided the sister in propping his shoulder and head so that he might drink the broth.

" 'Feel better, darling?'

" 'A bit,' he whispered and asked, 'How are you?'

" 'I'm all right now; but open your mouth so that this little sweetheart of yours can feed you.'

"And, Grace, he was a wonderful patient, never complaining and obeying all orders; his eyes moved constantly from my eyes to my lips and then back again. After breakfast, I asked, 'Darling, feel like talking?'

" 'To you,' he whispered.

" 'Do you know who shot you?' I asked. I had to place my ear to his lips to hear his answer.

" 'If I'd see him.'

" 'Why?'

" 'Because we both fired at the same time.'

" 'Would you hate him?'

" 'No, because that is war.'

" 'He is here, in this hospital.'

" 'Will he get better?'

" 'Yes.'

" 'Are they treating him well?'

" 'Very much so; and, Antoine, this morning he cried when he spoke of shooting you.'

" 'He must be a fine fellow. Can you raise me a bit so that I may see him?'

" 'Just a bit, sweet—now, over there; see, he raises his hand to you.' And, Grace, in return, Antoine smiled, and you should have seen the joyous expression on John's face; one could not help liking him.

"Then I lowered Antoine and said, 'Darling, you've proved, and I knew it before, that you love me more than life itself. You also know that I, too, feel the same way towards you. Now, sweetheart, my only concern is your health. As soon as you are well, I want you through life for my mate, my husband. Never mind smiling, darling; but, instead, close your eyes and sleep. See, I place my fingers gently over the lids. Now close them. I kiss you and will hold your hand while you sleep.'

"And, Grace, with the smile still on his calm face, he fell into a deep sound slumber; then I stole away and hurried to my home.

"When I entered, everyone rushed to me, asking excitedly, 'How is he?' I said everyone, but not Jeanette, for she knew by my satisfied expression, as she more or less always read my mind. She did ask, however, 'Is he alone?'

" 'Yes,' I answered.

" 'Shall I stay with him until you return?'

" 'Will you, please?'

" 'You know, Petite, I'd do anything for you.'

" 'Then please go—now.' And, Grace, she did, arriving just as Antoine awoke.

"Beckoning her to come near to him, he asked, 'Where's Petite?'

" 'Home.'

" 'Why?'

" 'To bathe and change clothes. Are you feeling better, Antine?'

" 'Very much better; I'd like a cigarette.'

" 'I haven't any.'

" 'Ask the Redcoat over there. Look under his bed.'

"And, Grace, she understood; and noticing the coat under the bed, now cleaned, darned and pressed, she walked to John and said, 'Antoine desires a cigarette. Have you one?'

"'Surely, take some. And here are matches. I believe you call them Alumettes.'

"'You know the French language?'

"'Fluently,' he answered in French and continued, 'I've spent years in Brittany.'

"'Oh! I see. And yet, you would fight the Frenchmen—here.'

"'Believe me when I tell you that I didn't want to, but I had to follow orders and only fired in self-defence. Tell me, are you Petite's sister?'

"'Yes.'

"'And your name?'

"'Jeanette. Why do you ask?'

"'Shall I be truthful?'

"'By all means.'

"'Well—because I could love anyone of her relatives. Please, don't go—I meant no harm.'

"And, Grace, there was so much sincerity in his tone that she felt ashamed of herself and answered confusedly, 'I want to take Antoine the cigarette, but I'll return.'

"Upon reaching Antoine, she saw that he was staring directly into her eyes and was grinning as if to say, 'Jeanette, watch your step.' She smiled, tossed her head to one side as if to say, 'Who cares?' and placing the cigarette in his mouth, she lighted it. After he drew she held it until he again asked for it. For five impatient minutes, John watched and waited. When she had disposed of the cigarette, she looked in his direction and, meeting his eyes with a full expression of tenderness, walked over to him.

"Grace, John was not handsome—Englishmen seldom are; but the goodness in him just emanated from that kind, smiling face. You've heard the expression, 'Wouldn't hurt a fly?' Well, I really believed that of him.

"However, when Jeanette reached his side, she coyly asked, 'Why do you like any of Petite's family?'

"'Because she is so sweet and you know, birds of a feather flock together.' And he added, 'Please take a chair.' And they talked for hours, about dancing—the various games played by young folks in England—various operas that he had heard in Paris—of Paris itself and of many other subjects that were of interest to her. Jeanette found the young Britisher with the kind eyes and the English accent very interesting—too interesting for she remained with him all afternoon. I had returned and was standing, admiring my darling, when Antoine beckoned me to lower my head; and placing my ear near his mouth, he asked, 'What progress is he making?'

" 'She's been with him for hours and is very attentive.'

" 'Good,' he replied.

" 'Why'

" 'Because I like him.'

" 'I do, too, Antoine.'

" 'I'm getting jealous.'

" 'I know better than that. For that remark, soldier, you must pay a penalty.'

" 'I am at your mercy.'

" 'Then I will not take advantage of you. You see, the penalty is a kiss.'

" 'Petite?'

" 'Yes, darling.'

" 'Kiss me.'

" 'But the pen—'

" 'Petite!'

" 'All right, soldier, but I do it under protest.' I kissed him, Grace, again and again; and each time he closed his eyes.

"Presently, he asked, 'Are they looking at us?'

"I raised my head and saw both of them staring directly at us, Jeanette with a smile and John with longing in his expressive eyes. He look at me, and I winked. That seemed to give him courage, and he reached for Jeanette's hand, which had been resting on the edge of the bed and held it. ' Please, Jeanette, sit on the edge of the bed so that—'

" 'Finish your sentence and I will.'

" 'So that I will be nearer you. Don't renege, Jeanette,' he said as she hesitated. 'You promised.' And with that, Grace, she sat on the bed, he holding her hand."

"Petite, that was the beginning of their romance?"

"Yes, for from that time Jeanette was as constant a visitor to the hospital as I was. However, John was permitted to leave before Antoine; but he with Jeanette, were daily visitors at the hospital. An affection grew between Antoine and John that was more than brotherly; and while John confessed to Antoine his love for Jeanette, she confessed to me her love for him."

"Were they engaged?"

"No, but before Antoine left the hospital, Jeanette said to me, 'Petite, I wish John would propose.'

" 'You love him enough to take him for your life's mate?'

" 'Love him, why I adore him. He is so gentle and good.'

" 'I'll admit that. But tell me, have you encouraged him?'

" 'Oh, surely! Why we even go to mass on Sunday together; and on one ocasion, we attended a wedding. And, Petite, when the priest asked the bride did she take the groom for her lawfully wedded husband, John's hand stole over the pew to mine, and he held it. When she answered yes, in her beautiful wreath and veil, he squeezed my hand; but when they kissed after the priest told them that he now pronounced them man and wife, he squeezed, he impulsively squeezed so hard that my hand ached.'

" 'And I'll bet that you did not make any attempt to move it.'

" 'No, Petite. It hurt, and yet it felt good. However, I thought then and there that he would propose; in fact, I am sure he wanted to, but he is as bashful as he is good. You know, I actually believe that he thinks me above him.'

" 'Do you feel that you are?'

" 'No; but I do feel that we are each other's equal—God-fearing human beings and I am certain that we would be a happy couple.'

" 'And, Jeanette,' I asked teasingly, 'would you find pleasure being held in his arms and being kissed?'

" 'There isn't a night that I lay my head on the pillow that I don't close my eyes and picture his face above mine; you know, how you do when you kiss Antoine; and my body tingles from head to foot. By the way, when will you and Antoine be married?'

" 'Well, we havn't set a date, but it will be as soon as he is able. I wanted the priest to call at the hospital and wed us there, but Antoine was adamant—he wants a wreath-and-veil wedding, 'For,' he said, 'Petite, my love, marriage, in your case, will happen but once. It is my desire that you enjoy it both spiritually and physically. A Catholic wedding,' he continued, 'is the most beautiful in wreath and veil; and the most spiritual when performed at Holy Mass.'

" 'I agree with him.'

" 'I do, too, Jeanette, but I long to feel that I am his mate. However, doctor has given his permission to move Antoine to our home; so tomorrow I shall have him to myself, for after you folks greet him I shall politely stand at the door and say, 'This way out, please.'

" 'You wouldn't dare.'

" 'You don't know me yet—you and I that cling so together.'

" 'I know you, but I'll wager that you wouldn't put us out.'

" 'Again, with Antoine's recovering, and he being taken to my home where we shall be inseparable, I felt as if I were treading on air; and deviltry again entered my mind. So I said, 'Jeanette, at the Ursuline Convent, when we girls wagered, since we had nothing to wager with, we always agreed for the loser to do the victor's bidding. Will you agree to do my bidding should I open the door and tell everyone to leave?'

" 'Surely I will; and should you lose, and I expect you to, I have something in mind that I want you to do . Incidentally, that wager is on our word of honor?'

" 'Definitely.' And with that Jeanette departed."

CHAPTER IV

The Engagement

"I awakened bright and early. Singing while I dressed, I eventually reached for the large soft powder puff, and finishing with that I raced down the winding steps, my feet keeping time with my singing of 'My Creole Belle.' I reached the hall and glanced at the old grandfather clock just as it chimed six. I looked for the long slender hand or, as father called it, the almanac hand, and found it pointing to twenty-three. Yes, Grace, it was the twenty-third day of January, eighteen hundred and fifteen—fifteen days after the glorious victory, the Battle of New Orleans. Today, Antoine was coming to my home. My, I was jubilant; I didn't want breakfast; I only wanted the hour hand to move faster. I wasn't alone in my happiness. Father, mother, Jeanette, and my other sister, Marie, all wanted to welcome him as son and brother. Jeanette seemed exceptionally happy; and on one occasion I noticed her staring at me mischievously with a big smile. Was it concerning the bet, I thought, and then said to myself, 'We'll see.' "

"Petite, was it concerning the wager?"

"Yes, it was. However, after what seemed an eternity, I found myself in the improvised ambulance sitting beside Antoine, his hand in mine. Neither of us spoke. He was still weak and moving him made him weaker. Finally we reached our home, and with everyone helping, even the slaves who crowded around, we managed to place him safely in Jeanette's room; for she unselfishly volunteered to use the spare room in the attic, and to deed to Antoine hers as it was next to mine with a door between. We had just made him comfortable when the priest arrived, adding to the already crowded room. In my excitement I would have forgotten completely about the wager had I not looked directly into those smiling eyes of Jeanette. Impulsively I decided to act immediately; and walking towards the door, I held it open and said, 'Folks, this way out, for he is mine now.' I must have been smiling broadly, for all laughed. Nevertheless, it had its result for, as I said he's all mind now, they filed out."

"Jeanette, too?"

"Yes, Jeanette and John. However, I asked those two to return alone in half an hour. After they had left, I immediately hurried to Antoine, who lay propped up on a large white linen-covered pillow. Grace, if I were to tell you how often I kissed that man, you would call me a kissing bug. Only those madly in love would understand. But you should know."

"I do. What next?"

"Well, before I could tell Antoine of the wager, there was a knock on the door. As slowly as Father Time moved those clock hands during the morning, he seemed to spin them since Antoine arrived.

" 'Come in,' I answered.

"Jeanette looked more beautiful than ever that morning; her cheeks were pink with excitement. I had expected her to look dejected at being at my mercy, for I had now won the wager; but she seemed jubilant. It then occurred to me that she always seemed to read my mind, and I felt cheated.

" 'Jeanette,' I said sternly, while she and John stood holding hands, 'Are you ready to pay your debt?'

" 'Ready, Your Honor,' she said, dropping John's hand and saluting me, chuckling all the time.

" 'Then, my dear sister,' I said, trying to act important, 'It's my order that you propose marriage to John.'

"She bravely turned to John, who, recognizing the seriousness of the situation, had turned white. Before she could speak, he ruined my plan completely by facing Jeanette and blurting, 'Will you, Jeanette?'

"Grace, as they fell into each other's arms, I turned and said, "Oh Hell!'

"Hearing laughter, I looked and saw Antoine holding his wounded side. Try as he might, he could not suppress his laughter; for he had then become wise to the situation. Still acting, I walked to Antoine and said, 'You, Antoine Floret, for disorderly conduct in this court, I sentence you to refrain from kissing the judge for the space of five minutes.'

" 'And if I say, "Petite?" '

" 'Then the judge will obey you.'

" 'Then, Petite,' he said smiling, 'you shall bring your prisoners before me.'

" 'Prisoners! You've heard the command.'

" 'Eh?' asked John.

" 'Huh,' uttered Jeanette.

" 'Oh, hell,' I said, seeing that they were in each other arms, and didn't even know we existed.

"Antoine was again laughing at me, and I then decided to act no more, but to be myself, and said, 'Jeanette and you, John, Antoine wants to talk to you.'

"They walked towards the bed and each placed a hand in Antoine's palms while he said, 'Sweet friends, let me congratulate both of you.'

"Jeanette bent and kissed him full on the lips, while John, good John, held his hands in both of his."

"And, Petite, what about the wedding?"

"You impatient blue-eyed doll!"

"Emile also calls me impatient."

"I can see why he teases you."

"But I like it."

"I know you do. We like being teased by our men, for this calls for, shall I name it atonement, and love's forgiveness which sweetens life."

"Yes, I understand that. But tell me, what happened next?"

"After being congratulated, Jeanette turned to me and asked, 'Shall we let you two alone?'

" 'Not necessarily,' I answered, 'for you both are unconscious and, by using the love-seat that Antoine and I like, you two will not disturb us.'

" 'But, Petite,' John said, 'at home, we have a crude seat shaped like this one, and we call it, as of yore, the she-and-I seat. It forms an ess like yours, which permits lovers to face each other while seated. But I like your name better—love-seat. Come, Jeanette, let's use it.'

"And, Grace, as I watched those two, in a world all their own, I heard the order, 'Consciousness, come to me.'

"I obeyed and, reaching him, lowered his head by removing the added pillows. Then, removing my shoes, I climbed into bed, on the opposite side from his wound. Resting on my side and holding up my head with my hand, I faced him with, 'At your command, lord and master.'

" 'You are wonderful, darling. But tell me, have you forgotten when you were unconscious?'

" 'I still am, for if I weren't I would have seen through Jeanette's plan to use me to cause John to propose.'

" 'Not so loud, honey; but tell me, I don't understand it all.'

" 'Well, I wagered that I would put everyone out of this room after you arrived. If she lost, and she knew she would, I was to order her to do my bidding. She knew that I was interested in her becoming engaged, since we had spoken of it, and she felt reasonably sure that I would act as I did. You may have noticed that she turned towards John and hesitated long enough to give him time to ask first.'

" 'I understand now. But I can see you are happy about their being engaged.'

" 'Very much so, darling. May I ask you something?'

" 'Yes.'

" 'I er—was wondering if you would object to a dual wedding?'

" 'Sweet, I was thinking the same thing and was about to suggest it. Ask them if they approve of it?'

" 'Jeanette and John,' I called.

" 'Yes, Petite.'

" 'Did you hear our conversation?'

" 'What conversation?'

" 'Oh! I should have known.'

" 'Can we do something for you?'

" 'Yes, tell me, are you two, by any possible chance, interested in getting married?'

" 'That is what we are planning now.'

" 'Have you set a date?'

" 'Not yet.'

" 'Then kindly release my love-seat and come over her. Antoine, you know, cannot talk very loud.'

"And, Grace, eagerly those two came to the bed."
"Had they been kissing?"

"Oh surely. You see, as soon as a Creole girl becomes engaged, kissing is permitted."

"But don't they have games like post office and—"

"Yes. But those kisses are merely the touching of lips,—not real love kisses."

"I see. What happened next?"

"First, young lady, let me ask you if you know what love kisses are?"

"Why, Petite, you forget that Emile is a Creole."

"Yes, I know; I was only teasing. However, when we made known our plans to Jeanette and John, they were elated for that would be an excuse for a short engagement."

CHAPTER V

CHOOSING FURNITURE

" 'Petite, you're neglecting me.'

" 'You said Petite, and not Petite, sweet. Are you serious?'

" 'Yes, very much so.'

" 'On your word of honor?'

" 'Well—no—not exactly, you see—'

" 'Oh, you darling.'

" 'Little sweetheart, your excitement on being measured for your wedding gown furnishes me the utmost pleasure. You know, sweet, you will be a picture.'

" 'Thanks, you old darling; but you know that I would have given up all of that excitement to have become Mrs. Floret long ago.'

" 'I know. You have been and I know that you'll always be the height of unselfishness. Each and every day I grow happier and happier when I think that I would not permit your doing it. Little do you realize, my darling, the thrills of walking up that aisle, in wreath and veil and—'

" 'And I will swear to Honor, Love, and Obey.'

" 'And obey?'

" 'Yes, darling, and obey.'

" 'And that will come from the very bottom of your heart?'

" 'Yes; and as Jeanette says, I am sorry that the vow does not include truthfulness and humility.'

" 'Did she say that?'

" 'Yes. Don't you think it was a beautiful thought?'

" 'Beautiful, yes, but much deeper than that.'

" 'Deeper, darling?'

" 'Yes, I am now convinced that Jeanette, like you, although in love, has not permitted her affection to warp her judgment. In other words, she is repaying John with his own clean sincerity, and I am happy for him. But I am further convinced that in her subconscious mind there is a slight doubt, or shall I say fear for the future.'

"'Darling, why do you say that?'

"'Well, as you know, I've been reared as a Frenchman, and I believe and regard that "and obey" as being sincere. Englishmen are different. As you know, I love your family as though they were blood relatives; in fact, I hope, at your father's age, to have the sweet, lovable, sincere family that he has. In my case, you obey me instinctively, because instinctively I demand it. Now, in John's case, Jeanette's great desire is to act towards her husband as she sees her mother act towards her father. What she doesn't realize is that John will permit her to make her own decisions, and that eventually she may regard it as weakness. In other words, his goodness, his desire that she be happy may lead to her having her own way, and, in that way, be the ruination of her life as well as his.'

"'I understand,' I said, and continued, 'You mean, that since his method will be entirely new and as she is totally ignorant of it, it will place her in a quandry and cause her to grope as to how to act as a wife?'

"'Yes, that's it. But I'm afraid that before one or the other learns and takes the initiative, she acting as an English woman or her as a Creole, their marriage will end disastrously; much as I dislike saying it.'

"'Can we do anything?'

"'No, nothing, for when two people are in love, they are in a world of their own and do not understand any language but their own. All we can do is to bide our time; and who knows, maybe in the future, we may be of help.'

"Grace, what Antoine had said was plain logic. It, however, bothered me; but, as he had said, we could not at present remedy the situation."

"But, I'm of English ancestry or supposed to be, and I dare say that I fit into Emile's life as snugly as any Creole would."

"In your case it is different, for inherently the female desires domination; and since Emile is the dominating type of male, it was only natural that you would just fuse into his life. Further, I feel certain that you are not of pure English parentage."

"I see—but how did it end?"

"By—"

"Please, Petite, don't tell me. I—"

"I wasn't going to tell you for that would end the story."

"What were you going to say?"

"By their getting married. But then you will not hear of the wedding scene, our emotions—"

"Please describe the wedding."

"Well, the Sunday following our agreement for a double wedding, the banns were announced from the shell-covered pulpit in the St. Louis Cathedral. That was on February third. The date was set for March twenty-seventh—a short time when one considers what had to be done."

"Almost two months, Petite."

"Yes, but you know, Grace, among Creoles, all friends give presents, from bedroom suits to towels and soap. In our case, that is Jeanette's and mine, father and mother insisted on giving us our bedroom suits. Leaving Antoine at home with his complete acquiescence, Jeanette, John, and I walked up Royal Street to the cabinet-maker. He had some stock; but it did not meet father's demand. He did have, however, many drawings of Louis the Sixteenth and what was later named the Empire Period furniture. In my mind's eye, I could visualize our bedroom. However, I permitted Jeanette to choose first, and she ordered a design that had beautiful, graceful lines. Jeanette and John were extremely happy; he permitted her to choose walnut while I was partial to mahogany. I should have been happy, too, but I wasn't. I missed Antoine, and I could not choose. I argued with myself that all of the sets were beautiful and that I could not possibly make an error, and that Antoine would be satisfied with whatever I ordered, for had he not said, 'Petite, you should choose the furniture, for, you know, you will have to live with it more than I.' And yet, Grace, I just couldn't, and was candid in explaining to the old French carver that I wanted Antoine also to choose. He solved the problem by saying, 'Take the prints with you. I know you will return them.'

" 'You'll let me have them?' I stammered, for I realized that they were valuable.

" 'Surely, but, if you want your furniture for your wedding, you and Antoine had better decide today.'

"Well, with that precious bundle of prints, I led Jeanette and John back home and raced up the stairs to Antoine, who smilingly said as I entered out of breath, 'I knew it; I knew it as surely as I am Antoine.'

" 'But, darling, I just couldn't, I—'

" 'You don't have to explain. You're so damn sweet that I want to hold you—to kiss you'—and, Grace, he reached for my hand and twisting me gently around forced me on my back on the bed, across his lap and then bent over me and kissed me until mother walked into the room with Jeanette and John, who wished to show her the print of the furniture they had chosen. When she saw the position I was in, she said, 'But, Antoine—'

" 'Now, Mom, you can stay, but the interference must go.'

"And, Grace, as I tried to rise, he again forced me down and kissed me all over my face. Mother stood by smiling as Antoine released me and said to her, 'Mom, try that with Dad.'

" 'Don't worry, we do.'

" 'But, Mom,' he continued to tease as he did every time she entered, 'you're not sweet sixteen any more.' And he continued, 'Mom, at what age does a woman cease to desire to be loved?'

" 'Listen, yong man,' she retorted, 'only last week I asked that same question of Madam Bére, and do you know what her answer was?'

" 'Yes, that it was so long ago in her life that she doesn't remember.'

" 'No, you are wrong. She told me she didn't know, for she was only eighty-five years old, and that I'd have to ask someone older than she.'

"And, Grace, everyone laughed, mother included, for she had a wonderful sense of humor. However, when they had seen the print they wanted, I again walked to the door, and holding it open, said, 'This way out, please.'

"When we were alone, I sat on the bed facing Antoine, and together we examined the prints. I could see that he was carefully trying to determine my choice while I likewise was trying to determine his."

"How did you two choose?"

"By Antoine's asking, 'What is your choice?'

" 'But, Antoine—'

" 'Petite!'

" 'All right, Antoine darling, I like this one, with the four-poster carved bed, the—'

" 'But the price is four thousand dollars.'

" 'Dad insists that we pay that price.'

" 'I believe I could afford that price better than he. At least, I should pay half.'

" 'Please, darling, don't ever mention that, for father will resent it. We may be able to help them at another time and possibly another way.'

" 'As you say, sweet, but return the prints by the maid and state your choice.' "

"You still have that suite?"

"Yes, and I want you to see it as soon as we reopen our home. However, Grace, after much fuss and confusion, and little neglect of Antoine, our trousseau with chemises, corsets, drawers, vests, petticoats, and what not were complete. Also, in the armoires were our wedding gowns. It was March twenty-second, and we had returned from the Cathedral where we had rehearsed the wedding; that is, our walking up the aisle and being handed over by Father—"

"Petite, that won't do. You will have to give me more details—that is, please do."

"I'll be glad to, but that porcelain clock is about to strike the noon hour and—"

"My, how time does fly! Let me ring for the cook."

"Did you ring for me, Ma'am?"

"Yes, Marie. Will dinner be ready at noon?"

"Yes'm."

"That's fine. But I hear the horses. It is Emile and Antoine. Come, Petite, let's run to meet them."

"Oh, you nomads! I wager you two covered the city."

"Almost, darling," answered Antoine.

"And did you enjoy yourself?"

"Immensely, and sister, you will have your hands full for the next three months for everyone asked where you were and how you are. And, if I would have permitted, Emile's home would have been turned into a reception hall."

"They knew I was here?"

"They surmised it since I was with Emile."

"But, Antoine, your breath smells of liquor."

"It should, but if we had accepted all the drinks offered, I should again be in the hospital. However, what you smell is Italian vermouth, and had I not drunk it outside, Emile would have insisted that I drink some here, for you forget that an ap-pertizer precedes all meals here in the grand old Vieux Carre."

"I'll forgive you this time, provided you pick me up in your arms and carry me to my seat at the dining room table; and, darling, I smell gumbo—that delicious dish that we haven't tasted for over two years. Grace, you think of everything."

"That is the reason I ordered it cooked today. And to wet your appetite further, we'll have crayfish bisque, red snapper court-bouillon—"

"Stop, Grace, for I'll have indigestion before I eat, for I can picture myself at the end of the meal, bloated like an over-fed pig."

CHAPTER VI

A Dual Wedding

"Well, Grace, it was four A. M., March twenty-seventh, eighteen hundred and fifteen. John slept with Antoine the last night, and I could hear them through the door—all excited. That night, Jeanette, in her pink gown and white wreath, was a picture; I, in my blue gown and white wreath, was all thrills. Mother, our good mother, said, 'Girls, your young men should see you now. But, as you know, that would be bad luck; so they will have to wait until you reach the Cathedral.'"

"Petite, I'll wager that you would still be beautiful in that gown."

"Some day, I'll dress in it for you."

"When?"

"After I reopen the house."

"My, that will be wonderful. But then you will leave us."

"Don't say that in so sad a tone, for we shall be daily visitors; that is, I'll visit you and you'll visit me."

"It will certainly be a treat—but tell me of your wedding day. Do you remember the details?"

"Not all, but if I had my diary—"

"We have it."

"Oh, yes, I remember. I gave it to Emile when he volunteered to write our romance. You know where it is?"

"Yes, Emile read from it last night."

"Not all, I'm sure."

"No, for he said that he would only read to me what he would write."

"And have you felt an urge to read it all?"

"No."

"Why?"

"Because Emile gave you his word that he would not permit anyone else to read it."

"And you have no desire to read it?"

"No, because I respect Emile's word."

"You have beautiful principles, Grace."

"Thanks, but shall I get it?"

"By all means."

"Here it is, in the secretary."

"You see, Antoine asked that I keep a complete diary, so I'll now read: 'The carriage stopped. Father opened the door and stepped out. My heart was pounding, and one glance at Jeanette's smiling face told me that she, too, was experiencing the same emotion. Father's hand was reaching for her. Picking up her train, she grasped his hand, and she, too, stepped out. The banquette was crowded with white and colored persons, Indians, Negroes—all friends of ours, all eager to see the brides. My blood was rushing to my head as though forced by a huge pump. I picked up my blue train and waited, not for long for there was Father's hand. One look at his neck convinced me that his heart was also beating as a trip-hammer. I grasped his hand and carefully stepped out.

"Someone reached over and said, 'Good luck, Petite,' and disappeared. It was a masculine voice. I looked at the line of faces to the left, from the carriage to the church; everyone was smiling, and over the heads I could see others apparently standing on their toes. They too were smiling. Little Toby in front called, 'Hello, Petite.' Father was waiting, but I turned and looked to the right. Many of my old boy friends were standing there, apparently choosing that side for the small door of the Cathedral opened on that side. There were not so many smiles from them, and I dropped my gaze.

"Then I looked at Father and he understood that I was ready. I remembered that Antoine had told me to keep a diary; so when I neared the iron fence, I stopped to look up on the façade of the Cathedral and noticed that the sun on its right was bathing it in pure white light. Then I looked at the massive folding doors. Inside those doors at the altar was waiting for me, my love, my all. My hand was on Father's arm, as was also Jeanette's, and carefully we three stepped upon the marble steps. Inside the entrance the other doors were now opened and were held in position by two altar boys. Before me was a full inner view of the beautiful Cathedral. Overhead I could hear distinctly the pumping of the organ, and then came the mellow notes of the wedding march. At rehearsal I was told to keep my eyes straight ahead—not for Petite, for in this crowded, holy edifice were my friends, all friends.

"We started through the inner doors. Looking to the right, I saw the Baratarians, headed by Lafitte and Dominique, all smiling. Dominique shaped his lips to 'Good luck, Petite.' I understood and lagged. Father whispered that we were out of step with the organ music. 'Make it every second step,' I whispered back, and he and Jeanette understood. I looked up, and through the stained-glass windows the sun was flooding the faces of slaves, some young, some old, who placed their finger tips to their lips and then waved their hands to me. I smiled and their faces lighted up; some of the older ones wiped their eyes; mine started too to fill, but this was no time for tears. To avoid them, I now decided to stare straight ahead. To my right and left I knew we were passing large, stained-glass windows depicting in life-sized figures various incidents in the life of St. Louis, for I had seen them thousands of times, and also the huge columns and small plaques of the Way of the Cross.

"We were now near the altar, and I remembered that Almonaster, buried in the church to the right, was responsible for my wedding to Antoine in so beautiful an edifice. We stopped. Standing to my right was Antoine, with the most kindly, the most tender, to me, the most beautiful face in the world. Our eyes met. This time, I could not restrain my tears—tears of pure, uncontrollable joy. I whispered to him as I placed my hand on his arm. I heard, from under his breath, two words, 'My Darling.' We stepped up the marble steps and walked to the prie-dieus. He placed my arm on his; and as our wrists touched, I felt that his heart too was faithfully doing its part, pumping hard and fast.

"To my left I could see, through the corner of my eye, John and Jeanette in the same position. I dared not look at her. We might both burst into tears. Instead, I raised my head to look full upon the beautiful white and gold altar that held the Blessed

Sacrament, to thank God for the ecstasy that was in my heart; and I remembered that He was to be a partner—three persons, man, woman, and God; and that as a partner, He was to guide us and cause a mutual self-surrender of two persons, Antoine and myself; and that we were to be fused into one—my thoughts continued—in the house, man is the head; woman, the heart. Our Partner will see that neither one will be moved; for, if one is moved, love is dead; hence, obedience from the heart, protection from the head. Head, Antoine—the man that would have given his life, from the sword—his life from an English gun, for me; 'God,' I said aloud, 'I, Petite, thank Thee.'

"The organ stopped! Everything was quiet; only occasionally one could hear a muffled cough. The priest stepped down from the candle-lit altar in his spotless white vestment, beautifully embroidered in gold, accompanied by altar boys. He stood before us, and I looked again at Antoine. Again Antoine said, 'My darling.' The priest heard and smiled; then he began: 'Antoine Floret, wilt thou take Louise Petite Champlin, here present, for thy lawful wife, according to the rite of our Holy Mother the Church?'

" 'I will.'

" 'Louise Petite Champlain, wilt thou take Antoine Floret, here present, for thy lawful husband, according to the rite of our Holy Mother the Church?'

" 'I will,' I answered. He then asked us to hold each other's hand and said, and Antoine repeated, 'I, Antoine Floret, take thee, Louise Petite Champlain, for my lawful wife, to have and to hold, from this day forward, for better, for worse, for richer, for poorer, in sickness and in health, to cherish and protect, till death do us part.'

"As he uttered those words, I realized that they came from his very soul, for the tone, the pronunciation, the sincerity as they left his lips were full proof of their being actuated by the supernatural.

"Just then the priest turned towards me and I repeated after him: 'I, Louise Petite Champlain, take thee, Antoine Floret, for my lawful husband, to have and to hold, from this day forward, for better, for worse, for riches, for poorer, in sickness and in health, to honor, love, and obey, till death do us part.'

"Our hands were still together and the priest continued, 'Antoine Floret and Louise Petite Champlain, I unite you in marriage, in the name of the Father and of the Son and of the Holy Ghost. What God has placed together, let no man tear asunder, Amen.'

"My body tingled; I could feel small bumps all over; my hand trembled as we both reached towards each other to kiss—a kiss that was long, lingering, and thrilling, a kiss that caused the congregation to break the silence with a murmer; a kiss that caused a mother to sob."

"Petite, that was beautiful."

"To me, Grace, it was more than that; for from that time I was his, to have and to hold, until death do us part."

"Did you listen to the ceremony which united Jeanette and John?"

"Yes, for when the priest began, we both faced them and listened. And I want to tell you that no two people were ever more sincere or more happy to have each other than those two.

"When the priest had completed the ceremony, all four of us remained on our knees before the altar and heard Mass, receiving Holy Communion. None of us complained of our aching joints; we were too happy."

"And after the wedding?"

"We drove home for breakfast and rest; and that afternoon there was a party in the ballroom."

"The completion of a wonderful day!"

"My most beautiful one—the one I will never forget."

CHAPTER VII

Madeau, the Fortune-Teller

"For one whole year we were extremely happy. Antoine and John jointly purchased a large double brick mansion on Royal Street. Only a hall on the second floor separated the two homes. The driveway was spacious, and it too separated the two homes on the first floor. The house was comfortable and airy, for the windows on the front reached to the floor, while in the rear large fan-shaped windows, placed on hinges, could be lowered to permit more air to blow through from the patio with its myriads of aromatic flowers. The rear walls were high and were entirely covered with evergreen vines; the evaporation from the leaves cooled the patio which, in turn, cooled the house. As I've said before, we were happy; but after the first six months, something happened that seemed to bother me. I spoke to Antoine about it, but he tried to allay my fears by explaining that it probably was harmless."

"What was it?"

"Well, John was fabulously rich; his inheritance from his father was known throughout the French Quarter, as was every and anything."

"Just like a small country town!"

"That's right, Grace. However, on Orleans Street, near Rampart, lived a mulattress, whose work was widely known; and this woman was feared by all of the colored folks and Negroes, and also by some of the Creoles. Her work was voo-dooing and fortune-telling."

"Petite, then this story is about voo-doo and fortune-telling?"
"Yes, Grace."

"Then, may I tell you of an incident in my wedded life?"
"Surely."

"Well, one day, about two o'clock in the afternoon, I was busy practicing the chain stitch in crocheting, when I heard the front

door open and close. It seemed to me that the door closed with
a slight slam; and listening, I heard Emile's unmistakable footsteps. But, like the closing of the door, it also seemed that he
was walking with, shall I say, determined steps. Reaching this
room, or rather the door, he stopped short, staring directly into
my eyes. The expression in his eyes was most determined; and
as I rose, he walked towards me. Moving the hassock to a position between us, he said, 'Grace, stand upon the hassock.' I did as
I was directed; and as he stood before me, I placed both hands
on his shoulders, while his hands were directly under my arms,
as if to steady me. As I was his height now, we faced each
other. I could see that he was much perturbed. I started to ask
what ailed him, when he interrupted with, 'Grace, we've been
married six joyous months.'

" 'Yes, Emile,' I answered, 'the happiest months of my life.'

" 'Yes, mine too. And, my sweet, whether it is six months, six
years, or sixty years, I am determined, if necessary, to move
heaven and earth to retain that happiness, that tranquility, our
devotion for each other."

" 'I'll help you, Emile,' was all that I could say as he continued,
'Grace, before you came into my life, my home was where my
hat was. This house I maintained intact with its slaves, as my
home; but it mattered little whether I slept at some friend's, at
the plantation, in a tent while fishing, or in a pirogue while
hunting.

" 'Since you've come, this home and especially this room have
taken on a different significance; and I now see that its beautiful
white walls reflect all of the colors of the rainbow, its large
heavy, panelled doors, the intricately molded centerpiece on the
ceiling—its every beauty that I had not seen before has taken on
a different significance since you, beautiful as a picture, sweet as
the word implies, have entered my life; and by God, Grace, it
shall remain that way.'

"As he paused, Petitie, I had time to say, 'Darling, you are
somewhat agitated.' He either did not hear me or he disregarded
what I had said, for pressing his hands more firmly against my
sides, he continued, 'Grace, as you are, you are a jewel, a treasure
more valuable than all the riches of the world—as you are I

said; and so that you may remain that way always, I am now ordering you, my first and I hope my last order, never to listen to anything whatsoever concerning voo-doo or fortune-telling. Grace, as long as you live, do not ever disobey this order.'

"Petite, he had spoken slowly, distinctly, pronouncing each word with complete conviction so that I could absorb its real meaning."

"And did you?"

"Yes."

"And what was your answer?"

"I started to draw him nearer to assure him with a kiss, but he held us apart as if desiring an answer. So I said, 'Emile, I swear, by the love I have for you, never to disobey your order.'

"Instead of kising me as I thought he would, he placed his arms about me and squeezed and held me, as one would an irreplaceable treasure. I enjoyed feeling helpless in his arms, and it was then that I fully appreciated the joy a woman receives when she is humble with the one man she loves."

"I'll wager you never have disobeyed that order."

"No, for I have the utmost confidence in Emile, he having steered our ship of devotion through calm and rough waters; there has never been a storm or a gale or even high winds to mar its straight sailing to the land of complete ecstasy."

"Beautifully explained, Grace; and I know you mean it. But haven't you ever heard of witchcraft?"

"Only once when the slave maid began to mention it; and I quickly told her that if she ever mentioned it again, I would recommend her sale to the master."

"One would imagine that it had the desired effect, for you certainly treat your slaves with kindness."

"It had. Now, Petite, I cannot disobey Emile's order, for I am certain he has a reason."

"But he knows I'm telling you this story."

"Would you disobey an order from Antoine?"

"No, Grace, I am only teasing. However, if I'm not mistaken, here comes Emile and Antoine."

"Back so soon?"

"Yes, we came for the barouche, for we are going to the plantation, and there are vegetables I wish to bring here."

"I see. Emile, you remember forbidding me to talk hoo-doo or fortune-telling with—"

"I know what you want; and you have my permission to listen to Petite; for after she finishes the story. I know that you will realize the harm that hoo-dooers and fortune-tellers do. Au revoir."

"Now, Grace, shall I continue?"

"By all means. I'm sorry if I acted rudely, but—"

"You forget that you are talking to a Creole, one that also obeys her husband. However, this hoo-dooer and fortune-teller, Madame Madeau by name, knew everyone's business, his family life, and what was most important the amount of his wealth."

"That seems impossible!"

"Not when you know her intrigues. First, she was known as the hoo-doo queen. The ignorant slaves and others who were superstitious believed her capable of doing bodily harm through black magic; so her word was law. In addition to being their head, she taught their children what we knew as chanting; this is the pure Negro's method of conversing secretly in song. The free superstitious colored folks and Negroes paid well. It was only natural that if she wanted information she questioned the children, her pupils, whose parents worked for the Creoles; and if the child did not know, it was told to ask its mother, for 'Mrs. Madeau wishes to know.' So successfull was she is keeping her subjects in abject fear that it was only necessary for her to voice to one that she desired an interview with one particular person. In this manner she was able to obtain complete knowledge concerning anyone's home in this section.

"Having been informed of John's inheritance, one day she sent word by Nini, Jeanette's slave maid, that she had a message of utmost importance, concerning her coming baby. Jeanette immediately invited Madeau to her home, who, as I was later informed, of course, brought her cards. Madeau knew much about Jeanette's homelife so that it was only natural that she, Jeanette, was amazed at the powers of this woman, especially when months later her prophecy that the baby would be a girl became a reality. Had I known of these visits sooner, I might have been able to dissaude Jeanette; but one day when I met Madeau face to face on her leaving I forgot what I was doing and immediately confronted Jeanette. I walked directly into her bedroom, and there she was nursing the baby. It was a plump, pretty child, and both Antoine and I were proud to be her godfather and godmother. 'Jeanette,' I started, 'What is the meaning of Madeau visiting you?'

" 'She cuts my cards,' she sheepishly answered and continued, 'Do you know her?'

" 'Yes, I do, and I know of no good that ever came of any contact with her.'

" 'But she predicted that the baby would be a girl, and she told of oh, so many things that happened here which I know are secrets that I believe and look forward to everything that she predicts.'

" 'And, naturally, you pay her.'

" 'Yes.'

" 'Very much?'

" 'The worth of her service.'

" 'And you consider her service great?'

" 'In a way. But you should try her.'

"For answer I left, slamming the door. Had I then known Madeau's method, I would have made it known to Jeanette, for I was certain that something was wrong. Then it was that I spoke to Antoine. 'But, Antoine,' I argued, 'even if it does not cause any harm, Jeanette is giving John's money away.'

" 'Oh, only a few dollars. And I'm sure John won't mind.'

" 'But, darling, that woman has been arrested by the police more times than I have fingers and toes.'

" 'Try talking to Jeanette again; you might explain to her that if any person had such power she would be immensely rich

through that power. Further than that, you might tell her that
with such powers those people could rule countries—in fact, the
world.'

"And so, Grace, I patiently waited for the opportunity to talk
to Jeanette, which was not long in coming. Excitedly, she came
into my room one noon after Antoine had left and said, 'Petite,
Henri is going to die.'

" 'He is?'

" 'Yes.'

" 'How do you know?'

" 'Because Madeau told me so.'

" 'I'm thoroughly disgusted with you.'

" 'Petite, please, don't act that way; but listen, did you know
that Henri was a protector for a quadroon?'

" 'No, I didn't.'

" 'Well, he was, and now he has left her.'

" 'So?'

" 'So she visited Madeau and pays her to kill Emile.'

" 'Through hoo-doo?'

" 'Yes.'

" 'How?'

" 'Well, the quadroon has Henri's picture; and with the aid of
Madeau and a candle, he will die.'

" 'A candle—'

" 'Yes, you see, the quadroon will place Henri's picture upside
down on a tomb in the cemetery and place the burning candle by
its side.'

" 'And that will kill him?'

" 'Surely.'

" 'Jeanette—'

" 'Please, Petite; not another lecture.'

" 'No, only what Antoine told me to convey to you.'

" 'Then Antoine knows?'

" 'Yes, I told him; and, Jeanette, you are being unfair to John.'

" 'He permits me to spend my allowance any way I see fit.'

" 'I'm not speaking of money matters. You know as well as
I that you should not hide nor keep secrets from your husband—
nor anything whatsoever. Mother never did, and no couple

we know of live a happier life than Father and Mother.'

" 'He wouldn't mind what I'm doing. But tell me what Antoine said?'

"Then I explained Antoine's psychology; and when I had completed my story, she angrily said, 'Petite, there are not many like Meadeu, and those that are not interested in wealth nor power; they only mean to help.'

" 'To kill!'

" 'She doesn't kill. She merely tells persons what to do; just as I would tell you how to shoot.'

" 'Jeanette, you are in a terrible state; that woman has completely warped your judgment, your mind. Wait, don't leave in anger. But let me warn you, you and I are sisters; and as all last children, we have been closer than with the other members of our family. Since birth we have loved each other dearly; together we took the sacred vow of matrimony; we should always be together in sympathy, in motherhood, with our husbands. Just now, you were about to leave me in anger. What I'm trying to tell you is that through hoo-dooism and fortune-telling, you and I shall be separated; and what is worse, you and John, as good as he is, will also be separated. Wait, let me finish. Think this over. We have lived happily and contentedly without sorcery for all these years. Let us live in the future in the same manner.'

" 'Im sorry, Petite, that I cannot see it your way; and since you think I'm hiding this from John, that I'm doing him an injustice, I'll tell him of Madeau tonight'."

"And did she?"

"Yes,, but it was four months later before I heard of the conversation. It seems that John listened patiently, never once interrupting; and although he was good, he was no fool, for when she had finished, he realized that it was not ignorance on her part, but rather trust that had caused her to be so imbued in Madeau's mysteries. However, he did say, 'Jeanette, don't you realize that those pieces of cardboard marked with black and red ink, those inanimate things, cannot possibly tell one's future.'

" 'But, John, it is not the cards, but the one that handles them— the gifted one that causes the cards to fall as they do.'

" 'Enough, Jeanette, for that subject will cause our first quarrel; and I love you so that I wouldn't want you to be angry with me.'

" 'But John—'

" 'Now, Jeanette, let's forget it. Tell me, don't you love me any more?'

" 'Surely I do.'

" 'Then kiss me.' "

"He was too good, Petite."

"Yes, for his own good. I know Antoine would not ask me to kiss him if I were to say 'But'. He would use one word. You know, don't you?"

" 'Petite!' Yes, and I know that you respect him for it."

"You bet I do."

CHAPTER VIII

John's Visit to Madeau

"Four months later, John, very much worried over Jeanette's mental condition, crossed the hall into our home and asked to talk to Antoine alone. I asked him if he wished to talk on the subject of hoo-dooism."

" 'Yes, Petite, why do you ask?'

" 'Because I may help you.'

" 'You don't believe in it, do you?'

" 'No.'

" 'Jeanette does?'

" 'Yes, I know, and I've tried to explain to her that such a thing doesn't exist—but without success.'

" 'What can I do? You see, I've never heard of such foolishness.'

" 'John,' Antoine asked, 'have you tried to prove that she was wrong?'

" 'No, I wouldn't know how to start.'

" 'May I suggest something, although I believe her to be too imbued for any proof,' I said.

" 'Suggest anything, Petite, anything.'

" 'Well, you meet this woman and have your fortune told. When she leaves, mark down everything that she prophesied. You see, until the time that I met Antoine, I was in everyone's home. For years I've heard of hoo-dooers and fortune-tellers, but through my faith in God, I realized that He would not give supernatural powers to any particular person, especially someone who would cause harm with those powers. In this way I've retained a level head and was able to notice how they worked. In telling fortunes, Madeau cuts the cards; the various suites mean various persons, places, etc. For instance, a ten of diamonds signifies money; and if it is preceded by a heart card, you will be told that you will receive money, the amount being in proportion to

the numeral on the heart card. If the ten of diamonds is preceded by a spade, then you will be told that you will pay out
money; other cards represent courts, fires, houses, etc., so that
money, to or from you, might be through the courts, a fire, the
sale of a house. In other words, cards, as understood by people
such as Jeanette, can furnish a complete picture, a complete story.
Now, have this woman cut your cards, as the expression goes.
Remember as much as you can of her predictions, and later show
Jeanette where not ten per cent of her predictions came true.'

" 'But doesn't Jeanette see that?'

" 'No, for the reason that people like her have their cards cut
weekly; and thirty prediction this week, thirty more next week
and so on—why they just don't remember them, except when
one happens. Then it is "Madeau told me so"; they do not realize
the number of predictions that never happened.'

" 'What a perfidy! and my Jeanette has fallen for that! But
what about the law? Can't it do something?'

" 'John, she's been arrested countless times; but addicts to fortune-telling, just like addicts to drugs, seek and find her.'

" 'I see. But, if what you suggest fails, what then? Why such
fortune-telling might have direful results.'

" 'It has been such. What would you do, Antoine, if through
her something serious would happen to us?'

" 'I'll tell you what I'd do. If I were convinced that she was
the cause of my losing you, Petite, I'd kill her.'

" 'That would involve scandal, court trials, and . . .'

" 'But, someone should do something.'

" 'Yes,' said John, 'someone should do something, for, for me to
lose Jeanette, my baby—God, what a thought!' "

"What did he do?"

"Just as I suggested and with the result that I predicted. One
month after the card cutting less than ten per cent of the predictions occurred, and those were only of a trivial or every-day nature; such as, receiving a letter, or having a female visitor.
Jeanette still held to the argument that the other predictions
would happen in the future. However, from that time things had
gone from bad to worse. John's home, his wife, his baby were

all influenced by the mulattress and her cards."

"How, Petite?"

"Well, I remember one particular case when he had occasion
to purchase a large tract of worthless land for a plantation.
In this case, as in every other, he permitted Jeanette to influence him, never once dreaming that her influence was from
the cards. Had he taken her advice, he would have purchased
that land. Antoine and I, realizing what was happening, followed the transaction, as a brother and sister would, told John,
and thus saved him a catastrophe.

"Another instance was about the baby. The slave maid was in
the very room when the midwife brought the baby into the
world. To this slave, that baby was 'My chile,' and she loved it
with the devotion of a mother. John had paid well for this slave
girl, for she could keep house and do hair-dressing; she was also
a good wet nurse. In general, she was really outstanding for a
slave. Madeau knew this and bargained with another woman
that she cut cards for to persuade Jeanette to sell her maid. It
was an easy matter for the cards to show that this maid only
feigned love for the baby and that she planned bodily harm for it.
To make a long story short, the sale was made; and when John
was apprised of the event, he went into a rage. Jeanette then
confessed why she had disposed of the slave; and, Grace, that interfering with his baby was the straw that broke the camel's
back."

"Did he get the maid back?"

"Yes, by paying more than Jeanette had received for her."

"Then what happened?"

"Well, that night he told Antoine that he was going to Madeau's
home.

" 'May I come with you, John?' asked Antoine.

" 'I was hoping you would ask.'

"Out Orleans Street they walked, passing Bourbon Street, Dau-
phine, and then Burgundy, until they reached the low squat
brick house. John knocked; Madeau answered. She asked
them in. In as few words as possible, he told her the harm she
had caused and demanded that she discontinue the cutting of
cards for his wife.

"She answered that she was a free woman of color and would do as she damn pleased.

"John's face turned red with rage; and he told her, with his fist in her face, that he would kill her if he caught her in his home again.

"On reaching his home he explained to Jeanette that he loved her and the baby more than anything on earth. 'But,' he said, 'Jeanette, this business with Madeau must end; of that, I am determined. I've called at her home tonight and made it clear that I will kill her if I catch her here again. Now, as wife and mother, I'm expecting you to heed what I say.'"

"His reaction must have been serious?"

"Let—me—see if I can recall his conversation. Oh! yes. I was alone in the parlor when he entered and said: 'May I talk with you, Petite?'

"'Surely, John. Unburden your mind, and I know you will feel relieved.'

"'I'm afraid it will take more than that.'

"'Tell me, what is troubling you?'

"'Well, Petite, I now realize that I cannot trust Jeanette in any one respect; for instance, if she makes a suggestion concerning anything at all, I can no longer believe that it is her personal judgment. This, however, I can possibly combat by forever being on my guard; but it is a hell of a life not to be able to converse with one's wife without questioning every word that she utters. To ask her suggestion about anything whatsoever is, of course, strictly out. But, as I've said before, I may be able to combat this. What worries me is just what she may be influenced to do next. If that witch should tell her through her blasphemous cards that I intend taking the baby away from her and return to England, why, she might leave with it and disappear.'

"'I don't believe Madeau would have the nerve to do that.'

"'If she did, I assure you, Petite, upon the word of honor that you respect, I'll be responsible for a new soul entering hell. I'll kill her; you hear me, kill her!'

"'Now, John, please control yourself. Listen well to what I have to say. Father has always regarded me as his pet, even though he adored all of his children. I believe the reason for that was the fact I was more daring than my sisters, and always did any and everything that the boys would do—hunting, fishing, even swimming in the Mississippi in my little drawers when I thought I was alone. Of course this kept father constantly concerned about me which, of course, led to more love, and more love led to more companionship.'

" 'That is good psychology.'

" 'Yes, but that companionship led to father's teaching me from early childhood the methods he discovered which helped to happier living. He did not say, but I am sure he meant that he was absolutely certain of one life only, and that that life should be made as happy as possible. Towards that end he had made certain discoveries and told them to me. It may be that I was a good listener; but be that as it may, I learned his philosophy of life. One thing he told me that has proved true was never worry, for he had found that out of one hundred times he worried, ninety-nine times it was useless, for things always seemed to right themselves. Not only in his life had he noticed these occurrences, but also the life of everyone with whom he came in contact.'

" 'Yes, but—'

" 'Just a moment, John—he further stated that at each new worry he would think of its being that one per cent, and that it was necessary to worry; but he found, as he felt I would, that the one per cent never came. If it should, he advised, then one shouldn't worry, but fight like hell.'

" 'But when shall I know that?'

" 'When it's so serious that, as in your case, the things that you are now worrying about come to pass.'

" 'In other words, I must not try to nip it in the bud?'

" 'No, I don't mean that. Nip it in the bud if you can; but when you can't, as you are now situated, then don't worry until your troubles have blossomed; then fight like hell.'

"This was my honest and truthful way of consoling him.

"However, he did ask, 'Petitie, you find that never worrying has helped you to live a happier life?'

" 'Yes, John, for when Antoine enters, instead of having a wrinkled brow that would possibly dissipate his desire to kiss me, I am happpy, full of smiles, and thus give him a desire to caress me, to love me more. I could not possibly imagine a husband as loveable and affectionate as Antoine, holding a wife with a wrinkled brow and loving her. Maybe he would for the first time in sympathy, but he would soon tire of it and plan to avoid her.'

" 'Petite, I begin to see your point. One would imagine that Jeanette would realize that her home was being broken.'

" 'Fortune-telling makes addicts of everyone, once one starts.'

" 'Never to be cured!'

" 'Oh, yes; but only after a serious occurrence.'

"However, for over a week everything was peaceful and quiet. They went out evenings pushing their little one in her carriage, proud of her being theirs. We were happy for them and on one occasion attended the opera with them. Never had I seen John so happy. He had known the bitter the better to enjoy the sweet.

"On July fourteenth, every year, we had a habit of leaving the city for the plantation. Our reason was twofold: first, to avoid the summer heat in the hot city; and second and most important, to avoid a yellow fever epidemic. Early that morning we bid adieu to Jeanette and John. They were to join us a few days later since John had some important business to attend. I was contented for I felt, with Jeanette soon by my side and away from Madeau, I might be successful in weaning her from that superstition. However, that afternoon, Jeanette and John were in their home playing with the baby when Jeanette, feigning suffocation, asked John to mind the baby, while she went out for fresh air. After an hour or so she returned; and upon John's questioning her as to how she felt, she simply answered, 'No better.' John noticed a change in her and decided to remain at home that night instead of attending the stag dinner which was given by the members of the Property Owners' League. The purpose that evening was to adopt a resolution to prevent the raising of taxes which the city fathers were advocating. However, by night Jeanette was supposedly feeling better and recommended that he attend."

CHAPTER IX

Result

"Petite, what did happen to Henri whose picture was placed in a cemetery with the burning candle?"

"Well, Grace, a few days before that incident I had met Emile's mother; and through tears, she explained that he was in the last stages of tuberculosis. We had known he was affected, but were not aware of the progress of the disease. Madeau knew this as she knew everyone's business, and capitalized on him to prove her power. You can imagine the furor this created among the superstitious; and directly or indirectly, they all knew of the incident. One morning three months thence, white placards appeared tacked on corner posts, rimmed with black, and with Emile's name at the top. At the bottom were details of the funeral. That is the custom in the quarter of announcing a death."

"I begin to understand now how easily and thoroughly fear could be inculcated into believers; and how more convincing her powers of hoo-dooing became to the ignorant."

"Grace, understand me correctly. It was not only the ignorant, but those of good education and sound judgment who sometimes were affected by it. You see, you know the facts in Henri's case; but suppose you didn't, and suppose many cases similar to his were brought to your attention; and again suppose that some calamity would befall you, for instance, like losing Emile, you might, as a last resort, be tempted to consult that woman."

"My, you've made that clear."

"Further, once you began, if you received your objective, you would continue to consult her at every little annoyance.

"Let me tell you of a case that on its face value seems unbelievable. I know that you have not doubted one word of what I've been telling you. Both consciously and subsciously you have absorbed everything I've told you as the gospel truth. I still believe that your conscious mind will accept what I will now tell you as also being the truth; but I sincerely feel that your subconscious mind will, and not without reason, doubt its authenticity. So that this mind might be more open, or let us say, more receptive, I want you to know that what I shall tell you is absolutely true on my sacred word of honor."

"Petite, since realizing what you have explained, I'm sure that both my minds will accept almost anything. However, proceed."

"Well, the woman I have in mind had accompanied a friend to a fortune-teller. When they were about to leave, she was prevailed upon to have her fortune told. Of course, this called for more visits; and on one occasion, she was told she would learn to love a blue-eyed man, and that he would be her main influence through life. Now, Grace, as you've seen, blue-eyed people are rather the exception than the rule in this city, dark eyes predominating. I should have told you that this fortune-teller was not Madeau's type, although she practiced hoo-doo, and actually believed herself everything the cards foretold so that it was only natural that she would ask her friend, practically every time they met, if she had met the blue-eyed man. Now this girl had among her acquaintance only one young man with blue eyes. She promptly hypnotized herself into believing that she was in love with this man; and subconsciously she not only did, but caused him to care for her. She had, however, become such an addict to fortune-telling and hoo-dooing that her sweetheart, being a strict unbeliever, felt, as did John towards Jeannette, that he definitely could not trust her in any manner, shape, or form. However, he still cared for her; but for fourteen years they remained single. The girl, or rather woman, was now thoroughly convinced that she was being hoo-dooed by his mother, and that this was the reason for their remaining single. This, of course, caused constant arguments which reached such proportions that they finally separated."

"What a fool!"

"It was not exactly her fault. But let me continue. Of course, we realize that fourteen years of intimate courtship would not definitely end with a separation, for one of the parties would endeavor to solve the problem; and in this case, it was the woman.

" 'Convince me,' she said to him one day, 'that I'm wrong by marrying me. I will then know that hoo-dooism does not exist, and I swear that I will be cured, and that I will never visit nor believe such people again.'

"Of course, Grace, the man, after fourteen years of cards, fortune-tellers, spiritualists, and hoo-dooers, fully realizing that like leprosy it cannot be cured, but eats deeper and deeper and deeper, avoided the wedding, until one day a month after when realizing her sincerity, he assented with the provision that they marry out of the state, that is, in one where a divorce could be quickly granted. You see, this man was emotionally more or less of father's type. He seemed to realize also that this life possibly would be his only one, and since he was getting on in years, he did not and would not, under any circumstances, permit a woman who would disregard her word to ruin his life. So they married; he definitely insisted on the justice of the peace using the words 'And obey'. Well, for one or two weeks, I don't exactly remember, they were extremely happy; the more humble she was the more he loved her. They had a really comfortable home with all conveniences, and their finances were in good condition."

"But, after the first or second week, she began to act as before and from that time for four years there was hell to play. Then, one day in an argument it leaked out. The woman, or addict, after the first or second week of marriage had again visited the fortune-teller. This time she was being hoo-dooed into a divorce although the man's mother was not aware of their marriage."

"Petite, it's no wonder you used your word of honor. How did it end?"

"In the inevitable—a separation. Whether it will be permanent or not remains to be seen. Personally I don't see how it could be otherwise, for this time it is definitely her fault.

"Let me cite you another case. I'll use her initial because this woman is alive and living not many squares from here. She is Mrs. S. She was happily married and was the mother of two children. Her husband had a responsible position that paid well, and they were able every month to meet the installments on their home for which they had paid over half. This Mrs. S. had some minor ailment, and feeling sure that her doctor was not candid with her, accepted the recommendation of a friend to consult a fortune-teller. She did and received the happy tidings that her ailment was minor, and was also told, in addition to many other prophecies, that her husband would receive an increase in wages, a fact her husband had known for weeks. Of course, when on Saturday his envelope bore larger figures, she was elated, not because of the increase, but because she had discovered a way to look into the future. So back to the fortune-teller she went for more prophecies. She gave the woman an extra dollar of her husband's hard earned money in appreciation for her prediction. This time, however, after her husband's card, the king of clubs, for he was a brunette, was placed face up on the table, came a queen of spades. 'The hussy!' A woman after her husband. She evidently knew he had received more money—yes, that was it, for the next card the ten of clubs revealed that she was after money. But, this card was followed by a spade, which denoted that he would turn his back on her.

"Now, Grace, it could just as well have been the ten of hearts, which, heavenly days, would have meant love. However, this day she was lucky and raced home, happy to meet her children from school and to prepare a meal. One can partially hypnotize oneself. Should you care to try it, one morning before Emile awakes, lie on your back, close your eyes, and picture Emile holding a woman in his arms, petting and caressing her as he does you."

"I've done that and never will do it again."

"Why?"

"Because I acted differently towards him and he quickly sensed it. I confessed, and playfully he placed me across his lap and pretended to whip me. Incidentally, Petite, that was the morning of the day that he made me promise never to permit fortune-telling and hoo-dooism to enter my mind."

"I see. Then you can readily understand Mrs. S., who, while en route to her home, had visions of her husband with the woman of the cards. 'For after all,' she mused, 'he was only a man.'

"That afternoon, as usual, his children were waiting for him at the front gate. When he turned the corner, they rushed to him; and after kissing the larger one first, he lifted the other one into his arms, and holding the larger one by the hand, strutted proudly through the center of the garden that he and his wife had planted, into their comfortable home. On that afternoon she didn't work in the garden, for she did not feel well; and the next morning, feeling the same way, she bade her husband good-bye in a cool manner.

" 'Strange ailments women have,' he thought as he carefully closed the gate.

"When the children had gone to school, she returned to the fortune-teller, for after a diligent search through his clothes the night before, she had discovered a faint odor of perfume. Probably her own, Grace, if there really was any scent at all. So the King of Clubs was again placed on the table and the next card was the ace of spades—meaning a separation in their home. Well, she decided she might as well know the worse—another one! This time it was the Queen of Clubs—'Yes, Mrs. S., you and your husband will separate,' said the fortune-teller. She tried one more card. The Jack of Diamonds, a blond boy friend turned up."

"How did it end, Petite? I feel sorry for the husband."

"You should also feel sorry for the wife too. Today the husband is living in a rooming house; his two children are in the convent, and he visits them twice a week—and the once dutiful wife and affectionate mother, a——, I'd rather not use the word."

"My God!"

"Yes, Grace, fantastic as this seems it is the truth. Those women, the fortune-tellers I mean, who believe they are endowed with supernatural gifts, are in reality far below standard, both mentally and morally. They unfortuntely have caused hundreds of such cases, so much so that a law has been passed forbidding them to operate. But they will nevertheless continue for years and years to come."

"Petite, I now can fully understand Emile's foresight; but tell me, do men also visit fortune-tellers?"

"Only about one to one hundred women. I personally know two who will consult such women before they consummate an important deal. In that case, like tossing a coin, if one does it often enough, one half of the time the fortune-teller is right; and the other half, wrong. Men are quicker to sense such fallacies and, of course, discontinue their visits. However, you should now realize that Jeannette is more to be pitied than blamed."

"I do. But it is surprising that some one doesn't dispose of women like Madeau."

"Many have tried and failed."

CHAPTER X

The Duel

"In a room in the rear of a saloon built especially for business men's meetings, and around a long table that was built of carpenter horses and flat boards, so as to be easily dismantled, sat a sober crowd, now listening to a speaker, and later sipping beer or whiskey, according to their pleasure, while from cigars smoke slowly curled until it reached the ceiling and as slowly was wafted towards the opening window. It was early and only one speaker had been heard.

"Presently the speaker called for order, when one of the attendants at this stag began to speak. John seemed somewhat worried over Jeanette's condition and was about to return home when he heard a resolution to be offered to the commission council to order Madeau to leave the city of New Orleans. There was a debate, and it was later learned that this debate was started by her white boy friend, Louis, who owned the house she lived in. Of course, John was highly in favor of her being tarred and feathered on her way out; and later while he had the floor in the debate, he actually recommended just that; and further stated he would be the first to sign the petition. Louis was furious; and when he was given the floor, he explained that if her morality was low so was that of the wife of Mr. John Lancaster, who that afternoon had visited Madeau, 'For,' he continued, 'birds of a feather—' and, Grace, he got no further. John had rushed at him; and instead of slapping his face with his handkerchief or glove he planted his five fingers on the man's face with all of the force in his body. The marks on Louis' face plainly revealed this fact. The crowd would have murdered Louis, for men of his type were despised, had not someone suggested a duel."

"What hell a woman can cause in a man's life!"

"That's right, Grace, and I want you to bear in mind that I'm telling this story as I know it, not as I learned it, for I heard it piecemeal. However, in less than five minutes, guns were procured, and two carriages were seen racing out on the old Bayou Road to Bayou St. John. Good John was good no more. He scowled at his seconds; he roared at the driver; he cursed his wife! Reaching the old historic Bayou St. John, they crossed over in pirogues. Then they walked about a quarter of a mile. Soon they came to century-old twin oaks, the duelling oaks, where red blood, human blood, from hundreds of men for over ninety years had seeped slowly down to the roots of these massive trees.

" 'How many paces?'

"John was impatient and yelled, 'Twenty-five.'

"They took their positions back to back, and both waited for the signal that was soon heard, echoing loud as if to break the deathly black silence. They moved apart over the mound which was built especially for dry, sure steps—one, two, three, four—until they reached twenty-five when both turned and faced each other.

"No one moved; all were as rigid as though they were statues. Although their hearts had quickened, they seemed scarcely to breathe. Then in the serene stillness, under the massive oaks, two guns barked as one. All eyes closed at the report, but quickly reopened, to see one man fall. Rushing towards him, they picked him up and rushed him to a doctor. He had a bullet in his lung. It was Louis.

"John hadn't moved from where he had fired, but stood limp, with lowered head and listless, hanging arms; the gun was still in his hand. His mind was in a turmoil, and he shook his head from side to side as if to clear it. Then the thought entered his mind that he had probably killed a man, and his mother's words rang in his ears, words uttered years age. 'John, rather give your life than take one.' He raised his head to find that he was alone. The loneliness caused something to snap for with long steps he walked away, back to the bayou. All of the boats were on the other side. Removing his coat, and with a determination unknown to good John, he dived, head first, into the brakish water.

"At about eleven o'clock, he reached Orleans and Rampart Streets. With a few more steps he stood before the squatty brick house. He raised his hand and knocked. Presently the door opened and the yellow face appeared. The shadows from the light of the candle on the inside caused the face to have the appearance of a fiend. Also from inside came the odor of burning incense.

"Madeau's face smiled as if in mockery. Then with the hatred of all hell, like a madman, he grabbed her gown at the throat with his left hand, and drawing her through the door on to the banquette, he for the second time that night planted his hand, not open this time but closed into a tight, powerful fist, directly on her flat nose, spattering blood over his wet clothes and smashing her nose even with her cheeks. Then, like a hammer, he let fall his fist over and over again; and grabbing the unconscious form with both hands, he threw it forcibly to the banquette."

CHAPTER XI

Punishment

"The following day I was at our plantation home. I've always admired the massive columns supporting the heavy slate roof, the verandas that circled the house on the first and second floors, and in the front, facing the river, the long double rows of oak trees that stretched from the home for one thousand feet to the river bank. I was seated on the second-floor veranda facing in the direction of the city. In my lap was a ball of pink yarn and in my hands were the beginning of a baby sock and the knitting needles. I was happy and contented thinking of the day when I would present Antoine with the baby we so ardently desired. The hall clock had just struck two, and the hot rays of the burning sun bathed the land with an intensity that caused one to see through the heat waves a cloud shadow falling on the sugar cane which waved in the wind like an endless green sheet. Presently the shadow drifted towards the house and slowly passed until it was lost over the levee. I turned my head; and looking in the direction of the city, I noticed a carriage in the distance along the winding river road.

"Keeping my eyes on the vehicle, I was thinking how pleased I would be to have a visitor when the carriage was hidden by a curve in the levee. Soon it emerged around the bend, and then I noticed that something about it seemed familiar. But, I thought, most of the carriages in this section are from France and except for some slight modification are all more or less alike. Notwithstanding, I continued to follow it until it reached the oaks by the river. I was elated to see it turn and roll down the shadowed lane. Dropping my yarn and needles in the hollow arm of the rocker, I raced through the house to the stairs, down to the first floor, and finally to the road just as the carriage stopped. I now recognized it; it was John's. My first glance through the windows led me to believe it held no occupant. Then the door opened; and as I reached it, Jeannette, lying on her side, thrust the baby forward with, 'Petite, take the baby.' I did as she requested and, placing it in my left arm, endeavored to assist her.

" 'Jeanette, what is wrong?'

" 'Let us not talk of it here.' And with that, we walked, she with an effort, up the stairs and into my bedroom. As I placed the sleeping infant on the couch, I said, 'Jeanette, have a seat.'

" 'But Petite, I can't sit.'

" 'Well, lie down,' I answered, not realizing the significance of her words. 'Come,' I continued, 'I will remove the spread. Now lie down—no honey, not on your side but on your back and relax.'

" 'But, I can't lie on my back. You see I've been whipped.'

" 'Been whipped?'

" 'Yes, I can' sit.'

" 'Wait, let me get a chair. Now, suppose you start at the beginning and tell me all.'

" 'Well, yesterday afternoon, while John tended the baby, I went to Madeau, for—'

" 'Jeanette! I thought—'

" 'Please, Petite, don't scold, for the urge was terr- - -'

" 'I'm not scolding, but you promised John to—'

" 'Yes, I know. But please let me continue. You see, she said the baby would become ill.'

" 'Through the cards?'

" 'Yes. Well, last night, after John had left for the stag, I washed the baby, powdered it, and placed it in its bed. Tears fell constantly; and when it raised its little hands and cooed, well, I burst into a heavy cry. About ten o'clock I realized that I could not sleep; so calling Nini, I ordered a hot bath. At about ten-thirty, she notified me that the bath was ready. Although it was hot, I told Nini to put on more coal.'

" 'I see, you used the new copper bath tub with the attached heater and ladder.'

" 'Yes. I remained seated in the tub for at least three

quarters of an hour, until my skin was red. Then, as I stepped
on the ladder, I heard the hall door open and close. I knew
you and Antoine were down here and naturally listened to
recognize the footsteps. They sounded like Antoine's, and
yet they seemed heavier. As I reached the floor, I heard the
knob turn; so quickly I reached for the bath towel and covered myself as best I could. The door opened wide; and
standing in the middle, on the sill, was John—hair dis-
heveled, no coat, and shirt and trousers wet and spattered
with blood. On his face were also some spots of blood. Before
I saw his appearance, I realized in a fraction of a second that
something serious was wrong, for John had never entered
my bath. As I started to speak, I stopped, for the expression
on his face was terrible, and—'

" 'Don't cry honey. And what?'

" 'And he started towards me. As he did, he seemed to
get shorter and his neck seemed to sink into his shoulders
which grew wider. I screamed; and as I did, he drew the
towel from me, and grabbing me, he sat on the wiping stool.
Then he placed me across his knees. I tried to extricate myself; but the harder I fought the more powerful he seemed
to become. God, I shudder when I think of it!''

" 'I can't believe it. Are you sure it was John?'

" 'Beyond question of a doubt. However, while I was still
screaming, he maneuvered me into a position in which I was
absolutely helpless.'

" 'I don't understand. But wait, Phoebe has brought us
coffee.'

" 'Good old Phoebe. You knew I was ill; so you bring
coffee.'

" 'Yes'm.'

" 'Tell me, Phoebe, if your man spanked you, what would
you do?'

" 'If ah deserves it, ah'd takes it. Can ah have de cups
please?'

" 'Now, Jeanette, do you feel better?'

" 'Yes, but my back certainly pains.'

" 'Now continue.'

" 'Well, you see, when he placed me across his lap, I was facing the floor. My left shoulder was under the pit of—yes, of his left arm. The crotch of his elbow was under my neck forcing my head up, while his hand was on my right shoulder forcing it down. In this position, I could not possibly move my shoulders nor my head.'

" 'You still contend that it was John?'

" 'Yes.'

" 'Go ahead.'

" 'Well, the Lord and John only know how he placed his right leg over my limbs, thus pinning me down completely.'

" 'Where were your hands?'

" 'Under me.'

" 'I see. And then? Now don't cry, please.' And, Grace, I stroked her head for she had placed her face in the pillow and was sobbing bitterly. I let her cry it out; and when she was somewhat composed, I asked, 'And then?'

" 'I tried to move myself by pushing up with my feet; and as my back side raised, red from the hot bath, I felt his hand strike and screamed with pain. He must have struck me seven or eight times; his last blows were weak and exhausted; and then he pushed, Petite, actually pushed me to the floor.

" 'I lay there and looking through tears at him, saw him totter towards the door. As he reached it, he held to the frame and turning, with a tired and mournful expression, he uttered three words which I'll never forget as long as I live— Hoo-doo, fortune-telling.'

"Again, Grace she drew the pillow to her face; and while she was crying, I walked over to the baby. She had awakened and I picked her up. Her blue eyes stared directly into mine. At the center of her chin was a dimple, the same as John's. I drew her to me, kissing her cheek. Jeanette had composed herself and asked for her baby. I handed her over and she placed the little one in a position to nurse.

" 'Jeanette,' I said anxious to know something about John's safety, 'what next?' She kissed her baby on the head and stared straight ahead for a full minute. Her face was sad and looked tired. Around her mouth had come an expression of sorrow. I began to fear for John; so I repeated, 'What next?'

" 'I'm sorry, Petite.' She brushed the hair from her eyes and continued, 'While I was lying there on the floor, even while he was still steadying himself at the door, I began to realize that John would never have done such a thing had I not deserved it; and since I had received such a terrible whipping, I further realized that I must have been terribly wrong. Oh, what a fool I've been and how I must have hurt him!'

"Grace, I rushed for the sedative water for she was nearly in hysterics. On returning, I found her moaning, and the baby looking directly into her face.

" 'Here, Jeanette, honey, take this and everything will be all right.'

" 'No it won't,' she sobbed, 'for he's gone.'

" 'You don't mean dead?'

" 'Oh, no, not that—thank God.'

"I breathed a sigh of relief and said, "Do you feel better?'

" 'Yes.'

" 'Do you care to continue?'

" 'I hate to bother you, sister mine; you've been so good.'

"I stooped and kissed her, and taking the baby in my arms, I said, 'Continue, Jeanette.'

" 'Well, when I heard the hall door close, I jumped to my feet; and although my back was bleeding, I threw a robe around me as quickly as possible, and stepped down the stairs in my slippers as best I could and followed him. When I reached the banquette, he was nowhere to be seen; so I walked towards Toulouse Street. Looking both ways I saw him heading towards the river, a block away. I started to cry out; but realizing how I was robed, I remained silent. Instead I tried to run, but couldn't. So I walked as fast as I could, but could not lessen the distance between us.

"Finally, fearing for the worse, I began to scream when I noticed that he turned to the left, down the river. I continued to follow; and with each step, I felt the pangs of hell. Finally he reached the new English ship, the one with the engines and sails, named the Ocean Queen. I noticed that a man was helping what appeared to be a drunken man, and saw him wave to John for help. Together the three walked up the gang plank and disappeared into the ship. I continued to walk until I reached the ship, and then I decided to wait for him to return over the gang-plank. As I couldn't sit, I moved from one foot to the other. Imagine my surprise when I saw that men were loosening the hausers, the whistle blew, and before my very eyes, the ship moved. I screamed at the top of my voice, but the noise of the engine drowned it, and away went the vessel down the river—with my John!'

" 'Now, listen, no more crying.'

" 'I'll be brave.'

" 'That's better. Now tell me what followed?'

" 'Well, I had barely reached home where Nini met me. She had witnessed everything, with the baby in her arms. When I reached the bed, I am certain I would have collapsed had it not been for my love for my baby who was crying to be fed. As I lay on my side, Nini placed her in position; and, Petite, you should have seen that little mouth move until it got located.

" 'Early in the morning, I sent for the mid-wife to treat my back; and as soon as I could summon sufficient courage, I ordered the carriage, and now I'm here.'

" 'Do you want to take my advice, little sister?'

" 'Yes, yours and Antoine's.'

" 'You did not sleep last night?'

" 'Not a wink.'

" 'I'll take the baby with me on the veranda, and I want you to sleep. See how the sedative water has calmed your nerves; and, Jeanette, honey, I predict that everything will end happily.'

" 'You have a plan?'

" 'Yes, but sleep and let Antoine and me do your planning.' "

"And with that, Grace, her sad, swollen eyes closed; and in a few minutes she was fast asleep. As a breeze had started, I placed a sheet over her. Then I tiptoed from the room and up the stairs, with the baby in my arms, to the veranda. Placing the yarn, needles, and unfinished baby sock on the floor, I hugged the little one, remembering that I too would have one of my own.

"I began thinking of how Antoine, busy somewhere in the cane field, and I would love my little one! Then, again in the distance, I saw, not a carriage, but a covered wagon drawn by two white horses. Surely this was not my family; so I busied myself talking to the baby who seemed as though it were trying to understand. However, after a few minutes, I noticed the wagon roll under the oaks towards our home; and again, I quickly left the rocker and raced down to the veranda on the first floor. Then I noticed that it was the patrol wagon; and as the policemen left it, I recognized one of them, an old playmate named Maurice. Leaping the stairs two at a time he asked, 'Petite, John is not here, is he?'

" 'No, Maurice; he is not.'

" 'Then, Albert, we cannot arrest a man that is not here.'

" 'No,' said the other policeman, winking back at Maurice, 'we cannot arrest a man that is not here.'

" 'Now, Petite, you may congratulate me.'

" 'What for?'

" 'I will be promoted to a sergeant. You see, the Chief said that if I should return without John, he would promote me.'

"We laughed and I asked 'Won't you two have a seat?'

" 'Sure.'

" 'And now, Maurice, tell me why the law wants John.' And, Grace, Maurice and Albert related the events of that night just as I've related them to you. They added that Madeau would never use her staring black eyes again; and since her appearance was completely changed, she had decided to leave the city for her followers were now convinced that she was not so omniscient as they had once believed, and so they had lost all faith in her. Maurice further stated that she fairly leaps out of bed when a man of John's build passes."

"She's got what she deserved."

"If you knew her as I did, you would have added the tar and feathers that John recommended. However, the wagon had barely reached the end of the oaks returning to the city, when Antoine, who had recognized it at a distance from his seat in the saddle, left the slaves in the field and raced home.

" 'Anything wrong, honey?'

" 'Yes and no,' I answered.

" 'What did the police want?'

" 'Let us go on the porch where we can sit and talk.' With that, he reached for the baby and up the stairs I again trod, he following. He drew another rocker next to mine.

"For one half hour I talked, explaining everything I knew. He listened attentively, only now and then interrupting when some event was not perfectly clear. As I related the events, his emotions changed; sometimes he compressed his lips and narrowed his eyes; other times his lips were slightly apart and his eyes became sad. Grace, he loved John as he would a younger brother.

"When I had finished, he rose, handed me the baby, lit a cigarette, walked over to the large column, leaned against it, and stared over the field, all the time puffing furiously. I remained perfectly quiet, for I knew he desired me that way. Suddenly, flipping the cigarette, he retraced his steps and again sat by my side.

" 'Petite,' he said, 'you've been an ideal wife, nay, more than that, you've been a wonderful, dutiful mate. Now tell me, since my prediction has come true, and I want you to believe me when I say that I'm sorry it did, just what would you do if you were Jeanette?'

"Unhesitatingly I answered, 'I would take the next boat for England.'

" 'Then, is that what you suggest?'

" 'I don't think that will be necessary. Look, down the road another carriage is approaching.'

" 'I've been expecting it.'

" 'So have I, Antoine. Our family is certainly clannish, one for all and all for one.'

" 'That is one reason why I love them so.' Antoine again took the baby from me, and we once more went downstairs to the front of the house and waited. When the carriage stopped, I opened one door while Antoine, on the opposite side, opened the other. Mother almost fell into my arms, crying; while Dad, after exchanging greetings with 'his son', asked, 'Where is she?'

" 'Asleep, Dad, and I would suggest not awakening her.'

" 'You know, Son, I'd like to place her across my lap and continue where John left off.'

"Just then, the big bronze bell rang, a welcoming sound to the slaves in the field, who, with their tools in the air, marched toward the house. It also was a notification that our supper was ready; so with my arms around Mother's waist, we led, followed by Antoine and Dad.

"Of course, John and Jeanette were the topic of conversation; and after I had said that Antoine had predicted the separation, Mother earnestly asked him what he thought of Jeanette's future.

" 'Well, Mom, for one thing, I now believe Jeanette is cured. Whether she will follow him, which she should do, or whether he returns, which is highly probable, because he certainly loves her and the baby, I don't know. He is on the high seas by this time, and anything can happen to that boat; steam is dangerous.'

"And so, Grace, towards eleven o'clock, with Jeanette still sound asleep, we retired.

"I had said my prayers when Antoine entered the bed at my side; and lying on his back, as was his custom, closed his eye and prayed, not the usual prayers, but as always one of his own that pertained to the events of the day. Just below his breath, and in the stillness of our plantation home, I distinctly heard him say, 'And I thank Thee for the mate Thou has so lovingly bestowed upon me. I could not control my emotions; and throwing my arm over him, I kissed him twice, long and lingeringly."

"It's odd, Petite, the emotions we arouse in each other—

humility and obedience from the wife—appreciation and tenderness from the husband."

"It didn't take you long to learn."

"No, it didn't. But tell me, your plantation home which you described is so much like ours—"

"It is the same."

"What?"

"Yes, that is the very one that Jeanette and Maurice visited."

"But are you, I mean is Antoine the partner that Emile spoke of?"

"Yes, one and the same."

"And you are to live with us?"

"Yes."

"Oh, Petite, darling, I am delighted."
"I thought you knew it?"

"No, it is a pleasant surprise. You know, out of the millions of women on this earth, I would choose you as my, let us say, confidante. And Petite, what happened next?'

CHAPTER XII

Jeanette's Resolution

"It was the morning of July 16, 1816. Being accustomed to retiring early, we naturally awakened late—all but Jeanette, who, awakening early, bathed her baby and, as I later discovered, walked between the row of oaks to and over the levee. I followed her; and when I reached the top, I could see the small open outhouse that Antoine had built at the water's edge where very often on summer evenings we were wont to sit, watching ships going to and fro. On the wooden benches were long leather cushions; and as I came nearer, I noticed that she was lying on her side, thinking deeply, for her brow was furrowed, while the baby lay asleep opposite her.

"So as not to frighten her I called when near; and rising, she answered, 'Thank God it is you, for I don't know how to face father and mother.'

" 'Well, Jeanette, honey, all agreed last night, upon Antoine's suggestion not to mention a word to you of anything that happened, but to act as we usually do.'

" 'You people are good to me.'

" 'We should be—you are our sister.'

" 'Antoine's also?'

" 'He couldn't love you more. Now, no more tears, for from this day forward you will be your own courageous self. Now let me arrange the cushions so that you can rest on your back; and if you bend your legs slightly, your sore back will touch nothing; that's it, now bend your legs—now rest.'

" 'My this feels good.'

" 'Now, are you ready to hear all that happened night before last?'

" 'Ready and anxious.'

"And, Grace, she closed her eyes and remained perfectly motionless while I explained to her slowly and deliberately all that had happened. At one time I almost believed she was asleep so quiet and motionless was she until when I mentioned the duel and again when I mentioned how John had pummeled Madeau's face, I noticed tears emerge from her closed lids and roll down the side of her face. During my account I saw Father coming our way, evidently looking for us; and when I motioned to him to go away, he immediately turned and returned to the house. For several minutes after I had finished, she still remained motionless except for her soft breathing. Finally, she opened her yes, turned her head towards her sleeping, pink-cheeked baby, and said, calmly, 'Petite, I will board the next boat for England.'

" 'I knew you would' was all I replied as she rose. I picked up the baby, and we both walked leisurely back to the house. We could see as we approached Mother, Father, and Antoine sitting on the veranda, evidently waiting for us. When we reached the steps, I led and walked directly to Mother and placed the baby in her outstretched arms. Jeanette had walked behind the chairs and leaning over kissed first Father and then Mother; and on reaching Antoine's chair, she drew his head backward and kissed him full on the lips, murmuring, 'Brother.'

"In the meantime I had walked into the house and quickly returned with two of my softest down-filled pillows. Placing them on Antoine's chair, which he gallantly relinquished, I motioned to Jeanette to sit. As she did, twisting, squirming, and making faces, her eyes met Dad's; and he, philosophical as he is, burst into laughter as did all of us, including Jeanette. The ice was now broken, as Phoebe would say; and after Jeanette had explained that she intended going to England, all offered suggestions; such as, what boat to board and what clothes to take, for the weather would not be balmy like New Orleans. Except for an occasional sigh from Jeanette, we passed a pleasant evening. It was made more pleasant for me when just before returning I made my rounds as all plantation hostesses do; and on my entering her room and reaching her bed, she said, 'I'm happy in the thought of seeing him again, and I will follow him around the earth if necessary.' "

"Petite, do you know what happened aboard the ship with John?"

"Yes, Grace. After the excitement at the stag dinner, the duel, the swim across Bayou St. John, the two-mile walk in wet clothes to Madeau's home—he was lucky it was mid July—, and the subsequent altering of her appearance, coupled with the whipping and the walk to the Ocean Queen, John needed help almost as much as the drunkard. The sober sailor saw this and appreciated his effort.

" 'Man, you're in as bad a condition as the sailor.'

" 'Yes, I know it, but I was not drinking.'

" 'I can see that; but your accent is British.'

" 'I am English.'

" 'Good, for I see you are spotted with blood.' "

" 'But man,' he stammered, 'I don't intend to leave—' And, Grace, that was as far as he got, for he reeled and fell just as Jenkins, the sailor, grabbed him. He then laid John beside the silent drunkard whom he had forced over to the side of the ship, and covered him; then taking a seat he sat and studied what to him was a transformation for what, only a few minutes before, had been a haggard face was now peaceful and calm; his features had relaxed with his body.

"Jenkins mused, 'shall I inform the Captain—well, there is goodness in that face, the clothes are a gentleman's; evidently he was in trouble. For otherwise why would he be covered with spattered blood; his right hand, too, is swollen, and between the fingers is also blood. Yes, he has struck someone with that hand, and to place him ashore might be to place an Englishman in the hands of an enemy. An Englishman—hum—better that he return to his native country. No, I will not inform the Captain, but will care for him as a stowaway.' "

"And he left Jeanette?"

"Yes, for he slept the sleep of the just, not awakening until noon the next day, when resting on his back he looked at the ceiling of the upper deck, recalling the scene of the night before. Yes, he had struck Jeanette! Good Lord, was he mad to have done that? She deserved a lesson, but not a whipping! Was she hurt, could she sit?

"He placed a hand on his forehead and rubbed it as if to remove tension. He began thinking again, and looking around said to himself, 'Yes, I'm on a ship, and we are moving for I hear the engine turning over. What will she think of me, believing me to be running away—me, a coward!'"

"Good John, again."

"Yes, Grace, and he leaped from the berth, opened the door, and was on deck before he knew that he was miles away. How long had he been asleep? For days maybe. Just then, Jenkins seeing him and not wanting the Captain to know, rushed to him with 'Man; inside the cabin.'

"John obeyed; and looking questioningly at Jenkins, asked, 'Why, in the cabin?'

"'Because the Captain doesn't know you're here, and if he learns of it, you will be put to work, while I'll be fined for harboring a stowaway.'

"'I want to work, for with nothing to do but think I'll go mad. Tell me, where are we?'

"'In the Gulf of Mexico.'

"'How long have I been asleep?'

"'Well you came aboard just before we sailed at midnight. So my friend you have been asleep just twelve hours.'

"'Twelve hours, and in the Gulf?'

"'Yes, for we've made the unprecedented speed of twelve knots, the engine being aided by the five-mile current of the swollen Mississippi.'

"'I see, but you are not an ordinary sailor: I can tell by your speech. And incidentally, my name is John.'

"'I understand, John; and, like myself, you haven't a last name. My name is Jenkins.'

"'Well, Jenkins, just why have you taken an interest in me?'

"'Because I know you are an Englishman; and seeing you spattered with blood, I felt it my duty towards my countryman.'

"'That is mighty kind of you. But just what do you propose that I do?'

"'Remain in this cabin until we reach Liverpool. Then—'

"'But, man, I'll go mad. Listen, let me walk directly to

the captain and declare myself a stowaway; I need not mention your name.'

" 'It's all right with me, but it will mean hard work.'

" 'That's what I want. And now, where will I find him?'

" 'In the chart room on the bridge deck. You know where that is?'

" 'I know where the bridge deck is and I can find the chart room. See you later.' Across the deck he walked and up the ladder; then he found himself before the captain. 'Are you the captain?'

" 'I am.'

" 'Well, I'm a stowaway and at your mercy.'

" 'Have any credentials?'

" 'None whatsoever.'

" 'Your name?'

" 'Just plain John.'

" 'But you have a last name?'

" 'Yes sir, I have, but I do not wish to reveal it.'

" 'I'll be compelled to hand you over to the police at Liverpool.'

" 'I'm satisfied.'

" 'Have a seat.'

" 'Thanks.'

" 'Now, John, you're not accustomed to being a stowaway. Your clothes, although soiled, are those of a gentleman. Why did you come to me so soon?'

" 'Because I was hungry.'

" 'John, you're lying.'

" 'But, sir, it is the——'

" 'You can't say it.'

" 'No, sir, I'm not accustomed to fabricating.'

" 'I can see that. I can also see that you've left behind someone that you love.'

" 'Adore, sir, two people. But how do you know?'

" 'By your wedding ring. That also tells me that you married a Creole.'

" 'You're right, sir. But what work shall I do?'

" 'None. You shall be my guest, John Lancaster.'

" 'But er——'

" 'Yes, how did I know it? Well, me lad, I knew your face

when I first saw it and noticing the J. L. embroidered on your shirt, and remembering the appearance of your father at your age—'

" 'Well, Captain, now that you know me, will you reverse this ship, and I will pay whatever you ask?'

" 'I cannot possibly grant your request, for freight is being shipped from inland to Liverpool to meet this ship on the fourth of August and I must be there then. Then, too, we never know how the Atlantic will treat us.'

" 'I understand, Captain; I didn't intend to embarras you, sir.'

" 'You're just like your father. However, we may meet another ship bound for New Orleans, and I'll gladly transfer you.' "

"Petite, why did he want to keep his identity, a secret?"

"Because, as he reasoned, one would hardly believe his story. Imagine an English Earl, owning a vast estate, in that condition, that is, a stowaway and too, to tell the truth about his being on board would have been to implicate Jenkins."

"I see. He would rather have suffered than harm someone. But tell me, did they meet another ship?"

"Yes, just when they were three days out."

"My, I bet John was happy."

"Not exactly. You see the Ocean Queen was riding out a heavy storm and to lower a boat over her side into the turbulent sea would have been almost suicide. Instead, however, they signalled a message to be delivered to Jeanette, a short one—'Love—will return soon—wait for me.'

"John's spirit was somewhat raised then; and he passed his time helping everyone—steering, oiling the engine, reefing in or hoisting sail when necessary, or repacking cotton bales when they moved in the heavy sea and threatened to list the ship; in fact, he was wherever work was, having made friends with the entire crew; of course, Jenkins, the old salt, was his favorite.

"However, Grace, after riding a minor storm when they neared the coast of England, they, on the fourth day of August entered the estuary of Mersey; there were only three more miles and they would reach Liverpool with its large quays on both sides of the tidal river, and its hewn-stone edifices of Italian renaissance architecture. There, too, his Majesty's port authorities would board the ship; they would take John to their office for questioning—"

"Did they?"

"Yes, and it was three days before he could prove his identity; for in addition to being without credentials, he was listed as having been slain in action in the Battle of New Orleans, an error unknown even to his father.

"John had decided aboard ship that since he would be in England, he would have his father's will probated. He did want to see more of Liverpool, especially Church and Bond Streets and the huge auditorium that was built in 1754, for he wished to hear once again the organ that his father and mother had traveled miles to enjoy with him as a boy. But, home, that is, his home in New Orleans where Jeanette and the baby were waiting for him, was more important.

"Well, his old feudal home, which dated back to the thirteenth century, with its historic background, was only a day's journey from Liverpool; so on August eight he stood before it, and gazed on the great stone walls. He turned and entered the medieval gates and walked through the passage into the courtyard that he knew so well; then he reached for an ever handy hammer and struck a huge bell. From up in the lofty, massive tower an old man's head emerged from a leaded glass window. Recognizing John, he shouted, 'John, oh John, look up here.'

"John saw him; and racing through the old castle, with its many turns, traps and dead ends, he finally reached the apartment, or palais as it was formerly called, and threw his arms around Jarvis, his venerable old tutor. They both sat on the massive, iron-bound chest at the foot of the bed, which was filled with the clothes of his good mother and stern father and reminisced. John had to tell all about his army life, his wound and capture, his meeting with and friendship for Antoine, and the reason for the wide gold band on the third figer of the left hand. About the ring, he was very explicit, telling Jarvis, as in his young days, secrets that only Jeanette, Antoine, and I knew, including the events of his last night in New Orleans.

"Then Jarvis said, 'Ah, John the stern old Baron! Do you

know, John, when I first discovered that you had two unusual characteristics? Well, it was the day when you so willingly fed and aided that old traveler at noontime, and later during that afternoon you thrashed a boy much larger than yourself for causing you to be unfairly punished. Yes, I then said to the Earl that you were John the good one hour and John the stern the next—probably inherited from your ancestors buried in this very castle.'

"'Yes, Jarvis, when I'm stepped upon, I'm not my natural self; but I'm thankful that this doesn't happen often.'

"'And what are your plans?'

"'To return to my wife and child in New Orleans.'

"'One would imagine that she had learned a lesson.'

"'I hope and pray she has, for I love her dearly; and Jarvis, when I hold her in my arms and—'

"'John, I have no record of John the affectionate.'

"'Jarvis, you've never lost your sense of humor. However, the Ocean Queen leaves in two weeks, and I should like to have all business completed by then.'

"'You intend renting the estate? You see, the Earl was offered a fancy price for it.'

"'No, I will keep it, for I've promised Jeanette to spend some time with her here, and to show her the oils, coats-of-mail—'

"'When will you return with her?'

"'As soon as she cares to come. But, Jarvis, suppose we gather the papers, my birth certificate included, for you see, I am dead in the eyes of the court and will have to prove my existance.'

"And Grace, off they went with the heavy iron box of documents dating back hundreds of years to the courtyard; and they left in the coach driving immediately across the moor to the family lawyer.'

CHAPTER XIII

In England

"It was August twenty-second; John was aboard the Ocean Queen as it slowly backed away from the quay; handkerchiefs, both on board and on land, waved furiously. Some faces were wreathed with happiness while others were sad with tears. John was happy; and as the ship left the Mersey and entered the open sea, the great wind jammer, Mistress of the Sea, silently with her massive sails slipped into the Estuary. She seemed to have cotton in her hold, so John thought she must be from New Orleans. What he did not know was that she, too, like the Ocean Queen had on board —in fact, at the rails—a passenger with her baby, who a little more than a year ago had knelt at the altar in the St. Louis Cathedral. As the ships met and drew apart, passengers on both vessels waved greetings to one another."

"Fate plays some odd pranks on us humans."

"Yes, Grace, there were two souls, each bound for a destination where each one thought with gladness he or she would meet the other."

"Petite, I just can't wait. Did they ever meet again?"

"Grace, I shall give you two minutes to decide whether I'll answer that question or—"

"I'm sorry. Continue."

"Well, I see your anxiety has reached fever height, so I'll simply give the important details. The next day, August twenty-third, Jeanette and Jarvis sat on the same iron chest.

" 'But, Jeanette, you should remain here for, when he reaches New Orleans and learns of your departure, I'm sure he will be on the return ship. Otherwise you two might again pass each other. You, see, I was his tutor; so I know his reasoning will be somewhat like mine. For instance, he knows that I'll suggest your remaining for two reasons; first, it is easier for him to travel, since he is a man, and has no child to look after; and second, he has explained to me his wish that you visit the castle, and since it is God's will that you remain apart longer, sweeter will be the days when you are together.'

" 'Jarvis, you are kind. But where shall we sleep?'

"The old man rose quickly, all agog at Jeanette's remaining, and answered, 'In this bed, the very one where John was born. And now, may I hold the baby? My, she's sweet. And Jeanette, I'll draw the curtains and light the long candle so that it will burn through the night as it did of yore, to keep away pixies and devils. Now here's the baby; she's lovely. And in the morning, mind you, I'll want her again. And tomorrow I'll show you the castle.'

"And, Grace, she prepared the baby for the night and lay down beside it on the down mattress. Then, she mused; and after darkness had enveloped the castle, the long candle with its flickering flame cast shadows on the canopy with its heavy curtains of blue taffeta of the old bed, upon the vaulted, exposed frame ceiling where beautiful carving ran across the masonry, and upon the great open fireplace that reached far out into the room.

"Long logs on andirons warmed the apartment and caused the stone work to glow for hours. All of this was interesting to Jeanette; and since she must wait for John, she philosophically decided to enjoy as best she could the secrets and beauty of the castle. Her anxiety concerning John's love for her was allayed after Jarvis had explained how determined and anxious he, John, was to return to New Orleans, and how he had said when Jarvis spoke of her having learned a lesson, 'I hope and pray she has, for I love her dearly.' And then, too, she realized John had not intended to desert her, and with a prayer that always since he had left included a plea for his safety, she closed her eyes. After the long, rough voyage she slept so soundly that she did not hear the storm, the worst in the history of Liverpool, that burst from out the sea."

CHAPTER XIV

Reunion

"For months now the English war department had been receiving secret documents from spies in America, especially those in New Orleans. There were men who could not understand why England had lost both wars with the youngest country on this planet, while they had won from old and war-trained countries the battle of Waterloo on land, and the sea fight at Trafalga, where Nelson had defeated the combined navies of France and Spain. It just did not make sense. Hence those at the head determined on a secret investigation which in the end revealed nothing that they could make public. And yet, the public was also asking why America won. Parliament knew enough to let well enough alone; yet the question could not go unanswered.

"The war lords passed days again looking through the long file when they discovered and remembered a report concerning the diverting of the Southern Cross. Yes, they would use that incident."

"Concerning Antoine?"

"Yes, but wait for—"

"At least I know that Antoine fared well, for he is here with us. But what did happen?"

"Well, we shall have to return to Jeanette, for it was during her stay that this plot was hatched. The next morning, that is, the morning after her arrival, she awoke thoroughly rested. The storm had gone inland, and the sun shone as it had set—first, as it emerged from the horizon, a ball of red which changed swiftly to orange and then to yellow and finally white. At eight o'clock Jarvis knocked on the door.

" 'Come in.'

" 'Good morning, Jeanette. Did you sleep well last night?'

" 'Soundly, Jarvis, for I was very tired.'

" 'I see, I see,' he said as he rubbed his chin and continued, 'Are you ready for breakfast?'

" 'I'm simply starving.'

" 'Then come into the dining room for the cook has prepared an English breakfast.'

"You've noticed, Grace, there was no mention of the storm, and one could not feel it in the strongly built castle for the reason that the good man did not want her to worry over the fate of the Ocean Queen as he had done all night.

"After breakfast, Jarvis took the baby in his old, practiced arms, for he had held many small ones in the surrounding country, and led Jeanette around the castle, explaining that it was built in the thirteenth century—to be exact, it had been finished in 1220. From morning until nightfall he led her over acres of stone buildings, all connected through various passages and staircases, some so narrow as not to permit invaders except in single file while the axman above could cut each down as he appeared. Then they went down another staircase to where they reached the outbuildings within this city of twelve-foot stone walls where families, hogs, chickens, cows, horses and dogs lived happily together. Crossing the courtyard, they again mounted narrow stairs that led to a bridge that connected the massive round donjon. Here he explained that it was customary to destroy the bridge when an enemy was successful in entering the castle. Once in the donjon the family and retainers could remain for six months, for during war it was stored with rations of all kinds. Then he showed her the various suits of armor, all in perfect condition, together with the family portraits. As I've said before, she spent the entire day inside, and only at nightfall did she re-enter her bedroom with its rare old tapestries that hid the ugly stone walls. She was fatigued. Up and down stone steps, on her feet constantly except for feeding time, in and out buildings—all caused her again to sleep soundly as she had the night before.

"And Jarvis, back in his room, fell into a chair and permitted the mask that he had worn all day to fall. His old wrinkled face now plainly revealed torture, for he had not spent seventy years in this neighborhood without learning that no ship, not even a sturdy one like the Ocean Queen, could withstand such a storm without being blown on the rocks. And Jarvis was right; for the storm first blew the smokestack into the sea, and then the great waves washed over the ship travelling down the smoke-filled opening to the firebox; and of course, without steam and unable to use sails, the captain could not prevent the ship and its occupants being dashed against the rocks where the mountainous waves with unleashed fury lashed the good vessel to pieces."

"My God! Did John drown?"

"No, Grace, for at three fifteen the next morning an improvised ambulance crossed the old moat and reaching the gate stopped while one of the attendants reached for the hammer and struck the heavy bronze bell that had been used in feudal days for an alarm. He had no occasion to strike the second time, for Jarvis, worn and worried, was just inside the second wall resting in an old chair. His expectations had become a reality.

"At the sound of the bell the old man jumped up from the chair and ran as fast as his old legs could carry him. On reaching the cart his first question was, 'Is he alive?'

" 'Yes, but badly bruised. Where shall we place him?'

"And, he led the way to his own room where he could care for him. And care he did, for he covered John's battered and exposed form until he was wet from perspiration and then removed the underclothes."

"Petite, it is surprising that he was not dead when they found him."

"It is. The authorities immediately sent all those who were not seriously injured to their own or other private homes which the people generously opened, using the hospitals for the more unfortunate. However, Jarvis replaced the wet underclothes with a dry nightshirt; and with a last feel of John's pulse, he lay down beside him. It was only at dawn that the worn-out old man closed his eyes and slept.

"It was nine-thirty. Jeanette and the baby were ready; they had waited for Jarvis since eight o'clock. 'He overslept,' thought Jeanette. She was right for, after the work of the day before, his almost continual explanation, and his remaining awake practically all night, the old man at five o'clock in the morning had closed his eyes and slept soundly until nine o'clock. On wakening, his first thought was of John. There he lay as he had done when Jarvis had gone to sleep—

the same rhythmic breathing with an occasional long deep breath that is common to those overfatigued, who, after long breaths, refrain from breathing for almost fifteen seconds.

"Now the thought of his telling Jeanette for, although it would be a pleasure to her to know that John was so near, would also be a shock, a shock that might cause a reaction, cause her to become uncontrollable for, after all he reasoned, she was John's wife, and naturally her orders would supersede his. So into the bedchamber he walked, since the door was open; and after exchanging morning greetings, he said, 'Jeanette, I've something pleasant to tell you, and I would like you to sit on the chest with me.'

" 'I'll be glad to; and, Jarvis, I'm delighted to hear it's of a pleasant nature, because this morning I feel blue.'

" 'And why?'

" 'Because I miss John more and more each day.'

" 'Well, it is about him that I must talk to you.'

" 'Jarvis, you said something pleasant?'

" 'Yes, now remove that fear from your eyes. Well, first let me tell you that John is safe and sound.'

" 'Why do you say that?'

" 'Because I want to impress on your mind that he is as much alive as you and I, and—'

" 'But why—?'

" 'Listen, you understand what I've said?'

" 'Yes.'

" 'And he is in this castle.'

" 'Here—here—but where, Oh where? Jarvis, where is he.'

" 'When you compose yourself I'll tell you and not before.'

" 'Now, I'm quiet; that is, I—I think I am.'

" 'That's better. Now, night before last, while you so soundly slept, a severe storm wrecked the Ocean Queen.'

" 'He is safe, Jarvis?'

" 'Upon my word. But his head is bandaged, and—'

" 'Oh, I knew it; I knew it!'

" 'Jeanette, the fact that he is here and not at a hospital should be significant to you.'

" 'Yes, I suppose it is; but please let me see him.'

" 'Only when you promise to obey my orders.'

" 'I promise.'

" 'You see, the reason I am so specific is that anyone suffering from shock should have at least a twelve hours' sleep. He arrived at three and now it is only nine-thirty. Another reason for my being specific is that your love for him may cause you to act dramatically, and a second shock may prove disastrous.'

" 'I understand. Where is he?'

" 'In my room.'

"Picking up the baby, Jarvis led the way with Jeanette at his heels. Noiselessly he opened the door and permitted Jeanette to enter. She tip-toed straight to the bed.

"There John lay on his back with his hands clasped as he was in the habit of sleeping on Royal Street. How peaceful and calm he was compared to the time she had last seen him.

"Then she realized that she was the cause of it all. In fact he might have drowned. Her heart began to swell and the pain reached such proportion as to cause her to sob. Quickly, Jarvis tapped her on the shoulder and motioned for her to leave. Instead, she placed her handkerchief over her mouth as the tears continued to flow.

"She dropped to her knees and with bowed head prayed. Jarvis watching her sympathetically stooped and petted her. Rising, she wiped her eyes and again tenderly stared at John. Since it was August, and the room was warm, Jarvis had removed the cover from his chest so as to keep him comfortable. Jeanette silently watched his breathing and counted the rise and fall of his chest with her heart beats, beats that she felt all over her body—one, two, three, breathe; one, two, three, breathe. Then came a long deep breath during which Jeanette counted eight, and his breathing stopped; she continued until she had counted to fourteen. In that one thousandth of a second in which the human mind so quickly acts, Jeanette was convinced he had died. With every muscle in her face tense with emotion, and with a shriek she threw herself on his chest and dramatically, as Jarvis feared, cried, 'Darling, darling come back—please don't go.'

"Jarvis reached for her, but just then John's eyes partly opened and closed again. Hardly had they closed then they quickly re-opened wide. 'Jeanette,' he cried, 'But, no, you are not Jeanette; she is in—where is Jarvis?'

" 'Here I am, John.'

" 'Oh! the baby, my baby!'

"Grace, Jeanette had recovered; and the muscles in her face had relaxed when John again looked at her and then realized that there, leaning over him was Jeanette—his Jeanette. With a cry of joy he threw both arms about her, holding her tightly."

"And, Petite, were they inseparable all that day?"

"Well, what would you have done with your extreme affection if that had been Emile and you?"

"Well, I would have taken Jarvis by the arm to the door and kissed him on his withered cheek; and with a smile and a wink I would have said, 'Jarvis, get the hell out of here!' "

CHAPTER XV

A Friend Befriended

"Petite, did they return to New Orleans?"

"But, Grace, darling, that is another story."

"Please, Petite."

"My, I'll wager that when you act in this way Emile just adores you."

"He grabs and hugs me and sometimes says, 'Precious jewel'."

"I can understand that. However, it being only three o'clock, I'll continue; but I'll condense my story."

"Not too much."

"Well, let me read Jeanette's letter of August twenty-fourth; I left it in the diary—ah, here it is. It starts,

" 'Darling Sister:

" 'One week of heavenly bliss! When I think back, I realize what a fool I was to jeopardize my wonderful happiness. John and I are inseparable and I have met many of his friends —wonderful, fine people. As for the peasant women, who are almost childless, as many of their husbands died in the Napoleonic wars, why, they are simply sweet. And, Petite, I too am almost childless, for Jarvis after the baby's morning bath takes her, and with diapers hanging out of his pockets is off to the peasant women who simply adore her. Sometimes at noon I see her again, but only sometimes.

" 'Incidentally, we are to be presented to the Prince of Wales next week. Rumor says the King is insane. John is somewhat elated; but, as for me, I feel no elation whatsoever in anticipation of the event. I'm beginning to tire of our castle and the acreage it covers.

" 'You'll notice that I wrote ours. John insists that I use this word, but I can't conceive being part owner of all of this; it is so colossal. Why, today it would cost millions of dollars to build the castle alone, not including its original antique furniture, suits of priceless armor, lances and shields —all of which should be in a museum.

" 'The original Saracen carpets on the floors, although priceless, cannot possibly replace in my heart our hooked rugs. And then, too, I would willingly trade the stone floors for our cypress one.

" 'I do so want to talk to John about our returning; and yet, I don't seem to have the courage. I have decided, however, to remain obedient, for I can live, uncomfortable though it be, with anything as long as I have him.

" 'Write me soon and give our love to all.

Your sister,
Jeanette.' "

"And, Petite, was she received by royalty?"

"Yes, Grace, and very much disappointed she was for over a month later I received another letter, or rather I called it a book. It is in a large red envelope, and may be where you found the diary. There, that's it on the second shelf. Now open it and read."

"My, it's long!"

"Dear Sister and Brother:

"There is a saying over here to the effect that one inherits one's relatives, but let us be thankful that one can choose one's friends. Well, folks, since you two are the relatives that inherited me, you've been choosen to be listeners or rather readers of my past months' experiences; I just have to tell them to someone.

"The day had come for the Prince's party. I would have given anything to avoid going. The day before John and I, incognito, had visited many poor people in the surrounding country; the fishermen who were repairing their decayed nets, were too poor to buy material to make new ones; farmers, thin and worn-looking, with just enough clothes to prevent blistering from the hot sun; coal miners and their families, so terribly in need as to make one shudder. However, with these wretched people in mind, John and I walked up solid marble steps past men in colorful livery and into a large hall where we were announced. After much ado about nothing we were presented to the Prince; and in turn we met other dignitaries, among whom was a Baroness, Louise, by name. She was a French noblewoman who had married into the English nobility.

"Baroness Louise, out of respect to my being of French lineage, warned me about the Prince, saying that he is a reprobate. And Petite and Antoine, she looks as if she has known many. However, the music started and I was surprised to find myself in the Prince's arms whirling over the marble floor. He had not asked for the dance, and I felt that he wanted me to know that he took what he wanted. He did not know our kind for, when he had waltzed me behind a huge, hand-cut marble vase on a pedestal of the same material, he freed me and, taking both my cheeks between his thumbs and over-jeweled first fingers, said he liked me. That was all, for I let fly my hand, as Phoebe would say; and it landed directly on the side of his face with such force that his monacle flew across the floor, while he, remembering the vase behind him, twisted his body so as not to strike it.

"Without saying a word, he quickly departed.

"It seemed as if no one had seen the episode; and walking from behind the vase, I nonchalantly again mingled with the crowd. After I had had a few dances, during which I was terribly bored, dinner was announced. Instead of a gentle-man (except for John, I don't believe there was one there) taking my arm, Baroness Louise accompanied me and said that she had been told I was to sit on the Prince's right.

"I asked was she certain, and she replied definitely so. Then I offered to trade seats with her; but she refused as she feared the Prince might be angry.

"I started to say what I thought of the Prince, but instead, reminded her that it would be an honor for her to sit at his right, for I had correctly guessed that she had been more than friendly with him. However, it ended by my sitting at the end of the table, and Louise, with her subtle wiles, at the Prince's right. So angry was he that I could hear him drink the soup from where I sat. I wanted to laugh, but controlled myself.

"I wasn't hungry, for my thoughts were far away. Then suddenly I began to realize that the food that was being served and wasted was the finest in the land. So I began comparing it with what John and I had seen in the hovels the previous day, and a terrible resentment came over me. Too, here were young men, in rich attire; two at the entrance with their heads high into the air, and their noses still higher; and dozens treading back and forth, some with food, others removing untouched plates. I thought how they could help the farmers, starved and emaciated, behind the plow.

"It was, folks, highly obnoxious. That crowd had no more desire to eat than I had to remain. As I afterwards was informed, their desire, male and female, was to drink, and in couples, to disappear.

"As all good things must come to an end, so must obnoxious ones. John and I were glad two days later to reach our home. We had met her ladyship this and his lordship that with his foolish monocle,—as if one needs to see better out of one eye than the other. As I descended from the carriage, I ran to my baby; and the peasant woman said she had been a wonderful child, not crying once.

" 'Listen,' I shouted, 'if any of you people address me again as My Lady, I will have you beheaded and burned in in oil. My name is Jeanette.'

"An old woman, wrinkled with age and a dearth of knowledge, said, 'Jeanette it shall be, for you are not the kind that oppresses and starves.'

"That night in our own bed John and I sat with pillows to our back; and after meditating for a few minutes, John said, 'Jeanette, do you know why we were invited to that party?'

" 'I should guess to make us uncomfortable.'

" 'No, it was for the purpose of my vote in Parliament, and those that I might control; that is, if they vote for some measure that I advocate, then I'm to vote for a measure that they desire, regardless of its merit.'

" 'They definitely don't know you, darling,' I replied, now

appreciating a real man after seeing so many nincompoops.

" 'They definitely don't know me, Jeanette, my sweet,' he repeated, 'I'll vote for anything that favors those poor devils you and I saw a few days ago; and I will vote against anything that will do them no good.'

" 'Good John,' I answered, Petite and Antoine, as I slid over to him and placed my head on his chest as his arm drew me tighter.

"I've been a widow for three weeks. John is poring over atlases and books. It is India, Australia, Canada; then finances—and oh, what not! I'm sick of it all. And one morning, the day before Parliament met, I asked him for an hour's conversation. I was never so homesick in my life, longing more and more for my quiet home and family in New Orleans.

" 'I know how you feel, Jeanette; but instead of an hour, let's hire a carriage, one in which we shall not be recognized, and just you, the baby and I leave for the high lands and have one of our old-fashioned picnics.' Folks, was I elated; to me, a picnic was one step nearer New Orleans. So we three found ourselves in a beautiful meadow under a large tree. We had finished our lunch; and, while the baby slept, John and I lay on our backs with our heads resting on our hands.

" 'John, this picnic reminds me of our courting days when, without a care in the world, we were so happy.'

"For answer, I heard a deep sigh; and then I noticed that he was moving. Rolling over and resting on both his arms, he looked directly into my eyes, and said, 'Jeanette, I know you are unhappy here and so am I. If, on the morrow, I find that I am unable to help the poor people of this country, we shall leave and move elsewhere.'

" 'To New Orleans?' I asked jubilantly.

" 'I'm afraid not, Jeanette; maybe France.'

" 'But, John, I swear, never to—'

" 'Honey, I would be afraid, terribly afraid.'

" 'John, please.'

" 'No, I—'

" 'John,' I shrieked, 'don't say no, rather say you you will see.'

" 'I will see, Jeanette.'

"And folks, I felt more contented as our carriage rolled over the drawbridge.

"We're in Parliament; John is upstairs while I'm in the first row in the gallery, a courtesy shown a lawmaker's wife. They are debating something that I, and I believe three-quarters of the members, don't understand. I know that John doesn't, for his gaze never rests longer than one minute at any one place; his mind seemingly is elsewhere.

"Now, folks, especially, you Petite, comes the best news in this letter. I would have stated it first, but felt that keeping events in order would be more interesting. Very often you told me you wished that the United States would close Antoine's case pertaining to his diverting the Southern Cross, as you feared English pressure. Well, dear brother and especially you, sister, you need not worry about such pressure for, when after hours of oratory, both John and I heard the name 'Antoine Floret,' I quickly looked down and saw that he had almost turned completely around. While his hand gripped the chair, his eyes were glued on the speaker, who said, 'And gentlemen, the war department has instructed me to demand that France force the United States of America to release that traitor to his country; and further demands that France deal with him as a pirate; for we have definite proof that this Frenchman diverted the Southern Cross to the United States with materials of war, such as flints, powder, etc., and further, we have definite proof, that without this flint, powder, etc., the United States of America would have lost New Orleans; and today, we would have control of that vast rich territory, the Mississippi valley. Now gentlemen, your pleasure!'

"Folks, I was angry. My United States of America to be forced by another nation to do Britain's bidding,—they whom we twice thrashed. My blood boiled, and I rose to tell them in no uncertain words that they were the traitors when, glancing down, I saw John rise and noticed that his knees were shaking. As he looked around, I noticed, as did he, that all eyes were on him. A gentleman at my side whispered to his friend, 'Look, the young Earl is rising. This should be good, for never before has a Junior member spoken on his first day, during his first week, or even in his first month.'

"I knew John's thoughts and was sure that he cared for nothing so much as to regain his seat, and to slink into it; but, folks, a Lord had mentioned the name of his friend, one he had slept with on his wedding eve, one who had lived in the same house with him, his wife, and his baby. That friend would be sacrificed to save the honor of the undeserving, blundering English war board. Yes, he would have his say, just as Antoine would have had his under reverse conditions. And folks, I was trembling with rage when I heard from below, 'My Lord,' and then he hesitated for a moment in that dreadful silence, and continued 'And gentlemen, I beg of you to bear with me if I'm not in order, but—'

" 'You're in order, Earl of Lancaster, continue.'

"I looked around to see if there was some way I could get to him, but quickly realized that the chamber below me was well guarded. Peering down, I seemed to think that John did not seem so hesitant when he continued, 'Gentlemen, I know the history of the Battle of New Orleans and—'

" 'Better than the War Board?' queried a Lord.

" 'I shouldered and fired a musket and was wounded in that battle.'

" 'Others have fought in that battle; and, yet, they don't claim knowledge of its history,—others, of whom we have proof of their fighting.'

"I could see John had turned red at this insinuation, and I further noticed that other members seemed to disapprove of the speaker's tactics in taking advantage of John's youth. However, I could see a change in John; and I remembered that night he whipped me. His head seemed to sink into his shoulders, as it did then, and his eyes wore a different expression when, loud and clear, he asked, 'My Lord, are you, by some chance, biased?'

"I could see members smile; and as the speaker groped for words, a few of these men applauded. However, not waiting for an answer, John, now John the stern, continued, 'Gentlemen, I bear in the left side of my body a lead fired from the musket of Antoine Floret; and he carries in his body a lead that had left my musket. We both fired and fell at the same instant, and were both taken to the only hospital and placed opposite to each other; and we both received the same kind treatment from the loving hands of those descendants of the French.'

" 'At this time, you speak of the loving hands of the French when so many English lie buried in the sod caused by Napoleon's French soldiers!'

"Ignoring the speaker entirely, he continued, 'Gentlemen, I am speaking of the Creoles of New Orleans.' Again, a hum of voices was heard and John continued, speaking very slowly and distinctly, 'I am an Englishman—a nationality that is regarded the world over as just, honorable, and charitable. Now, I'll ask all of you to picture yourselves in a distant land attacked by a foreign power. Further, I'll ask you to picture an Englishman, with a shipload of ammunition to be delivered to an enemy with which he would kill you. Tell me, what would you think of that countryman if, knowingly, he delivered that shipment, indirect though it might be, to your enemy when you were in need of what he had, to defend yourself? An Englishman, gentlemen, could not possibly act that way—nor could a Frenchman.'

"Folks, I forgot myself completely; and like Phoebe when the cocks are fighting, talking to her pet, I cupped my hands and, amid applause, yelled to John, 'Give him hell, John; give him hell.'

"As my voice was the only one from the gallery, it could be heard distinctly by everyone below; and after John had looked at me and smiled, I saw the members of the body all gaze at me.

"And then I heard John say, 'Gentlemen, that was my Creole wife; may I apologize for her?' And they chorused, 'No apology necessary.' Then John continued, 'Now, this gen-

tleman, Antoine Floret, and I do mean gentleman, did exactly what you, and you, and you, and I would have done. Let
us not for some unscrupulous purpose so foreign to Englishmen, sacrifice a brave, fine, God-fearing man, regardless of
his nationality. I say sacrifice with a reservation, for the
United States will not comply with the demands of any nation as we have so disastrously found. Now, if we have the
privilege to love our countrymen; then, before God, I contend that he also has the privilege to love his countrymen.'

"Folks, the house applauded again, but this time I kept
my neck in, as John continued, 'Now, Gentlemen, I'll tell
you why we lost that battle.' And folks, he looked directly
at the speaker as he continued, 'We lost because our soldiers
fought as they did at Waterloo—a system that will fail with
the Americans, if, instead of four soldiers on our side to one
on theirs, and that was a fact I don't believe you know, we
had fourteen or twenty-four soldiers to one American. It is
not a disgrace to lose, but it will be an ignominious act on
the part of this Parliament to blame that defeat on one man
—and more so since he is not our countryman. Further, Gentlemen, let us not antagonize the United States of America,
the only other English-speaking nation on this planet—a nation with predominant English blood, which in 1776 was so
shamefully spilled. You know, I know, and the world knows
that when we signed the treaty of peace after that war, we
did it as an act of convenience, for England had intended
at its first opportunity to reopen the war, under guise, as it
did, and failed to suppress those people. We—have—done
—enough harm! I'll not ask for atonement; I do not ask
for an admission of guilt; but I do ask you, Gentlemen, to
treat that child of this nation, for they call England the
mother country, as a mother would treat her child, with
tenderness and justice and equality.

" 'Now, since on one occasion we failed to keep it, and
on another occasion we failed to retake it as a colonial possession, then let us have it as a friend. Let me add further,'
he continued, raising his hand to check the applause, 'in a
hundred years or so, that nation will have a navy second to
none, as Napoleon predicted, and as a friend, will help the

mother country, maybe, when that mother country, your England and my England, may be on her knees. I thank you.'

"Exhausted, folks, he sank into his seat; but only for a moment, for amid deafening applause, other members of Parliament sought to shake his hand—the hand that pulled the trigger to an undying friendship for you, Antoine.

"Petite and Antoine, let me add but one thing more, and then you can rest your tired eyes. John is interested in steamships, having made this his hobby. I may have a surprise for you soon; no, not our return to New Orleans, for his honesty of purpose, his foresight as some of the papers printed it, has made him an important man to England; and my hope of return seems doomed.

"With love to all and hoping to hear that all are well, I am
Your loving sister,
Jeanette.

"P. S. We've visited France, and John has contacted the relatives of a personal friend of his. Their hospitality reminded me so of my Creole city that I was again homesick. Returning over the Channel, John, too, was meditative."

CHAPTER XVI

Get The Hell Out Of Here

"My, Grace, that sigh came a long distance."

"Yes it did, for your mentioning England and France has re-kindled an ember that has lain dormant a long, long time. You see, Petite, the desire to travel reaches back to my school days. Later, when I left Boston, I had intended travelling first all over the United States of America and then Europe. When I reached New Orleans, I met Emile, and here I am."

"Are you sorry?"

"No, for I would give up everything for him."

"That was what I thought. But tell me, have you spoken to him about traveling?"

"On many occasions. In fact, every two or three months he has said, 'Grace, or darling,' according to whether he was in a business-like or loving mood, 'I'll never forget my promise of that trip abroad when, for me, you curtailed your tour;' or 'Grace, won't it be wonderful when some day you and I will board a ship for Europe?' "

"And you would give up everything, except Emile?"

"Yes, as much as I love my home, I would give it up too for that trip."

"Well, should Emile decide suddenly, why, my trunk is filled with clothes; and since we are the same size, you will have but to take the trunk."

"Where is it?"

"I haven't moved it yet; it is still on the boat. However, let me continue the story.

"It was the season of laziness, as Antoine called it. The cane was cut and delivered to the refinery. That year, as there was no ditching to be done, the slaves, except for caring for the winter crop of cabbage, lettuce, and a few other vegetables for home consumption, had nothing to do but sing and play. Every afternoon for over a week Antoine took me by the hand, and we ran under the oaks to the river and to our outhouse. On this particular afternoon, he lay on his

back and placed his head in my lap, placing my right hand
between his; while I stroked his black hair with my free
hand, he promptly proceeded to sleep. He had hardly closed
his eyes when from down the river I heard a loud, low whistle, one I had never heard before. His eyes opened and he
looked at me; we both listened. After about ten minutes
he again closed his eyes when again over land and water
came the same whistle, this time clearer and louder. Antoine
rose, and we both walked to the edge of the wooden walk
that he had built for those of our guests who cared to swim.
Reaching the end we sat on the floor of the walk, our legs
dangling beneath us. In the distance we could see clouds of
black smoke billowing up—up—up into the sky. Presently,
about a mile farther down and around a turn we noticed
first the bow of a pure white vessel, and then the smokestack amidship. We both stared in wonder; and as it neared,
we noticed it was void of sails, and that it must have been
all of a city square in length. As it came nearer we noticed
that on the black funnel was the silhouette of a face; and
the more I looked at it, the more it seemed familiar. Without moving my eyes, I asked, 'Antoine, doesn't that face seem
familiar?'

"'I was thinking the same thing, and look, Petite, the
name of the boat, 'Jeanette.' A thrill ran up and down my
spine as I again looked at the silhouette; and whether it was
my imagination or not, I saw it was a picture of Jeanette.

"The ship had passed and the waves it left in its wake
were moving nearer and nearer. To us there was something
about those waves that affected me; and as I stared at the
first one coming nearer and nearer, I absently asked Antoine if I were losing my mind."

"'No,' he replied, 'for I believe you are watching that approaching wave with the same awe that has overcome me.'

"We continued to watch. Now it was fifty feet away, then
forty, thirty—nearer and nearer it came until, as with a
pleasant surge, it reached up to our feet. Others followed,
and a desire to visit the ship seemed to dawn on us both, for
we both suggested at the very same moment a visit to the
city. Holding hands, we raced back to the house and the
stable, and Antoine ordered the horses hitched. In less than

ten minutes we were off. It seemed on this trip that Antoine urged the horses for more speed, more than usual. Upon reaching Toulouse Street we turned left towards the river. There, in all her glory, and surrounded by Indians, white, colored, and black people, floated gracefully the Jeanette.

"Antoine reigned the horses; and after helping me out, he fastened the heavy weight to the horses' bit.

"We both again noticed the silhouette, and it seemed to urge us on. We climbed the gangplank that had just been lowered, without an invitation. On board Antoine quickly asked for the Captain, and he was directed to a clean shaven man on the bridge.

"Up the ladder we climbed; and when we reached the bridge, the Captain turned to face us. Both men stood still eyeing each other, while I, puzzled, looked from one to the other. Finally, I heard the Captain say, 'Antoine!' and Antoine cried, 'Pierre!'

"Those two men threw their arms around each other while I looked on, smiling at Antoine's happiness. I could see the resemblance between the two men so that I was not surprised when Antoine, placing his arm around me said, 'Brother, this is my wife, Petite.'

"Pierre took me from Antoine, held me by both hands and, looking directly into my eyes, said, 'So you are the girl that followed Antoine through the swamps and to the battle grounds?'

" 'Yes, I'm the culprit; and Pierre, this is indeed a pleasant surprise. My, I'm glad to know you.'

" 'A mighty pretty culprit, Petite. Jeanette and John should have told me how cute you are. And oh, here is a letter from them; I took it from the safe this morning coming up that beautiful river of yours so as not to forget it. Now, let's go into the cabin.'

"So, Grace, into the cabin he went; and while Pierre was showing John the various instruments, I read the letter. Here it is. Read it."

"Dear John and Petite:

"Did you ever receive such a surprise in your life? Imagine how I felt when before it was launched I walked from under the ship and I looked up at the heighth, and saw the silhouette. It was familiar, but the truth is I didn't recognize it; and only later, when I saw the name Jeanette did the thought come to me that the silhouette was a picture of me. Again imagine my excitement when I was told that I was to christen the ship; and the added excitement when I struck it with the champagne bottle. And, Petite, how do you like Pierre? He and his family were the ones I spoke of searching for in France in the last letter. And you, Antoine, are you glad to see your brother? I'll wager you are.

"Here in England, we have free speech—provided one does not mention the state or the crown; that crown should be melted into wedding rings for the poor who can't afford them.

"Incidentally, and I do mean incidentally, John is very much in disfavor with the Prince (King) since he has caused to be enacted a law that abolishes all taxes on boats or property belonging to those worth less than six hundred pounds and raised the taxes on larger boats and buildings. Those who surround the King are up in arms, claiming that it was done in an underhand way. And, folks, I must admit that John 'pulled a fast one,' as Phoebe would say, by inviting the members to a Louisiana hayride. This being new to them they turned out en masse. As you know, they were to bring their lunches; and in four hay-filled wagons, with their wives and children, these men were driven, happy and contented, to open ground in one of the most destitue neighborhoods. It made me sorrowful and sad to see the poor children, half-naked, begging for something to eat. Now, folks, these Parliamentarians are smart men; and since they realized to what extent John had gone to make them see for themselves the poverty of these people, one recommended and the others agreed to visit as many poor localities as the time would permit. John was acclaimed everywhere; and when these men saw the true condition, they shook their heads. However, it all ended with the law being passed; and further, the farmers will get a better price for their vegetables, the fishermen for their catch, and the miners an increase in wages.

"Of course, this led to John's being loved by the poor and despised by the rich, the royalty, and the Prince. Intrigue here is so rife that one feels it in the air; and now that John has done his bit, as he said, we may have to move to France to live a peaceful life. My, how I would love to say New Orleans! But I'm doing as father has taught us, that is, taking things philosophically.

"Now, let me make a suggestion and an earnest plea. Please brother and sister, board the Jeanette and come to England. You can place your plantation in the care of some one capable (maybe Emile would help) and visit me. How I do miss all of you! Should we leave for France, it will have to be after the arrival of the Jeanette.

Your loving sister,

Jeanette.

"P. S. John knows that I'm writing you; and although he does not know it, I am looking at him and can see, as it happens everytime I write you, that he is in a pensive mood; and I'm sure that he, too, is homesick for you all and our home; our brick building with its patio, its hand-painted iron lace-work, our only true home."

"Petite, I can imagine her, away from all of this beauty, surrounded by crude stone with its crushing feeling. My, I wouldn't want it. But tell me, what happened next?"

"Well, we were so happy to have Pierre that we went to our Royal Street home, the same that Jeanette speaks of, for remember that we both occupid one half; and after sending for Father, Mother, my old maid sister, Marie, though she's only twenty-six years old, and my married sister and her husband, you know the one in whose home Maurice and I cut the brush on their wedding night, Antoine opened some rare old liquor. It was three o'clock in the morning before all of us realized that we had drunk a bit too much; so we decided to retire."

"And you like Pierre?"

"He is just like Antoine; and Grace, the next day he and Marie were inseparable."

"Another romance?"

"Yes, you romance fiend, but it was short; but wait, I'm ahead of my story. You see, while Marie was with Pierre, Antoine and I came to this building. The maid answered the bell; and knowing how friendly we were with Emile, she showed us into this very room. Everywhere were papers—

on the bed, on the dresser, on this very chaise lounge; and his secretary was also covered with them. In his hand was a wooden pad, and under its snap were more papers arranged in book form. On it he was writing, when Antoine asked, 'Writing, Emile?'

" 'Yes, folks. Have a seat. Now, what brings the hero of the Battle of New Orleans and the conqueror of the swamps here?'

" 'You do, Emile, but tell me the name of the book you're writing?'

" 'As You Desire Me.' "

"Petite, may I interrupt?"

"Surely, Grace."

"Did Emile ever finish his romance, 'As You Desire Me'?"

"No, you see, when he received the coin with two heads he wrote that he would reclaim, not two hundred acres, but all of the land reaching to the lake except a ridge where he would build a levee. He further stated that he would drain this land with the slaves during the winter when they were idle, and that he had experimented with an automatic water pump that used an air-tight ball to pump the water over the levee and into the lake. Since then, we've received word that it was a complete success.

"However, what I'm leading to is that with all of this work at hand he wrote that he would discontinue writing; and, Grace, in the drawers of the secretary I'm sure you will find that romance, incomplete, but well started."

"As You Desire Me! My, the name alone seems to promise that it is a beautiful romance. And, knowing Emile as I do, I can look forward to an interesting evening—an evening when I'll find him at his best, full of sentiment and affection."

"Why, Grace, those words are exactly the same I told him."

"You did?"

"Yes, for after he had told me the name of the story, I said, 'Emile, with your system so full of romance, affection, and sentiment and with this beautiful home, you could make a girl very happy. I know a few that would say Yes.'

" 'I do too. But, as you know, everyone more or less in the Vieux Carre confides in me; so that I have seen some unhappiness—little of course among our friends. But, unless I find the right one, I will die a bachelor.' That, Grace, is a compliment for you."

"Yes, Petite, I know. He has told me over and over, that I was the only girl that would make him say, 'I do'—the dear."

"However, we finally told him of our intended trip, and that we would desire him, not only to supervise the plantation, but to become a partner at its original purchase price."

" 'But,' he said, 'you've reclaimed over two hundred acres, and that would not be fair. I'll be glad to supervise it, however.'

"Well, Antoine explained that our ground was bound by the lake, and that he, Emile, could, with the slaves reclaim another two hundred acres, and between him and Antoine, they would own the largest plantation in the South.

"Emile claimed that this wouldn't be fair to Antoine and me, and Antoine contended that it was; so I suggested the toss of a coin. Either Emile would be a partner or a supervisor. I tossed the coin, called for heads and Emile became part-owner. However, the coin that I had taken from Phoebe had two heads. Antoine knew it, but Emile didn't."

"I've seen a coin like that in his strong box."

"It's the same one; for when we reached England, we mailed it to him. However, ten days later we ascended the gangplank and sailed with the bride and groom, Marie and Pierre, to England."

"My, it must be wonderful to travel! Tell me all that you saw."

"I'd rather not, for I would ruin your trip, er—I mean—er when you travel. But we spent two years abroad, and now we are glad to be back home."

"The home that Jeanette loved, Petite?"

"Yes—but why the sigh?"

"I was thinking of Jeanette. But there's the bell; the maid will answer it."

"Aunty, Oh! Aunty, where are you?"

"In here, Baby."

"Oh! Aunty, I've missed you."

"I know—but where were you all day?"

"Well, Mommy, Daddy, and I were in the house Mommy used to speak of so often—the one on Royal Street, but I was outside with the slaves. And you know, Aunty, before I left the room I saw Daddy and Mommy in the center, and Daddy was holding Mommy, and Mommy was holding Daddy; and Mammy's head was back, like this; and oh! I've seen a picture like that somewhere."

"And what else, Baby?"

"And Daddy looked straight into Mommy's eyes, and Mommy said something about 'and obey,' and Daddy's head dropped like this; and he kissed Mommy long, long, long; and he said just one word, Aunty, and Mommy cried. I don't understand it."

"You're a cute little sweetheart, Baby; but tell Aunty, what was the word?"

"Home."

"Petite, if you tell me that sweet child with its English accent is Jeanette's and that Jeanette and John are here, why, Petite, I'll—Oh, there's the bell again."

"Grace, this is Baby—Jeanette's baby. Wait, for here comes—Come in here, John, and you too, Jeanette. And now Brother and Sister, I want you to meet Emile's sweet and adorable wife, Grace, John and Jeanette."

"Grace rushed over to them, saying, "I don't know which of you to love first."

"Grace, with those tears in your eyes—we know we shall love you, and on your return—.""

"But where is Emile?"

Just then, Antoine rushed in with "All set."

"But, Antoine, where is Emile?"

"On the Jeanette, and he sails with her in an hour."

"Without me? Oh! There's something wro—. Say, he can't do this to me; oh! that man!—But all of you are smiling, and, you Petite, you're laughing."

"Wait—Grace—please until—I compose myself."

"But, but—."

"Yes, but—why, Grace, I believe you would die without Emile; and you remember your answer when I asked, what would you do if you and Emile were in Jeanette and John's place when her screams awakened him?"

"Yes I do, but what has that got to—."

"Sister, kiss me! and then you had better get the hell out of here if you care to see Europe."

FINIS

MINE

PART ONE

"THE EPIDEMIC"

CHAPTER I

The Request

"Emile! Emile, wake up!"

"Huh?"

"Emile, it is six o'clock, and you will be late at the plantation."

"Oh, this bed is so comfortable and so warm!"

"Move your arm so that I can lay my head on your chest. And Emile, it is raining terribly hard and—"

"That is February weather; and, Grace, I don't think I shall go to the plantation today."

"I wouldn't, for the thermometer through the window is registering thirty-two degrees—regular pneumonia weather. —And Emile—"

"No, Grace, no romance today. Ring for Virgie. The fire needs more coal. Incidentally, Sweet, she has been your slave maid for some time."

"Yes, quite a while. Why, darling, she always held the candle at different needful angles when I dressed and made myself pretty for you during our courting days. And I love you as much today, as I did then, you brute—ouch!"

"Take back that word brute."

"I take it back, darling; but please, let me send for Petite. We three can make ourselves comfortable, that is, spend a happy day together, and—"

"Yes; so I can tell you two another capital romance of the French Quarter. No soap, little sweet, as Virgil would say. But you know, I've avoided the tragedies. Some day I shall relate one of them, beginning as though it will end as a sweet romance, but in the end it will be a tragedy."

"I'll appreciate anything; this is an ideal day for a thing of that kind; what, with the rolling thunder, the flashing lightning, and the heavy rain and hail striking the glasses in the fan-shaped window as if in an effort to force its way through—why, it would almost seem as if witches were abroad."

"Huh!"

"Emile, you big brute. You're not sleeping."

"Who's a big brute?"

"Please, may I send for—"

"So I'm a brute, eh? Well, I am now going to tame you—you can wiggle and fight—and turn and twist—Now I've got you where I want you. Now tell me, am I a big brute?"

"Please, darling, the story."

"Oh, hell! I can't strike where there is no resistance—and after mussing the bed so."

"Emile, you're exasperating! But I'll forgive you, and kiss you, see, on your lips, your nose, your eyes, and—"

"You vixen!"

"I win, honey?"

"Provided we breakfast in bed?"

"Oh, you darling! I'll ring for Virgil."

"Wants me, Miss Grace?"

"Yes, Virgil. We wish breakfast in bed this morning. And, Virgil, send word to Mrs. Petite that Mr. Emile is remaining home today. She'll understand."

"Yas'm."

"Now, my sweet, let me rearrange the bedclothes. Oh there's the bell. I wonder who could be calling at this hour and in such bad weather."

"Oh! So I've found you two in bed; lazy things."

"Why, Petite, what brings you here?"

"To try to induce that man of yours to remain indoors. Emile, icicles are hanging from trees, houses, and everything else that they can cling to; there's ice in the gutters—and br-r-r-r, it's below freezing."

"Of course, I'm to remain indoors for that reason?"

"Come now, you know what I mean."

"Yes, and I'm beginning to believe that you, like Grace, are fast becoming a romance fiend."

"Well, from what I've heard of Lizette and Philippe, I know it will be interesting. Grace, aren't those pretty names?"

"Very. Have breakfast with us, Petite."

"I've finished mine an hour ago. Emile, please, the story."

"Yes, the story."

"Listen, if you don't get out of here, I can't dress—or is it possible that you expect me to crow in my night shirt?"

"What slang! You could—"

"All right, if you women won't leave the room; then I'll dress before—"

"Come quickly, Petite, into the dining room. You know, he might do it."

"I don't doubt it; but, Grace, he knew we would run."

"At any rate, he promised to tell us a story."

"I knew he would, for last night when I lay in my Frenchman's arms, he asked: 'Petite, did you know that I am psychic?'

" 'Honey,' I said, 'you can't keep a serious face when you're fibbing.'

" 'All right, but I'll make a wager with you that I can tell what Emile will do tomorrow.'

" 'That should be easy; you know the plantation routine.'

" 'But he will not even go near it.'

" 'Then what will he do?' I asked.

" 'Well, Petite, my psychic mind tells me that he will relate the story that this French Quarter has tried to solve for for years.'

" 'As You Desire Me?'

" 'Yes, sweet; however, events have so changed that this title alone will not be appropriate; so he will change it to Mine, at the same time merging As You Desire Me into it.'

" 'About Lizette and Philippe?'

" 'Yes. It is so amazing that it haunts me.'

" 'You know it?'

" 'Yes, from the very beginning to the inevitable end.'

" 'Inevitable end? Is it not complete?'

" 'No, Honey. If I had not made my reservations on that stern-wheeler bound for St. Louis tomorrow morning, I would want to be there, at least for the ending. I tell you, honey, considering that you and I are like brother and sister to Emile and Grace, this story will leave you dumbfounded.' "

"Grace, he was lying on his back. I raised my head from his chest and, bending directly over him, pleaded: 'Darling, please tell me some of it.' And he said: 'Listen, to tell you any more would be to do you an injustice, for, after leaving me at the steamboat, you should have Oscar drive you directly over to their home, where you will be graciously entertained.' And Grace, that was all that he would tell me. Now you know why I'm here. You know, whenever I heard an opera in Europe, and just when the hero or the heroine desired an expression of love, I would think of Emile's title."

"Then you knew it before you left?"

"Oh, yes. I spoke to Emile one day about it, and he told Antoine and me that he had been delving into the mystery and hoped to put it in print when it was solved. He also said that he was sure to solve it. I asked under what title he would publish the story, and he said it would be 'As You Desire Me.' Grace, those two people, Philippe and Lizette, are as common a topic of conversation as Anthony and Cleopatra must have been in Egypt, for they are called the lovers of the Vieux Carre."

"My, Petite, I thought that you and Antoine would be entitled to that title."

"Our romance was beautiful, but I understand that—"

"Well, you two women can re-enter now. I have on my blood-red flannel underwear. And ladies, now that you are looking, that underwear is under my pants and smoking jacket."

"Now, Emile, the story."

"Not so fast. First, let me confess. You see, I had intended relating 'As You Desire Me' today, but it has a prelude and an aftermath. Secondly, I want you two to make yourselves perfectly comfortable, because you will be in that position for six or seven hours. Thirdly, as I unravel this story, it will be necessary to consult some of the books in the old secretary at times in order for you to understand fully its event and appreciate them. In fact, it will be necessary that I explain some history."

"We're ready, Emile."

"I see that. But will you two, one at a time, tell me how in hell you can be comfortable sitting together in one rocker?"

"But, darling, we love each other more than if we were sisters."

"Yes, I know that; in fact, at the plantation I noticed how you two did everything possible to make each other happy this past summer. Yet, neither of you neglected your husband."

"'Emile, I'm thankful that we have Petite and Antoine as partners."

"Yes, Grace, we have much to be thankful for. Our plantation now extends from the winding Mississippi River to salty Lake Pontchartrain, and it's the largest in the South. Further, one third of the seven hundred acres is in first-year sugar cane stubble, another third is in second-year stubble, and the remaining third will be seeded this spring by the slaves."

"You know, Emile, Antoine said our slaves are the healthiest and the happiest in this section; and that as they are all either Mulattoes or Octoroons, they are smarter and more gifted. He added that they would go through hell for you."

"I am kind to them, Petite. But there is also a bit of selfishness in my motive. You see, they notice that I give them the best medical treatment and the costliest medicines, not realizing that to lose one of them would be equal to losing fifteen hundred dollars. Why, even our animals are worth only from one hundred to two hundred dollars, and they are treated by the best veterinarian."

"There must be something more than selfishness, because Antoine said that some of the slaves who were able to buy their freedom wished, instead, to return to their former status. Why, Emile?"

"Well, to be truthful, it is not for love of me, although they appreciate the help I give them. But the real reason is that in the summer and fall of the year, when they are able to make fair wages, they immediately spend all their money, not understanding finances, so that in the winter they go hungry. Another reason is that while they live in houses with paper stuffed cracks in order to exclude the cold, icy north wind, our slaves have well-built, warm homes— again our selfishness in keeping our property healthy.

Then, too, we protect our slaves from the possibility of bites from rattlers and other venomous snakes, by hiring free men of color and Irish labor.

"In other words, we pay labor to do the dangerous work so as to conserve the health and lives of our valuable slaves."

"Exactly. But, Grace, while Petite and I are talking, you seem to be dreaming."

"The story, Emile, darling."

"All right, sweetheart; but first, let me ask you two to listen to the explanation of a bit of history so that in your mind's eye you will be able to have a true mental picture of two of the greatest and sweetest characters that this old French section has ever produced."

"You mean Philippe and Lizette?"

"Yes, Petite; I know you have heard of them."

"I have, and some of the stories are as conflicting as those of Madam La Laurie. They say that when one of her female slaves, I mean Madam La Laurie's, became pregnant and was about to deliver, she would put that slave in a pit and cover her with earth up to her neck. We know she was cruel to her slaves; in fact, the Creoles are beginning to call her mansion the haunted house."

"Grace, you're pensive again."

"Yes, darling, because I am eager to hear the story; and I'm on pins and needles, fearing that you and Petite while conversing may eventually leave this earth, and I'll find you roaming around the milky way, in and out among the stars."

"Oh, Grace, I do want to say this. What we shall hear from Emile is authentic, for he has documents and other valuable papers to prove it."

"Thanks, Petite. Now Emile, the story."

CHAPTER II

Philippe

"Well, in the year 1605, a boatload of Frenchmen were landed in Acadia, or what is now known as Nova Scotia. That was fifteen years before the landing of the Mayflower at Plymouth Rock.

"Acadia was alternately ruled by France and England. When under English rule, the English unsuccessfully endeaverod to force the French Acadians to swear allegiance to the English king. The result was that in the year 1755, when they refused again, the Englishmen herded them into small boats and forced them to leave what they believed to be the earth's most productive land. Those who landed in the Carolinas, although they received kind treatment, could not understand the language of the inhabitants, and there were no Catholic churches where they could worship God according to their belief. Further, they were still under the English rule and knew that at a future date they would again be ordered to take the oath of allegiance to King George.

"Hearing of a French city with French priests and a Catholic church to the south somewhere on the Mississippi, those uneducated, but loyal and pious peasants found their way west through the hostile Indian-peopled wilderness; and, reaching the river, they managed to travel towards their goal, which they reached on October 12, 1758.

"The Creoles accepted their countrymen with open arms. Since they were penniless, all homes, even the modest ones, were thrown open to them.

"The Acadians worked and toiled with the grit of their ancestors. As time passed, they realized that the new land was more fertile and the new climate permitted two crops instead of one; so with what money they had acquired, some of them pushed westward to the beautiful Teche country.

However, many remained in and near New Orleans; and one family in particular, named de la Tour, cleared a small piece of land just outside the ramparts, near the center fort, in fact, opposite Orleans Street. They permitted two huge magnolia trees, with their large, aromatic, leathery-like white blossoms to remain. Between them they built a small but comfortable home with the help of the Creoles, using greased paper for window panes and torches of ill-smelling myrtle wax for lighting.

"Each day they cleared more land and soon received sugar cane from the Jesuits, who had brought it from San Domingo in 1751. They planted and cultivated their fields from dawn until after dark. On Sunday, of course, they attended mass in St. Louis church, after which they rested, as the Good Book said they should.

"For three years these good people toiled; and, as with all toilers, they were prosperous enough to aid another Acadian, Andre Ney, who had come with his wife that fall on a lone small boat, also down the Mississippi.

"In 1762 both of these families had become extremely friendly. One might expect them to, coming originally from the same locality and becoming neighbors in a distant land. That year, providence sent to the de la Tours a baby boy and to the Neys a baby girl."

"Emile, then a romance begins?"

"No, Grace, but I'm explaining this so that you and Petite can understand the stock that Philippe came from. However, twenty-six years later, when de la Tour's boy returned to the city, having completed his medical studies in Paris, he and the Ney girl planned marriage in the wooden church on Easter Sunday; that was March 23, 1788. Two days previous, on Good Friday, a horrible incident occured. A fire, started by the ignition of a drape when blown in contact with a lighted candle before an altar at 538 Chartres Street, consumed eight hundred and fifty-six buildings in the Vieux Carre, including the wooden church, and rendered over five thousand people homeless. The wedding, naturally, had to be postponed until June of the same year, when they took their vows before an improvised altar at the Ursuline Convent while a more beautiful, more lasting church or cathedral was being built.

"These two Creoles of French Acadian descent lived happily, for the doctor progressed in his profession. When he had to remain in the city during the summer months to treat the victims of yellow fever and cholera, his wife went to the suburbs with the children.

"They had a family of seven children. On March 21, 1823, their last child was born, a blue-eyed, blond-haired boy. The tiny baby, in a long lace dress, was christened in the beautiful St. Louis Cathedral as 'A Creole child of Creole parents and Acadian grandparents, with the name Philippe Jean de la Tour.'"

CHAPTER III

Lizette

"In 1727, Bienville, who you two know was the founder of this city, sent over to the colony the Casket girls (Filles a la casquette), so called because each had received from the king a casket-like box containing a complete trousseau. These women left their comfortable homes to become wives of the early French settlers.

"Into the Gulf a sailboat limped, having weathered a terrible storm, and thence through blue Lake Borgne, through Lake Pontchartrain, into Bayou St. John, and up this winding stream, with swamps on both sides, to its banks at the head of a road leading in various directions, sometimes southeast, other times southwest, but always in a southward direction. The passengers journeyed through the moss-covered cypress swamps infested with hideous alligators ten and twelve feet long, slippery water moccasins, and vicious rattle snakes that seemed to slithe across the road known as 'the Grand Route St. John', the only possible piece of land connecting Bayou St. John with la Nouvelle Orleans.

"Along this road came the French Casket girls, following the hired Houma Indian guides always so plentiful in that region, who carried the casket-like boxes on their bronze shoulders. Upon reaching the city the girls were temporarily placed in an old building with the Ursuline nuns, while their new building was underway, the ground having just that year been broken at Chartres and Ursuline Streets. Incidentally, the builders took seven years to complete the building which cost five million francs. Here the Casket girls met and wed men whose character and integrity were beyond question."

"Darling is that the same building that now stands at that corner?"

"Yes, Grace, for over a hundred years. I am sure some future generation will prove it one of the oldest buildings, if not the oldest building in the vast Mississippi Valley. As it was built of brick and hand-hewn cypress, it will last for hundreds and hundreds of years."

"I see. Petite, shall we visit it some day when Emile and Antoine are occupied?"

"I would love to take you. I know every inch of it, because I received my education there."

"You know, Petite, I had almost forgotten Emiles telling me that when he related your romance. However, continue the story, Emile."

"Well, among those women was Lizette Chateau, who, when told to choose her man, asked them to show their hands palm up. To her their appearance was of secondary consideration. The man she choose to be the father of her future children was not the handsomest according to the well preserved charcoal I have here of him, which reveals the face of a clean-cut young man of about twenty-two years, two years Lizette's senior."

"May we see it?"

"Surely, Petite, but be careful as it is glued between glass."

"As you've said, he is not handsome; but I do admire his determined chin and wide forehead. Don't you, Grace?"

"Why I'd say he was nice to look at."

"Now that you women have taken the poor man apart, look at this old map made just one year later, that is 1728. Notice that the entire city is only five by nine squares, and that many of these squares are void of buildings. Also notice the Bayou and how the Grand Route Bayou St. John snaked through the swamps."

"And that was la Nouvelle Orleans?"

"Yes, and in one of those huts Lizette and her 'good husband', as one of her letters call him, tenderly and wisely reared their family of four children, one of whom was named Lizette. When this second Lizette reached womanhood, she also married a Creole and through storm and fire, floods and yellow and malaria fever epidemics this Lizette the second, and her little daughter, Lizette the third, born one year later, passed miraculously; and when the girl reached womanhood she also married, becoming a mother in 1751, seven years before the Acadians arrived. The city had grown to the size of six by twelve squares, and was completely protected by palisades and forts, over which flew the white flag with the three golden Fleur de Lis, the flag of monarchial France.

"Her husband, the record reveals, was a Creole lawyer, who had not made any great success, preferring his home and family to the filthy courts of those days, supporting his family in moderate or average style and rearing them as God-fearing young men and women.

"During the first year after their marriage, that is, in 1776, the year in which the United States of America declared its freedom, Lizette, the fourth was born. She was a beautiful child as this small oil will reveal. See the long light golden curls that hang over her sweet little shoulders, and her large black eyes and the expression of innocence."

"Emile, how old was she when the artist painted her picture?"

"Records state that she was eight."

"Was she as beautiful at eighteen?"

"Well, I've found no picture of her then; but I do have a letter from her sweetheart, and he writes of her virtues and also extols her hair, eyes, shape, lips, nose, ears and even carriage."

"And you have a record of her marriage?'

"Yes, Petite, for that was an easy one to get. The St. Louis Cathedral had been rebuilt, and a search of their archives for the year 1798 reveals that she married; and papers I've found spoke of it as being the largest attended wedding of that year. The groom was a young lawyer whom she had met in her father's office, named Jules Monnot.

"They built a beautiful home on lower Royal Street, she choosing an exquisite floral design for the iron lace-work to support the second story roof. Of course, a law had been enacted to the effect that all buildings had to be built of brick since a second fire in 1788 almost again razed the city. Hence their home was built of that strong, lasting material."

"And, they too had a Lizette?"

"Yes, three boys and two girls. Lizette the fifth was born, as the records show, on June 17, 1825—"

"Emile, may I ask a few questions?"

"Surely, Petite, I've been expecting them, for I've noticed on several occasions, while relating this story, your brow wrinkle as though you did not understand, and yet, what I've explained has certainly not been complicated, and surely was concise and correct."

"That's exactly it. But before I start, should your answers to my questions be of a secret nature, please don't hesitate to tell me. But, Emile, you're smiling."

"I believe I've read your mind; however, proceed."

"Well, the research in this case must have taken years of constant hard work. Is that correct?"

"Correct, Petite."

"You're smiling again, Emile."

"Yes, because I know your next question."

"What is it?"

"And at great expense?"

"Yes, that was my next question. Well, was it?"

"Yes, at great expense. Now continue."

"Then, you didn't go through all of that work and bear the expense just to satisfy your curosity nor to write of it?"

"Again, mon ami, you are correct."

"Emile, but I'm again asking you to refuse to tell me, unless I should know just what was your motive, that is, if it is any of Grace's or my business."

"Yes, it is indirectly your business as it also is Grace's busines, but—"

"Then, it is about you."

"No, it is not about me; but I am not at liberty to tell any more."

"Emile, darling, please."

"I'm sorry, Grace, little sweet; but there must be no more questioning."

CHAPTER IV

The Organ Grinder

"Let me tell you first of the organ and the organ grinder as we call him. You see the organs were very heavy two-wheeled instruments that were either laboriously pushed or drawn, usually by one man. At times, two men would handle the instrument, one pulling while the other pushed through the uneven black muddy streets.

"The instruments that created tones were various-sized brass strips held mechanically firm at one end, while steel pegs on a fourteen inch cylinder, as it turned, would force the strips to one side; and it was so adjusted that the steel pegs would release certain intended springs so that they would vibrate furiously, creating a sound or tone much like a harmonica but so loud that it could be heard about three or four city squares away. The steel pins were adjusted for the various dance songs of the times, and a twist of the wrist would cause the large steel-pegged cylinder to move forward or rearward, each position intended for a certain tune, there being about sixteen or eighteen different changes or songs.

"Usually the organ grinder on reaching a corner played the chorus of a song and, when finished, peered in four directions for someone emotionally inclined for terpsichorean amusement. Not seeing anyone, he moved to the next corner, and again he repeated the music.

"Now, it was June seventeenth—Lizette's birthday. That evening, she was permitted, after being well admonished concerning her behavior, to dance with the other girls of her age.

"It was six-thirty, and supper was over; the dishes had been placed in the mahogany china closet and the silver was back in the plush-lined drawers of the wide sideboard, while the pots and pans, scrupulously clean, hung from nails at various vantage points, near the large brick fireplace in the kitchen.

"Lizette, stepping from her bath, applied the large soft,

pink, downy powder puff. And finally she stepped into her over-starched gingham dress. Down the stairs she tripped, two at a time, for from all directions came the strains of music from brightly colored organs, whose handles were being turned by free men of colour.

"Reaching the banquette, she was greeted by other girls; and while they were in the center of the square, the boys congregated at the corner.

"Presently on organ grinder with his musical instrument arrived; and before he actually stopped, one of the boys was at the crank, turning the handle slowly and methodically, even stopping for a fraction of a second at times when he thought a pause was effective; the other boys were now dancing in each other's arms.

"The organ grinder realized too late that he had made an error in stopping at the corner for, when the last strains of the chorus died, the boys en masse pushed the organ to a position midway between the corner and the girls.

"Having released the organ to its dusky owner, the boys raced back to the corner while he played his organ; and since he had also learned where to pause in turning the crank, the pause being intended for some added fancy or comical steps, laughter was heard from both boys and girls."

"It was good, clean, wholesome fun."

"Yes, Petite. However, towards dark, when the strains of the organ could still be well heard, the boys danced closer to the music, as also did the girls, each dance bringing them nearer together, while their parents sat on their respective second-story galleries.

"Of course, the girls could not dance with the boys except in their own homes or at a chaperoned ball. So, when father saw the girls and boys together, he reached over the iron railing and peered down at them. When he had made sure that the girls were dancing with their brothers, he resumed his seat.

"Now dancing with one's brother or one's sister does afford some pleasure, but being in the arms of a non-relative, of course, adds to the enjoyment. So, towards eight-thirty, what father had smiled upon, the boys and girls frowned upon; and presto, partners were changed. They were lucky that father did not again peer over the railing."

"I've done that, Emile."

"Yes, Petite, and so have I. However, although Lizette and Philippe knew each other, for they heard mass in the same church, this night, for the first time, they became really acquainted; and for that one hour, from eight-thirty until nine-thirty, when father paid the organ grinder, which was the signal for finis, they danced continually together.

"Of course, that night when Lizette retired, as with everyone who feels that she has met for the first time someone of the opposite sex who appeals to her, sleep came late. Philippe had the same experience."

"I can understand that, darling."

"You can, Grace?"

"Yes, for the first night I met you, I didn't sleep at all."

"You've been hiding something from me, sweet."

"You knew it, darling, for you knew the effect of the kiss on the first night."

"Well, little honey, I can assure you I fell for you, too. Well, let us get back to the story—but wait, Grace, there's something you should know; and if you promise not to question me, I'll tell you—"

"'I promise."

"Well, I loved you even before I saw how lovely you are. No, no questions, now! Now let's see, where was I?"

"The organ grinder."

"Yes, that's right. Well, that organ grinder or another, according to which one arrived first, was a nightly visitor as was also Philippe until one night months afterwards when Lizette's father stepped downstairs for some purpose and discovered the deception. Although the organ grinder was permitted to continue to come nightly, her father made certain that the boys remained at the corner, while the girls remained under his gallery."

CHAPTER V

The King And The Queen

"It was Saturday, February the fourth. Lizette was now fifteen years old; and Philippe, eighteen. On January 12 they had attended a 'King party' at the home of one of the boys who had danced on the corner. For the past two years they had gone on hayrides and on these occasions were always together, so much so that even though she was too young for 'steady company', they were regarded, in their circle, as being sweethearts; their fathers and mothers also regarded it practically as such with Creole complacency, since both families were very much respected."

"Emile, darling, may I interrupt?"

"Certainly, sweet."

"What is a 'king's party?' "

"Well, it is a party given at little Christmas or twelfth night—Kings' Night. The young people celebrate the visit of the Magi with their gifts to the Holy Infant by gathering at someone's home. When the special cake is cut, the girl or boy who finds the bean is Queen or King. She chooses the king or he, the queen. They rule until the next party of which there are many, which is given at the King's home, where the special cake is cut. The fortunate girl or boy again chooses a partner. And thus the custom goes on year after year. So on the night of February fourth, slaves had moved the furniture from the two first rooms with the large folding doors, including the large rug with its vari-colored flowers. They left the small rosewood piano with its two candle cups on both sides to furnish light for the music. At this piano sat the mother of the King; and as she played, the King and his Queen led the grand march with the others following. When the march was over, all applauded; and, when quiet was restored, the King said, 'Subjects, it is my order that you choose your partners and make merry with a dance.'

"Then all chose partners, Philippe choosing Lizette; and

to the strains of the piano they danced the steps they had learned at the corner and under the gallery.

"During an intermission in dancing the 'King's Cake' was cut and served with light refreshments."

"Emile, describe the 'King's cake'."

"Yes, sweet; it's an oval cake with hollow center, resembling a life preserver, in which is one bean. Each one at the party receives a piece of the cake, holding it in one hand while in the other is another refreshment. Usually the excitement is at fever pitch, for the one who bites on the bean is king if a boy or queen if a girl. And more so was the excitement in this case as the next and last party would be on St. Joseph's day, March nineteenth, the only day during Lent on which a party can be given. You see the Tuesday following March fourth was Mardi Gras, or fat Tuesday, and the next day Lent began.

"So, all sat, waiting for the command when suddenly the word 'Bite' was heard. Everyone placed his piece of cake in his mouth, each eager to shout the one word, 'Bean.'

"Amid much laughter, and a chorus of 'Who has it?' A male said said 'Bean.'

"The old King then walked up and said, 'Philippe, you are King from this day, and I now place you on my throne. My last act will be to place the ladies in line so that you may choose your Queen. Girls, all in line. Now your Majesty, the ladies are waiting.'

"Philippe hesitated tantalizingly and scanned the standing girls, purposely avoiding Lizette's gaze, whose heart had quickened, for she knew that the King would kiss his Queen.

" 'Have you chosen, your Majesty?'

" 'Yes. It is my order that—Lizette reign with me as my Queen.'

"Shyly and coyly, Lizette stepped forward; the King, who was now standing advanced to meet the blushing girl who was red from her shapely neck to the roots of her hair. Slowly she moved her head backward to one side, while Philippe held both her hands between them. Looking directly into her staring eyes, he dropped his head and kissed her gently but firmly as the boys and girls shouted, 'Long live the King; long live the Queen.'

"The parents of the former King, the only elderly couple at this party and incidentally the chaperons, realized their love, and the father said to the mother, 'Sweet and innocent.'

"Towards midnight, an order was given to hitch two carriages, one for the boys while the other was for the girls and also the mother, who saw each girl safely home; that is, those that would not sleep in the spare room at her home."

"Emile, do you know how Philippe and Lizette felt?"

"Well, when Lizette reached home, her mother asked, 'Did you enjoy yourself, Lizette?' You must have, for I see you are all a flush.'

" 'Mother, I'm queen!'

" 'Give me one guess to name the King.'

" 'Don't tease; and you know we had our first kiss; and, Mother, he took my hands and held me like this and pressed his lips against mine like this.—And, oh Mother, I was sorry when it was over.'

" 'Yes, I know; and as it is past mid-night, hurry to bed; and Lizette, knowing your thoughts, may I suggest that you not forget your prayers.' "

CHAPTER VI

Mardi Gras

"It was Monday, February sixth, Carnival or Mardi Gras eve, which is the day of Misrule. Grace, the word Carnival is derived from two Latin words, Carne meaning flesh, and Vale, meaning farewell—hence, farewell to flesh. Now Mardi is French for Tuesday, and Gras is French for fat; hence Fat Tuesday means the same as Carnival, which is the eve of Ash Wednesday in the Catholic religion."

"And, where did it originate?"

"Carnival began with the Pagans, and then spread to Rome and Paris. New Orleans naturally borrowed it from Paris, but has improved upon it so greatly that today it has no equal anywhere on earth."

"I should like to know more about Mardi Gras, as you know I was ill on those days when I was here. Petite, do you mind?"

"Not in the least, for I, too, am learning, for instance, its origin."

"Well, the parades reproduce scenes from history, literature, art, or mythology. The first started not long ago, in 1831; they cost now between thirty and forty thousand dollars each. Grace, in about a hundred years from now, let us say 1950, I predict that one of those same parades will cost over one hundred thousand dollars. However, one of the most important factors about them in arousing the Mardi Gras spirit is the secrecy and mystery enshrouding these great pageants; the public knows nothing of them until they appear on the streets, for the 'floats' as we know them are built behind closed doors, usually in abandoned cotton warehouses. They are made of all sorts of materials: the figures; such as life size horses, serpents, or elephants, for example, are made of papier mache.

"Of the usual eighteen or twenty floats, the elected king sits on his handsome purple throne on the first, where he toasts his Queen en route to the French Opera where the pageant ends and where a grand ball with the King and Queen at its head is held. However, let us get back to the story. In this small old city everyone was astir on this particular Mardi Gras eve. Mothers were putting on the finishing touches to the various masking suits, some of which were fashioned out of rich, gaudy expensive material, while others were made of materials not costing a penny.

"It was five-thirty, Mardi Gras eve. Father was in the yard with the boys and girls, and a four-wheeled sugar cane wagon was brought through the wide carriage entrance to be decorated, for wagons like people must conceal their identity.

"The boat with its oars that hung from the ceiling of the driveway, held close to the ceiling by block and tackle and fastened to large iron rings, to be used in case of a flood, had to be lowered and placed in the rear so as to permit the large wagon to enter.

"Father wrapped the spokes of the wagon wheels with cambric in the Mardi Gras colors—purple, yellow, and green.

"One of the boys wrapped the single center shaft spirally with the same material, while some of the girls placed rosettes over the decorated lath sides; others tied on bells of various sizes. The harnesses, two in number, also received their share of the colored cambric.

"In the stable was the riding horse, belonging to a younger brother, who laboriously decorated its head and saddle with gay carnival colors.

"Mother was in the kitchen frying doughnuts. You know, Grace, the kind you ate at the coffee stand in the French Market, for tomorrow there would be no time for cooking, and the various masked visitors would be hungry.

"In one corner of the yard the free men of color, quadroons and octoroons, were practicing the music they would play on the morrow; the cornet; the bass with its umph, umph, umph; the wooden clarinet; the flute like oboe; the big bass drum with its large metal discs; the trap drum and the castanets; and the large, cumbersome bass viol— seven pieces in all.

"It was nine o'clock when the work was completed. While the men returned the lanterns to their respective places in the covered driveway and about the patio, the girls stole home, each for a final inspection of her costume and for a good night's rest, because the next day would be a day which would exact every bit of stored energy. The boys also retired early."

"Darling, at what time does the masking begin?"

"Well, at nine o'clock next morning the wagon drawn by two horses rolled out of the entrance, while the seven dusky musicians played the Marseillaise.

"Philippe and Lizette were just like the pictures one sees of royalty, having at the last minute rented costumes since they were selected King and Queen. He wore a large hat with a plume gracefully attached to one side, while she had a jeweled tiara. Their costumes, made of velvet and trimmed with stones, glistened in the sunlight as did the jewels on their gilded slippers.

"Now the King and Queen ruled a realm of all kinds of subjects: colorful shepherds and shepherdesses, barons and baronesses, gay peasants, a miller and his wife with her cream-colored skirt and shirtwaist, a Chinaman and his wife with long pigtails and long loose fitting pants, a tramp and his wife with costumes cleverly made of basted oat sacks which fitted them loosely and on which were sewed over a hundred playing cards. There were also Mr. and Mrs. Devil, the pranksters of the crowd, in their fiery red suits, from the hood of which projected two sawdust-filled red horns; monkeys with suits of brown sateen; a cave man with part of a goat skin across his chest and groin, holding a chain fastened to a similarly attired girl; and last, one of Lizette's country cousins, who came to town unexpectedly and whom her father attired in an old ragged slave suit, blackening his face and giving him large painted red lips. He too was a prankster. Of course, all wore appropriate masks except the painted face."

"My, what a crowd!"

"Yes, sweet, a happy set of young people. Up Royal Street they drove while the musicians, to the tapping of their feet, rendered gay strains of the day. As they proceeded, they waved and shouted to those behind the varied colored lace-work on the galleries, hearing every now and then, 'I know you, I know you!'

"Reaching Royal and Conti Streets, they leaped from the wagon; and on the new brick banquette they waltzed to the strains of the Blue Danube, while some of the maskers on foot, old and young, grasped their partners and added to the merriment. Presently, Lizette spied an onlooker, an old lady friend of her family; her face was wreathed in smiles for she, no doubt, recalled her youth, and Lizette said to Philippe, 'Look, there is Mme. Jaque. Grab her and dance.'

"Philippe took Lizette to the wagon and, amid music and shouts, walked up to the old lady and placed his arm around her. Accepting the spirit of the occasion, she waltzed off with him and asked, 'Who are you?'

" 'You promise not to tell.'

" 'Yes.'

" 'I am Philippe.'

" 'I should have never known it. And the Princess is, of course, Lizette.'

" 'Yes, no other.'

" 'And when will you have nerve enough to visit her as a 'Beau'?

" 'When I'm invited. You know the precedent here. No girl is allowed steady company under sixteen years of age.'

" 'Maybe I can help you. But now the dance is over, re-turn to Lizette. See, she is facing this way.'

"And then they crowded back into the wagon and were off again. Through the narrow streets their decorated wagon rolled; they called those who weren't masked by their names; who, in turn, waved and shouted 'Who are you?'

"When they reached an acquaintance's home, they again leaped from the wagon and waltzed. This time the boys grabbed the girls of the home while the girls drew the men off the banquette steps. All danced, the acquaintances endeavoring to penetrate the masks.

"When the dance was over, they still withheld their identities, for those outside must not know who they were; then inside they trouped, one and all, while the surrounding neighbors guessed. Everyone that was not masked remained outdoors on that day, seated on his front steps.

"Once inside, the masks were removed; and amid much jollity, they ate doughnuts with their soft drinks. But, as one chewed on his doughnut, he found something that just didn't taste right. An examination revealed that his host had on this day of 'Misrule' inserted cotton in the doughnuts. Of course, the good-natured crowd laughed. However, their host returned with more doughnuts and cake, assuring them this time there were no false fillings.

"They visited more friends and towards two o'clock in the afternoon met other decorated wagons. Being fatigued by the arduous five preceding hours, the maskers ordered their drivers to form a parade; other wagons joined until there were about eighteen. With their bands playing, they paraded until six o'clock in the evening when, by law, masks had to be removed.

"Then, Philippe, Lizette, and the crowd went back home. There the chairs had been removed from the wagons and placed on the gallery on the second floor; and while Mrs. Jeanfreau distributed cakes and other refreshments, the masqueraders reseated, and awaited the last parade which could be advantageously viewed from Lizette's home. Then Mardi Gras would be over for another year."

"But you have not described one love scene."

"No, I haven't; you see, my mind is on the next chapter, which is so heartbreaking that I wish it were over."

"Is it so sad?"

"Very—possibly the saddest and most ghastly two weeks in this old city's history. However, I'm ahead of my story. All were seated while waiting for the parade. Philippe, who was the last to enter, noticed the only vacant chair was in the rear; so he drew himself up to where he sat on the wooden banister which surmounted the railing, facing the others. So as not to topple over, he twisted both feet, wide apart, firmly into the iron lace-work. Lizette left her seat and walked to him. While the others chatted, she placed her hands in his, saying, 'Philippe, this has been the happiest day of my life.'

" 'Mine too, honey, for I had you all day. But I see no justifiable reason why we cannot see each other oftener; and, with your permission, I should like to consult your father.'

" 'It will be no use, for Mother has spoken; and when she fails, no one succeeds.'

" 'I know, but to see each other only at mass on Sunday or at a party once every two or three weeks, considering how much we've learned to care for each other, is a penalty I don't think you or I deserve.'

" 'I agree with you, honey—agree fully; and yet, we know the commandment, "Honor thy Father and thy Mother." Then, too, we must remember that I am only fifteen years old.'

"You are not fifteen, for in June, which is only three months away, you will be sixteen; but I suppose we shall have to content ourselves with these spasmodic meetings.' "

CHAPTER VII

The Cholera Epidemic

"Petite and Grace, I have now reached a part in my story that threatened the very existence of this city. It was of such a ghastly and terrifying nature that I would rather read an eyewitness's account for he was on the scene, nay, was in everyone's home, because he was a pastor for a local church on Canal Street. So I shall read Dr. Clapp's vivid account.

" 'On the morning of the 25th of October, as I was walking home from market, before sunrise, I saw two men lying on the levee, in a dying condition. They had been landed from a steamboat which had arrived the night before. Some of the watchmen had gone for a hand barrow or cart, on which they might be removed to a hospital. At first, there was quite a crowd assembled on the spot. But an eminent physician rode up in his gig, and gazing a moment, exclaimed in a loud voice, "Those men have Asiatic Cholera." The crowd dispersed in a moment and ran as if for their very lives in every direction.'

" 'Those two men had the usual symptoms of Cholera; cramps, convulsions, cold and blue feet, icy perspiration, with a great pressure on their chest, intense thirst.'

"He goes further to describe the weather, saying, 'The heavens were covered with thick, heavy, damp, lowering clouds, that seemed like one black ceiling spread over the whole horizon. Everyone felt a strange difficulty of respiration. I've never looked upon such a gloomy, appalling sky before or since. Not a breath of wind stirred. It was so dark that in some of the banks, offices, and private houses, candles were lighted that day.

" 'That same day,' he continues, 'as many persons left the city as could find a means of transportation.' "

"My, that must have been terrible."

"Wait, for you haven't heard the worst. Let me continue reading: 'On the evening of the 27th of October, it (the cholera) had made its way through every part of the city. During the ten succeeding days, reckoning from October 27th to the 6th of November, all the physicians judged that, at the lowest computation, there were five thousand deaths— an average of over five hundred every day. Many died of whom no account was rendered. A great number of bodies, with bricks and stones tied to the feet, were thrown into the river. Many were privately interred in gardens and enclosures on the grounds where they expired, whose names were not recorded in the bill of mortality. Often I was kept in the burying ground for hours in succession, by the continual arrival of corpses, over whom I was requested to perform a short service. One day, I did not leave the cemetery till nine o'clock at night; the last interments were made by candle light. Reaching my house faint, exhausted, horror-stricken, I found my family all sobbing and weeping, for they had concluded, from my long absence, that I was certainly dead. I never went abroad without kissing and blessing them all, with the conviction that we should never meet again on earth.' "

"Emile, I've heard people speak of that epidemic, but I never dreamed it was that severe."

"Let me read further: 'After bathing and taking some refreshment I started out to visit the sick. My door was thronged with servants, waiting to conduct me to the rooms of dying sufferers. In this kind of labor, I spent most of the night, returning home at three o'clock.' He continues, explaining the odd cases of Cholera he witnessed, about one of which he says, 'The patient was perfectly free from pain, with mental powers unimpaired, but suffering from debility and moral apprehensions.'

"In another chapter, he adds, 'At six o'clock I stepped into the carriage to accompany a funeral procession to the cemetery. On my arrival at the grave I found a large pile of corpses without coffins, in horizontal layers, one above the other, like corded wood. I was told that there were more than one hundred bodies deposited there by unkown persons, at different hours since nine o'clock the evening previous. Large trenches were dug, into which these uncoffined corpses were thrown indiscriminately. The same day a private hospital was found deserted; the physicians, nurses, and attendants were all dead or had run away. Not a living person was in it. The wards were filled with putrid bodies, which, by order of the Mayor, were piled in an adjacent yard and burned, and their ashes scattered to the four winds.' "

"My, that doctor must have suffered mentally!"

"Yes, Petite, but physically as well, for reading further, he says, 'At many a window into which was flung the sickly, flickering light of these conflagrations could be seen persons struggling with death, and rigid, blackened corpses awaiting the arrival of some cart. Many times, on entering these apartments and putting my head under the mosquito bar, I became deadly sick in a moment, and was taken with vomiting, which, however, passed off.' He further adds, 'Let the reader imagine a close room, in which are laying a half dozen bodies in the process of decay, and he may form a faint conception of the physical horrors in which I lived and moved for two entire weeks.' "

"A living hell, darling."

"Yes, sweet, he did go through a living hell, for let me read just once more, when he speaks of the cholera of the following year, saying, 'Two of my daughters, the eldest four, and the youngest two years of age, died of cholera about the same time. I was so fortunate as to procure a carriage in which their bodies were conveyed to the family vault in the Girod Cemetery, which had been constructed and presented to me, some years before by the trustees of Christ Church, Canal Street—a church characterized for large, generous, and noble sympathies. I rode in the carriage alone with the two coffins. There was not a soul present but myself, to aid in performing the last sad offices. Most desolate and heavy was my heart at the thought that they had left us to come back no more.'

"Now, Grace, and you too, Petite, wipe away those tears."

"It was terribly sad."

"Yes, I know; but in your present mood, I can't continue

this chapter—on second thought, I believe I'll omit it, and I am very desirous to have it over."

"Please,—darling, continue—we'll compose ourselves."

"Suppose all of us compose ourselves; Grace, ring for Cafe au Lait."

"But, Emile, you had a motive in describing that dreadful cholera."

"Yes, I did. You see, having so many uncoffined bodies to bury, after they were placed in the shallow trench, they were barely covered with porous sod so that with the weather dark and heavy, and without wind, the emisssion of putrid gasses from the process of putrefaction had permeated the air in the quarter and also for miles around. It was no wonder that on November 2, Lizette's brother contracted the fatal disease, and that on the next day, as they moved her brother's corpse, Lizette became a victim."

"Emile!"

CHAPTER VIII

The Prayer

" 'Listen, son, listen to reason. If cholera continues for a few more weeks, the entire community will be de-populated; and since Lizette knows you're no coward, you owe it to yourself to—'

" 'Father, I've always been an obedient son. But I know that if Lizette recovers, it will be only through my presence.'

" 'Just how, Philippe, will you accomplish the impossible?'

" 'Father, last night after I overcame Mr. Jeanfreau's objections, he led me into Lizette's bedroom. On seeing her sad, sweet face I was overcome with sorrow; and my heart ached so that unconsciously I lifted the mosquito bar and sat under it on the edge of the bed. Chokingly I asked her how she felt. She smiled, Father, you know, a sad, sweet smile and said much better since I had come. And I told her that I would be there every day and all day.

" 'Then she said I should avoid seeing her.

" 'I found myself talking soft and low; and almost pleading, I asked her whether she would say the Our Father with me; she nodded; so we began and prayed for at least a half hour. Then I asked her whether she felt any better.

" 'She replied that she did, for the heavy feeling had left her chest and her head was clear. And, from over my shoulder and through the bar, Mr. Jeanfreau said she looked better.

" 'So you see, Father—'

" 'But, son, just an hour ago, as I returned from market, drays, wagons, and carts passed filled with dead bodies, which had been found lying all over the streets.'

" 'I know, Father, but I'm no coward.'

" 'Coward! Coward you say! Philippe, you've made me very angry; but listen, at Milneburg, I met old Mr. Boisblanc with his aged wife, his children, and grandchildren. They were entering a chartered schooner to cross the lake; and seeing me, he asked my mission. I told hi mthat I too wished to flee from the pestilence. Then he said he had fought under Jackson, receiving a medal for what they called heroism. He was no coward, but common prudence caused him to run away from the common enemy that was now desolating the city. At Chalmette they could see the enemy and cope with and resist him, as he was visible, and they had arms; but here, we have a foe that is invisible, who is mowing down hundreds of his friends each day. In battle, they rested at night; but cholera gives one no rest, neither night nor day. So you see, son, the word of coward—'

" 'I'm sorry, Father, please forgive me. But again, please don't insist on my leaving. You and the others leave; take the slaves with you; but let me remain on the plantation. And, Father, with your kind permission I should now like to go.'

"And he left the old plantation home with double strides; he crossed Rampart Street and headed towards Royal Street. As he neared Burgundy Street, he saw a man lying on the banquette as if he had fallen from the steps. Looking up Burgundy Street he discovered two more, one a youngster, and the other an elderly man, evidently father and son. Continuing on Orleans Street, he smelled a putrid odor which filled the air around a long, open window. Peering inside and under a mosquito bar, he saw the corpses of two small children and their mother, while on the floor was the corpse of the father and husband who had evidently used his last bit of energy to summon help.

"Nauseated, he left. When his thoughts connected that scene with Lizette, he shouted aloud. 'No! No! And as if in a frenzy he ran as fast as his young feet could carry him. Without knocking, he opened her front door; and taking the steps two at a time, he soon reached her bedroom where he heard voices.

"Trembling and out of breath, Philippe peered through the open door and saw the doctor with his small black bag. Mr. Jeanfreau still wore his black tie and coat, evidently having just returned from his son's burial; while the mother, with her handkerchief to her eyes, was gazing at the doctor pleadingly. Just then, they moved towards the door; and, unnoticed, he entered. The room had begun to smell of the peculiar putrid odor common to abodes of the deadly disease. His hope fell, his knees began to sag and fold under him when he heard faintly, 'Morning Philippe.' With renewed energy, he reached the bed and, again sitting on its edge and under the bar, asked, 'Lizette, how are you feeling?'

" 'Not so well, but listen. The doctor is talking, and oh! what was that, it must have been Mother—Oh! I'll bet she fainted—she has, and I can hear Father gather her in his arms—and now he is taking her to their bedroom. Oh, well, Philippe, I'm sorry to disappoint you.'

" 'You can say that and smile?'

" 'Yes, for I've never harmed anyone and I've been a good Christian, and—and—but those lines have come back to me; yes, they go like this:

'Jesus can make a dying bed
Feel soft as downy pillows,
Whilst on His breast I lay my head,
And breathe my life out there.'

"As she closed her eyes, as if to picture the future, Philippe recalled this stanza:—

'How sweet the scene when good men die,
When noble souls retire to rest!
How mildly beams the closing eye,
How calmly heaves the expiring breast!
So fades a summer cloud away;
So sinks a soul, when storms are o'er.
So gently shuts the eye of day;
So dies a wave a long a shore.'

"As the last words ran through his mind and he recognized the significance of the stanza, he shouted, 'Lizette! Lizette!'

" 'Yes, Philippe.'

" 'Please, let us repeat what we said last night; let us pray.'

"And they did, Philippe holding her hands. Hardly had they begun when Mr. and Mrs. Jeanfreau noiselesssly entered and hearing their earnest supplication, they also knelt and prayed before the small white altar that hung from the wall, with its burning taper showing red through the glass holder.

"And again those two pure souls prayed for one half hour

and again their prayers were heard, for she seemed stronger
and breathed less rapidly. They stared directly into each
other's eyes for fully two minutes—she was smiling, while he,
with wrinkled brow and aching heart, was recalling the scene
of the dead mother and her two young children.

"Shaking his head as if to cast away the vision of that
gloomy scene, he said, 'Lizette, honey, please, let me pray
alone. And as the words left his saddened mouth, they
seemed as if influenced by some divine being, some supernatural, unexplainable something, to form into verse as he
began in soft, low tones:—

'Our Father, who art in Heaven, who heard our plea,
Please continue to listen to me.
For Lizette is your offspring, as so am I.
Then why should I live? Why should she die?
Pure as a new born, with mind just as pure,
She's always been faithful to You, I'm sure.
As fathers on earth grant the wish of their children.
May I hope as much from Thee in Heaven?
As Fathers on earth chastise them when bad
But whose hearts go out to theirs when they're sad,
May I hope from Thee whom I love with my soul,
Sympathy for goodness, and badness, a toll?
If we're to believe this, then some one's in error,
For Thou doesn't wish us to remain in terror.
Then Lizette is well; and for a later day
She will remain with us, never Thee to betray;
And now, dear Father, if this is not true,
And if this be Thy will, that she return to you,
Then see, I kiss her lips, without any restraint,
That I too may come with a soul free from taint.
And now, dear Father, we await Thy will
Together we come to Thee, or together we stay till
We fill our earthly mission, as we hope to do,
When our souls, united, will soar direct to You.'
                                        Amen.

"That was a beautiful prayer, Emile."

"Yes, I thought so as did her parents who, when Philippe
began, rose, walked over to the bed, and stood directly behind him."

PART TWO

"AS YOU DESIRE ME"

CHAPTER I

The Engagement

"Twenty-four hours had passed; and the doctor, more out of respect than for professional service, reigned his horse before the house on Royal Street—the house that should have had a white crepe on the frame of the door. He was puzzled and wondered whether the remaining occupants were in no condition to hang one. But no, for someone was answering the heavy iron knocker. As the door opened, he was greeted with, 'Doctor, she is much better. Oh, much better! Come, let me show you.' And with the doctor also excited, the two men raced up the stairs and into the room.

" 'Lizette, why, Lizette, God—child, I'm glad to see you better. Here, let me feel your pulse and tell me, how do you feel?'

" 'Well, Doctor, I haven't vomited since Philippe came. And I breathe quiet easily, and my chest feels almost normal and—but, I'm worried about Philippe; he kissed me yesterday while praying for me, and I'm wondering—'

" 'Well, since his prayers have worked this miracle then surely no harm can come to him. Come here, young man, let me look at you. Ah! you look fit, but you seem to need some sleep. Haven't you slept?'

"Lizette answered, 'Not a wink, Doctor, for every time I awoke last night he was sitting on the edge of the bed, while Mother rested in that chair. Make him sleep, Doctor.'

" 'And why don't you want to sleep, Philippe?'

" 'Because, Doctor, if I awake and find her in the condition she was in yesterday, why—'

" 'You will never see her in that condition again. She is definitely on the way to recovery. But, what are you to her?'

" 'Her sweetheart.' Her father proudly answered.

"On the evening of the eighth of November, exactly two weeks to the day when the two men ill with cholera had been found on the levee, a terrible electric storm passed through this city. The polluted, evil-smelling air was replaced with salubrious, fresh, life-giving air; and from that moment, not another case of cholera was reported. It was estimated that during the fourteen days, seven thousand persons had died. Although everyone was happy that the unseen foe had disappeared, nevertheless, the community was a very sad one, for there was not one family that had not lost a loved one or a very dear friend. And, Grace, knowing these people as I do, they being very affectionate, I can imagine the tears, especially on the cold, wet, wintry nights that were slowly edging in, when they thought of their dear ones, many of whom were buried in the wet ground.

"However, Christmas came and with it some happiness, for even though many seats remained vacant at the table, there were some, especially those of the younger set that found Yuletime happiness. For instance, in the St. Louis Cathedral, at mid-night Mass, Philippe, standing in the rear with Lizette so as to leave seats in the much crowded church for the elders, on rising after receiving the Holy Sacrament, gently took her hand in his and handed her a small, purple, velvet-covered package."

"Emile, an engagement ring?"

"No, Grace, but a beautiful studded lavalliere watch. When she opened the case, in the dim candle light, her eyes beamed with joy. Now, those two were only sweethearts and, of course, not permitted to kiss; but when she turned her head in the position familiar to those in love, he forgot all about honor; and while the entire congregation returned to their knees, he gently but firmly placed his lips on hers."

"And what did she give him in return?"

"Well, his present was on the Christmas tree. On it were the words, 'To my Sweetheart from Lizette,' of all things, a solid gold penknife."

"Why of all things?"

"Because knives are said to cut friendship; I mean that is the superstition in the Quarter. New Year's quickly followed and was ushered in with whistles of all kinds and tones, even to those of the stern wheelers, or steamboats, varied so that plantation owners would recognize the individual boat before it reached his plantation. Some of the whistles measured four and one half and five feet in length. The din was almost indescribable—tooting of tin and red, white, and blue paper horns, the loud noise of the spinning racket and the deep clang of cow bells—besides the pop of firecrackers and the louder report of the larger crackers. Every now and then one saw the varied colored glowing balls from roman candles and the stars from various sized skyrockets bursting in a canopy of flame and sparks.

"With tears many greeted the New Year, remembering one or more who were missing. Others did something they would dare to do only on that night—exactly one minute after mid-night, they kissed their sweethearts. The old superstition says what one does during one minute after twelve, one will do most of the coming year."

"What a superstition!"

"Yes, but it's a harmless one. Soon 'King's Day' or twelfth night followed with its various parties as did summer and winter. In fact, except for two minor epidemics of yellow fever, two uneventful years passed in which the families of Jeanfreau and de la Tour became intimate friends, so much so, that on June seventeenth, the de la Tours and some few intimate friends including Lizette's personal friend Marie, who, by nature was a wit, attended Lizette's eighteenth birthday.

"Mrs. Jeanfreau was at the piano; and after the first dance, Marie hoisted herself on top of the instrument and said in a loud clear voice, 'Ladies and gentlemen, I was wondering just why this party is taking place. What reason have we to be happy that Lizette was ever born? Now—' Lizette rushed at Marie; everyone laughed, and all knew that those two gentle girls always confided their every secret to each other. Towards ten o'clock Philippe danced Lizette towards the gallery and, expertly separating the two long lace curtains that reached to the floor, danced through the long window to the porch. While the tones of the piano floated through the open window, Philippe, holding both hands and drawing her closer to him, said, 'Lizette, my little sweetheart, I have much to be thankful for, that you were born eighteen years ago today. We've been real sweethearts and have been, except for the kisses that we stole, very honorable. Tonight I have a present, a birthday present that I'm sure you will lovingly wear for the remainder of your life.

" 'Lizette, darling, take this ring which represents my love even to the minutest fraction and tell me that your love for me is as strong as mine is for you.'

" 'Philippe, the tears that you see in my eyes, tears that I make no effort to hide or wipe, I know are more significant to you than all the words I could use; and Philippe, we will, with Father's acknowledgement of our engagement, be able to kiss honorably and at will. Now, will you ask Father so that we can announce it tonight?' "

"And, darling, they became engaged?"

"Yes, Grace; and, as is customary in the Vieux Carre, the engagement was for one year, which is the shortest possible period; so they were to be married on her following birthday."

"Why so long an engagement?"

"Well, I believe the custom was established so as to enable the couples to send to and receive from France various necessities and presents. For instance, in this case, Mr. de la Tour had an artist draw a beautiful wreath design of flowers with their marriage initials, P. De L., in the center. The flowers were in their natural colors and the initials were in gold. This design was sent to Dresden with instructions to have it placed on every piece of the one hundred and thirty-two piece dinner set. And, Grace, since we've been married, you've learned that the captain and first mate made purchases in gay Paris and other European cities for us Creoles and are paid a fee for their trouble. In the case of the newly engaged couple, their parents, aunts, uncles, cousins and friends, nearly all sent for their presents."

"Have you seen any of those presents?"

"Yes, practically all of them."

"Please describe one piece."

"Well, I'll describe a mantle set that consisted of a clock, two vases and candelabra. The clock was of transparent white porcelain; and along the edges were porcelain roses, in their natural colors, that is yellow, pink, red and a very dark red, with their green leaves; all were applied in relief as though glued on. The face or dial was also of fine white porcelain with raised golden numerals; and the hands were of onyx, held to the rotating center with gold metal. The vases had a pleasing design to match and were also decorated with colored flowers in relief; the candelabra were equally ornamented. To give you an idea of the value of this set, it cost over four hundred dollars."

"My, it must have been exquisite!"

"It is exquisite, and some day soon, you and Petite will see it. And, Petite, you have been a patient listener."

CHAPTER II

Yellow Fever

"Well, Emile, I've been trying to place their house, for, as you know, I've been in everyone's home in our little city; but we've heard so many stories of Philippe and Lizette, that I begin to realize that it is possible that they never married. But tell me, who gave that expensive present?"

"Lizette's mother."

"And, Grace, did your mother send something for your wedding?"

"No, for I'm an orphan, having been reared in a convent in the North."

"Oh, I'm sorry!"

"There's nothing to be sorry for, Petite, because I was well treated and only suffered when some of the mothers visited their little girls, holding them to their breasts and kissing and loving them. I remember how my eyes would become moist; and when I asked the Superioress about my mother, she would take me in her arms and would say, 'Now, I'm your mother.' Well Petite, that is the past and I've given all of my love to darling Emile—and—would you mind if I left this seat and sat on his lap."

"Not at all, Grace. But, suppose Emile should mind?"

"He won't, the darling; for whenever I've spoken of my mother he has always placed his arm about me and held me tight as though he were taking her place."

"Then come and make yourself comfortable and let me kiss those moist eyes."

"Emile, you are sweet."

"You see, Petite, why I treasure this bit of femininity and why I said yes when she proposed."

"Emile, you fibber. You—"

"No, I proposed; and I'll tell you how I did it. You see, I came in unexpectedly, and changing my voice and hiding behind closed doors, I said, 'Grace, will you marry me?' and she answered, 'Yes, who are you?'"

"Emile, you fibber; Petite knows better."

"Yes, honey, I do, for I know Emile. However, on with the story."

"Well, all plans were made for the wedding—the furniture was completed, the presents were safely stored, and a large corner room at the plantation home was done over in the Empire style, that is, the style of Napoleon. When it was finished, it was one of the most beautiful rooms near this city. Philippe had been taught the duties of the master of a plantation; consequently each day found him with added responsibilities so that Lizette quickly accepted the offer of the de la Tours to live with them. You know, Grace, this little city has proved, contrary to common opinion, that two or more families can live in harmony together, provided they are of the same nationality, for then their likes and dislikes are practically the same; for instance, their cultured taste for highly seasoned food, besides many other things that, with strangers living together, might cause petty argument and bitter remark.

"However, just eleven days before the wedding, this peaceful city was visited by the worse plague of Yellow Fever in its history."

"Emile, have you an eyewitness account of it?"

"Yes, Petite. Shall I read?"

"Please."

"Well, the same Reverend Dr. Clapp who gave us so graphic an account of the terrible cholera epidemic was in the North at the time the epidemic started and immediately embarked for home. He writes: 'On the day of my arrival, it rained incessantly from morning till night. In the space of twelve hours, the interments were over three hundred. The same day I visited two unacclimated families belonging to my church; they were all down with the plague. In these families were nine persons; only two of them survived. I knew a large boarding house for draymen, mechanics, and humble operatives, from which forty-five corpses were borne away in thirteen days. A poor lady of my acquaintance kept boarders for a livelihood. Her family consisted of eight unacclimated persons. Everyone of them died in the space of three weeks.'

"Notice, Grace and Petite, he says unacclimated persons, for the Creoles were acclimated and not usually subject to the disease, while the Negro slaves were immune. He continues: 'Six unacclimated gentlemen, intelligent, refined, and strictly temperate, used to meet once a week, to enjoy music, cheering conversation, and innocent amusement. They had been told that a great safeguard, in a sickly summer, was to keep up good spirits and banish from their minds dark and melancholy thoughts. They passed a certain evening together in health and happiness. In precisely one week from that day, five of them were in the tomb. One of the most appalling features of the yellow fever is the rapidity with which it accomplishes its mission.

"He continues, 'There is some difficulty in arriving at the true statistics touching this epidemic. It was supposed by the best informed physicians that there were fifty or sixty thousand unacclimated persons in New Orleans when the epidemic began; and in four months the whole number of deaths reported were ten thousand three hundred. Of course, eight thousand were on account of yellow fever. The physicians estimated that thirty-two thousand of those attacked this year were cured. Of course, if this calculation is true, the whole number of cases in this year was forty thousand.'"

"And he continues: 'The horrors and desolation of this epidemic cannot be painted; neither can they be realized, except by those who have lived in New Orleans and have witnessed similar scenes and participated in them. Words can convey no adequate idea of them. In some cases, all the clerks and agents belonging to the mercantile establishments were swept away, and the stores closed by civil authorities. Several entire families were carried off—parents, children, servants, all. Others lost a quarter or a third or three-fourths of their members; and their businesses, hope, and happiness were blasted for life. The ravages of the destroyer were marked by more woeful and affecting varieties of calamity than were ever delineated in the pages of romance. Fifteen clergymen died that season—two Protestant ministers and thirteen Roman Catholic priests.

"'They were strangers to the climate, but could not be frightened from their posts of duty. The word fear was not in their vocabularies. Four Sisters of Charity were laid in their graves, and several others were brought to the point of death.'

"He futher writes, 'In a letter which was written by myself to a minister up North are the following lines: Let us look for a moment at a rainbow of beauty spanning this dark cloud of pestilence. During the past season of gloom and affliction, the inhabitants of New Orleans have displayed a degree of heroism, a power of philanthropy, to me, absolutely unparalled. Families of wealth and ease, instead of going over to the delightful watering places in the vicinity on the sea shore to enjoy themselves, have passed the whole summer in the city and devoted their days and nights to the taking care of poor, stricken forlorn strangers who had no claims on their charity but the ties of our common humanity. I know one gentleman and lady in independent circumstances who have had under their charge in the course of the summer as many as thirty poor families, all strangers to them. These they have taken as good care of as if they had been their own kith and kin. Such things have been common all over the city, and in all cases of our heterogeneous population. The members of the Howard Association have achieved miracles of benevolence. I hesitate not to say that this city, in this fearful visitation, has given to the world an example of Christian philanthropy as lofty as can be found in the records of all time. I have often thought that if our Northern brethern could have been in New Orleans this summer, they would no longer entertain a doubt but that a slave holder may be a Christian—the highest type of man, the noblest work of God. Every means which ingenuity could devise or benevolence suggest has been employed to avert and mitigate the evils of the plague. More than two hundred children have been made orphans, and the ladies within and around the city are making clothes for them, and doing everything possible to promote their welfare.'

"He further states: 'In New Orleans, I have often been struck by admiration to see persons in the lower walks of life making every possible sacrifice of time, ease, and money in attending the sick, soothing the dying, and providing tombs and a decent burial for those who were absolute strangers and utterly destitute. I go so far as to say that I have never, in a single instance, seen poor and wicked people (as they are called) declining to perform all the offices of charity in their power to the ill and distressed around them!' On another page I read: 'I knew a woman who was impoverished and so ignorant that she did not understand the meaning of the phrase self-sacrificing benevolence, yet she took a sick child from an adjoining house; its father and mother had just died of yellow fever, and she watched over it till she was worn out with fatigue and anxiety, without the slightest hope of any reward—even her own children were dependent upon her daily labor for subsistence.' Again he writes: 'I have seen poor young men close their stores and suspend all business to give their days and nights, their toil and money, to the relief of sick, indigent, and helpless strangers from whom they could neither wish or hope for the smallest remuneration. I have known them to carry on this work of charity until their health was undermined and their lives were offered up in sacrifice on the altar of philanthropy.' "

"And, Emile, since Philippe and Lizette were part of these people, I would imagine they did thir share."

"Right you are, Grace, for I've found in the archives of the Cathedral that the Sunday before the wedding, the priest announced from the pulpit that it, the wedding, had been postponed indefinitely. Further traces through a letter that I have here reveal—"

"Darling, can you read us the letter?"

"Yes, sweet. Here it is; it was addressed to her friend Marie, who, having one unacclimated parent, that is, her Creole father married an American woman, was advised to leave the city for the Gulf Coast. After the salutation and the account of the ravages of the mysterious disease, Lizette writes: 'I have charge of nineteen baby orphans, living with us day and night. After I place them in bed, using my bed for nine and placing an extra mattress on the floor for the other ten, I sit and talk with Philippe, who is dead tired after building all day tombs to house the bodies. He is using as many slaves as the plantation can afford and with them is kept busy from five in the morning until eight at night, sometimes not eating until he reaches my home.

" 'Day before yesterday, the corpses arrived in such numbers that he and the other men had to bury them in the ground until they can catch up with the tombs. That night we had a downpour; and the next morning, the corpses, in their pine boxes, were floating in their trenches; fortunately the lime that the local authorities had poured over the bodies in an effore to stem the epidemic had made the coffins water tight.

" 'The moment I move to attend one of the ailing babies, Philippe falls asleep on the large sofa that I have purposely made comfortable with soft pillows during the day; and rather than be parted from him by his returning to his home, I let him sleep through the night while I take a cat nap for, with nineteen babies, I am awake practically all night. Mother takes over for me during the day, permitting me to get some much needed sleep.

" 'As for our wedding, we have decided to postpone it indefinitely, for I could not act the part of a wife that I so desire to do, and further, could not possibly remain hidden for fifteen days after our wedding night, as is our custom. Marie, he and I had planned a wonderful time in my large, beautiful room, where he would every day bring me my meals and where we would be free from prying eyes; but we are happy to make the sacrifice to help those not so fortunate as we are. As for you, for God's sake, remain where you are, and do not, for one day visit the city, for the doctors claim this epidemic is the worse on record; and it is becoming worse daily.' And then she closes her letter with love, etc."

CHAPTER III

Basin Street

"It was October of the same year. The yellow fever cases were becoming fewer and fewer and in good time, for Lizette's weight of one hundred and thirty-five pounds for her five feet, six inches had been reduced to one hundred and five pounds, causing her to look, what she terms in a letter, 'like a bean pole'. Philippe, too, had dropped from one hundred and seventy-two to one hundred and thirty-eight pounds. Everyone, whether he had the miserable fever or not, had lost weight; and all the population looked thin and haggard. The priests, ministers, nuns, doctors, nurses, servants, slaves, all but the children looked wretched, and even some of them showed signs of malnutrition, their parents' time being consumed in giving much needed help to the victims.

"Lizette had just completed washing a sweet, plump, little black-eyed baby and was pinning on the diaper and giving it a dash of sweet smelling powder when Philippe entered.

" 'Philippe, isn't she sweet?'

" 'Yes, honey, a little darling.'

" 'And, Philippe darling, I was wondering if you would care to adopt her. You see, she is the orphan child of the Tremblins. The others all have been adopted or claimed by relatives.'

" 'Lizette, only if no one else can afford to care for her, for we want one of our own, you know, one that was actually at one time part of you and me.'

" 'Then Mother can have her, for she expressed a desire for her; however, Mother is not young any more, and with the trials of this last plague—'

" 'I understand, but let her have the baby so that when we have one of our own we can give it all of our love and yet keep an eye on this one. And, honey, would you care for Christmas as a wedding day?'

" 'That would be wonderful.'

" 'Then Christmas it will be.'

" 'Yes, Christ's birthday.' "

"And were they married on Christmas?"

"No , Grace, for two weeks later, at a meeting of the carnival club, Philippe was elected King of the carnival parade, for, in addition to being one of its most popular members, he was to be married; and they thought that they might be able to induce him and Lizette to wed on that glorious night amid all the beautiful decorations; and too, the ball would be a substitute for the wedding party, but on a grander and more embellished scale.

"When informed of their desire, Lizette thought for a while; and realizing the intended honor the members wished to bestow on them, she just could not refuse. Of course, she was to keep secret the fact that Philippe was to be king and, instead, was to infer that he would be one of the dukes. Then it was that superstitious tongues began wagging—'never two postponements without a third'."

"Darling, was there a postponement"

"What have you heard, Petite?"

"That there was one or a substitute marriage."

"Well, darling, which was it?"

"To tell you would be to ruin the story, and to ruin the ending would be sacriligious—for there will be a great revelation. Now, shall I consider your question retracted?"

"By all means."

"And Petite, why are you smiling?"

"Because, Emile, I've been trying since you've started this story to find a clue to the ending, but you have successfully hidden even the faintest hint."

"Now, tell me, if this were a book, would you be tempted to turn to the last pages?"

"Definitely."

"And if I were to tell you that you would ruin the story, as far as you're concerned, and that I would emphatically urge you not to, would you then read the last pages?"

"Definitely no; for since you would have my pleasure in mind, I would take your advice. However, what happened next?"

"Well, some years ago the local authorities built with

slave labor, a canal or basin from the old Bayou St. John into the rear of the city, right through Mr. de la Tour's plantation permitting sailboats to discharge their cargoes just one square in the rear of Rampart Street, thereby saving a distance through the swamps of over two miles. The street where this basin terminated was named Basin Street.

"Now, immeditely after the yellow fever a woman had given a contract to have a two-story residence built; she wanted it raised, with an imposing entrance and a marble vestibule and large leaded-glass door. The woman, twenty-three or twenty-four years old, was a foreigner. She was tall and lithe with large blue eyes and hair between golden and red; she was, indeed, a picture worth gazing upon. She was a divorcee, something the Creoles frowned upon; and it was rumored that she intended using the house for immoral purposes, for she had been seen repeatedly in earnest conversation with beautiful, shapely quadroon and octaroon girls, ones who had been discarded by the Creole boys when they married.

"Months later this proved to be correct, for a male visitor to the city who cared to spend from ten to two or three hundred dollars for a night's private entertainment would hie to this residence. The girls, thirty to forty in number, would all rise at his entrance, exposing, under a very thin veil, their sylph-like bodies. Their faces were perfectly formed, with olive skin, large jet black, liquid eyes, and a pair of expressive lips that revealed a pearly set of teeth. Picture these faces with their background of curly, black glistening tresses, together with their thin, shapely forms, and you have an alluring picture.

"Choosing one of these girls, the stranger would retire with her to a highly, voluptuously decorated room when, on entering, he was confronted by a neat and formally dressed maid who inquired as to the drinks, which varied upwards from three dollars for one bottle of beer.

"Now, girls, all of this was not generally known until near Mardi Gras. It was common knowledge, however, in the Jeanfreau home that the blond owner of this house looked on Philippe with much favor, having mentioned it before her girls, who in turn mentioned it to one of Mr. Jeanfreau's slaves. However, Lizette had confidence in her Creole fiance, all the confidence in the world, until three days before the Carnival parade."

"Oh my, Petite, there goes the wedding."

"I wouldn't jump at conclusions, Grace, for one version that I've heard was to the effect that they married. However, Emile, that old meany husband of yours looks on placidly and smiling, tightens his arm around you.

"Well, if you two have completed your conversation, I'll continue. But jokes aside, girls, I can only relate the events as they happened. So I'll continue. Everything has been made ready for the wedding to the minutest detail, even to the stage which would permit Lizette to cross from the club gallery to the high throne on the parade float. Masked as a queen, she would wear glittering gems around her lovely throat and on her head a tiara; and her gorgeous purple gown and mantle would be bespangled with sparkling jewels.'

"Now, queens don't usually ride with their kings, but since the pleasure of walking up the aisle in wreath and veil was denied Lizette, one of the committee conceived the idea of Lizette riding with her king, and the throne was then ordered to be made large enough to seat two.

CHAPTER IV

Green Eyes

"Lizette and Philippe had fully recuperated after the strain of the epidemic and were once again perfect specimens of manhood and womanhood. They were, as one would suspect, exceedingly happy; Lizette dreamed of the time when she would be queen, with her king, undisturbed for fifteen days, to love and be loved, to enjoy the bliss which nature provides for every living thing. As birds build their nests together as mates, so Philippe and she would build their

"He was living also in the clouds, for he was to be king nest for the baby girl he had so tenderly spoken of. and his queen was to sit by his side on the throne on the first float; the other seventeen following would be peopled with members of his royal court, and the entire population would be loyal subjects. He had visited his float, hidden with the others in its barn, and marveled at the magnificence of its splendor; its huge, high, jeweled crown canopy from which hung beautiful royal purple drapes trimmed with rich ermine; the throne seats inlaid with radiant gems, at the bottom of which rested two large fiery red foot rests; the seats that will sit two handsome child pages whose heads will support two long, curly, colored plumes; the large vari-colored, irridescent jewels that surround the float; and other highly decorative material all put together by master craftsmen for his Royal Highness, the king of mis-rule.

"And above all, Lizette was to be his—to have and to hold until death would them part.

"Now, as you know, March weather in New Orleans is beautiful. Combined with the balmy spring days, when everything returns to life, the Carnival season with its purple, gold, and green decorations made everyone gay and light-hearted. La Nouvelle Orleans was, indeed, the city that care forgot. And I believe this was the reason why when Philippe was walking on St. Peter Street to meet Lizette, who was waiting for him to visit the dressmaker to have the final fitting of her royal robe, the blonde woman walked from behind Philippe and placed her arm in his.

"Now girls, I'm not one to believe in devils and pixies, but there are times when one feels something causes fate to act evilly against us. In this case, Lizette saw the actions of this brazen woman.

"Now, as you girls know, there is so much chivalry here that for Philippe to move the blonde's arm was, of course, unthinkable.

"Lizette, permitting jealousy to get the better of her judgment, especially since at her home her parents would tease her, saying that it would be a race to the altar between her and the blonde, turned face and doubled back towards Royal Street and her home.

"Philippe, having noticed what happened, quickly excused himself and hurriedly followed Lizette, only to have the door shut in his face—an insult that is considered unforgivable, and one Lizette would never have committed had she taken time to reflect.

"Philippe, exceedingly angry now, walked through the carriage entrance past the large iron gates and entered the hall from the rear without knocking. Correctly guessing that she had entered her bedroom, he leaped the winding steps two at a time and again, without knocking, opened the door and met Lizette, face to face, she having heard his footsteps and being prepared for him.

"Now, Grace, although the French lead a philosophical life, they have, when angered, terrible tempers. So, on entering, Philippe said angrily, 'Lizette, before I say another word, I demand an apology.'

" 'I don't apologize to anyone who, in the future, intends living a double life.'

" 'A double life?'

" 'Yes; and furthermore, I now realize why I am told that it will be she or I.'

" 'You were told no such thing; you were teased, and now, as far as that woman is concerned, she may reside in her home adjoining our plantation the remainder of her life—I do not propose living in a miserable state of insane jealousy; so unless you become the sweet, loving, pure thinking girl you've always been, I've no wish to marry you. You will have until tomorrow noon for reflection. Come to me, as I desire you, or not at all.'

"And turning, in his rage, he left the house.

"Now, girls, you may not have experienced it, but I've seen it dozens of times, where jealousy, the master builder very small molehill into the largest mountain imaginable. of all times, can change in almost a twinkling of an eye a

"Lizette lay on her bed; and as she cried, the green-eyed monaster led her to believe that when Philippe remained away from her to repair the pump that forced the rain water off the plantation or to repair the rear levee where a crevasse had occurred to prevent the brackish lake water at high tide from inundating the plantation and ruining it for three years, he was holding the blonde woman in his arms and kissing her. Then, too, weren't there some nights in which his ardor was not so forceful or sincere as others, thus proving that he was in love with someone else, and that his story of a toilsome day was a lie? Further, what woman would brazenly walk up to a man and place her arm in his? No such woman existed to Lizette's knowledge unless the man was interested. And it was only after one became engaged that the two walked arm in arm. She rose, locked the door so as not to be disturbed, and lying on her back with both hands behind her head, resumed her thinking and reasoning. The more she thought, the more his loving the other woman became a reality; and when she thought of the night that he supposedly remained at the veterinarian with the French coach stallion, and again supposedly remained up with his best friend, the one who was to be the groomsman, she was certain that those nights were spent with the blonde woman.

"You know, Grace, you never have experienced pangs of jealousy and perhaps don't realize how the mind is warped to a point where, in proportion to the depth of one's love, one hypnotizes oneself to believe only the calamity of the loss. I don't believe you have either, Petite."

"Not in jealousy—but I could swear that I saw Antoine wounded on the battlefield in the Battle of New Orleans when

I was in the Cathedral, praying for his safety."

"Yes, love will cause those things; and the more we love, the more we permit our imagination to run rampant. This was just what Lizette did, so much so that she was now convinced, beyond the shadow of a doubt that the best she could hope for would be to share his love with that woman.

"At supper that night her father noticed her swollen eyes, but said nothing until later when he followed her to her room and seating himself in a comfortable rocker addressed her quietly asking, 'Lizette, what is wrong?'

"For answer, she dropped on the bed and sobbed convulsively.

" 'Come on, Lizette, compose yourself; maybe I can help you.'

" 'No one can help.'

" 'All right, all right, but I demand to know what this is all about.'

"Then she explained the facts, not as we know them, but as her deranged mind would have them, never once saying that 'she believed it to be,' or 'it may be,' but rather as definite events, and with so much conviction that considering her veracity Mr. Jeanfreau was convinced that Philippe was no fit husband for his daughter. So, in no uncertain terms he ordered that she from that moment forget him as he would not countenance for one moment the thought of him as a son."

"In other words, he forbade the marriage?"

"Yes; and, Grace, a Creole father's word is law in his home. However, later, when alone in his study with his French briar pipe moving to and from his mouth, he slowly and pensively puffed smoke into the air. His first thought was to avenge Lizette's honor. But then, were there not hundreds of Creole boys who were protectors for quadroons, and who even had children by them, and when the time came for marriage, did they not, in most cases, abandon those girls, giving them the furniture and the house? No, until they were married, neither he nor Lizette had been dishonored.

"And then he began to reason more sanely, for he did not have her crying before him to influence him. And the more he reasoned, the more he became convinced that an error had been made somewhere, and that the worst that could have happened was that Philippe was tricked. However, he would let matters remain as they were until he could investigate, considering too that both he and his wife preferred a wreath and veil, a wedding at mass.

"He did, however, send for Marie, who was to be maid of honor. Asking that she would not interrupt, he explained everything and further suggested that she would act as queen, as it was his duty to see that post filled since he had forbidden the wedding. Marie, being Lizette's size, could use the royal gown which was still at the dressmaker's.

"Of course Marie agreed with Mr. Jeanfreau that the whole thing was preposterous and even went so far as to agree that a church wedding was the proper thing. However, she had plans of her own and immediately started to put them into effect."

"Emile, must those plans remain a secret from us?"

"Not necessarily, but I do like to tease."

"Please, darling, tell us the plans."

"Well, Marie knew better than to visit Lizette that night, for to explain that Lizette was in error would only complicate matters since Mr. Jeanfreau was adamant in cancelling the wedding until further investigation. She then induced her fiance to aid her, and sent him with a message to Philippe to the effect that she, Marie, would act as queen. From there, he went directly to the dazzling blonde woman whom Marie believed to be a good woman at heart, for she was donating money monthly for the support of yellow fever orphans and had him explain to her everything in detail, asking that she meet Lizette at her, Marie's home about six o'clock on the parade night."

"How did you gather this information?"

"From a letter I have here that was sent to one of Philippe's relatives who since has returned to New Orleans."

CHAPTER V

The Mardi Gras Parade

"It was eight o'clock, and the gorgeous pageant was under way. The strains of the brass bands, eight in number, reached the happy crowd that thronged the banquettes and galleries. The King sat on his throne of state alone. The throne of the float was almost even with the decorated second-story galleries. His majesty waved to the men and threw kisses to the smiling women, at the same time his retinue on other floats tossed colored beads and other souvenirs to the shouting children with their upraised hands.

"At the sides of all of the gayly colored floats, which this night depicted various old love stories; such as, Romeo and Juliet in the balcony scene surrounded by countless flowers of all colors; and Anthony and Cleopatra in their boat gorgeously decorated with papyrus and other plants while under were small waves, painted in blue and silver. Negro slaves in red coats and hoods held the colored torches that cast their light on the floats, while others laboriously carried cumbersome contrivances on which were five burners fully ablaze, consuming what had been introduced that year for the first time, the magic fluid, oil.

"The Negro slaves were in perfect step with the grand music; and, as with the tom-tom, they shuffled and made the African dip, bending their right knee until it almost touched the earth beneath their wide feet.

"The King, alone with his thoughts of what might have been behind his smiling mask, mechanically waved his scepter to the right and left, towards the banquette and the galleries; and, at least a half dozen times he thought he saw Lizette's little face, sweet and penitent.

"The local police who proceeded the parade were mounted on shapely French coach stallions; they stopped, as did the officers of the Krewe in their resplendent court uniforms, also on horses whose backs were covered with long, flowing silken capes of the riders. The band continued to play as it halted, while the Negroes, whose hands were at the bits of the docile mules, led them from the center of narrow Royal Street towards the curb, for they had arrived at the club house; the gallery was gayly decorated with Mardi Gras colors. On it were the club members and their wives seated on a platform that tapered upwards toward the rear. In the center front sat a figure gorgeously robed in the purple attire that Philippe had failed to see, surrounded by her ladies of the court with their various colored silk and satin robes.

"The float stopped as the wheels rested perilously near the open, dirty black gutter, directly in the center of the gallery which was filled with gay, smiling faces.

"The wild, shouting mob had now broken through the cordon of police and were crowding around the float; everyone was pushing into a position where he could see the King and the Queen.

"The band from the second float had marched up directly to the rear of the King's band, and a bandmaster from the gallery wielded his baton, while music from the two bands now playing as one filled the air with strains that were heard above the noise of the fun-loving, gay, howling mob, all eager to get a glimpse of the King's face as he lifted his mask to drink the toast.

"The portable bridge, with its protective sides also covered with the royal colors, was now in place; and the King, with his sorrowful, aching heart, rose and walked towards his queen. He thought 'Why couldn't it have been Lizette, instead of Marie, as we had planned.' However, reaching that part of the gallery where the colored iron lace-work had been removed, he and the queen were offered silver goblets, into which was nervously poured sparkling French Champagne from an ice-cold bottle. With shaking hands, they raised the goblets to the center of their masked faces and tremblingly extended them forward until they touched; and amid a roar and cheer that momentarily drowned the royal music, the king partly lifted his smiling mask, while the queen placed her goblet under her silken face covering, and they drank, having dexterously kept their identities secret. They returned the silver goblets, and the king extended his right hand, which was quickly grasped by the queen, and gently he led her to the throne beside him. Again an uproar came from the milling crowd as the chief of police blew loud and long on his whistle. Then the parade slowly rolled along while the crowd returned to the banquette, and those on the galleries rose, shouted, and applauded. If one could have lifted those two masks, one would have seen pain plainly written in every feature of the face behind the smiling one, and fear and remorse behind the silken one, which later changed to sweet understanding and love as she noticed how he searched every face, from right to left, looking for only one as they passed her own gallery. And then, too, not finding what he was looking for, he seemed to slump in his soft, spring seat.

"The band now began playing a familiar song, starting with the chorus, and he waved his shining scepter, a duty he owed his subjects, regardless of his agonizing emotions. The crowd joined in singing, the words floating from below and from both sides as the float slowly rolled on:

" 'As you desire me,
So shall I come to you,
How'er you want me,
So shall I be;
Be it forever,
Or be it just a day
As you desire me,
Let come what may.
I care not what you will,
Do what you will, with me;
I give myself to you
For you're my destiny.
And now come take me,
My very soul is yours.
As you desire me,
I come to you!'

"Philippe dropped his scepter, but the Queen quickly raised his arm, and again it mechanically moved while the music played the song; and as it neared the chorus again, he bent his head towards the queen and asked, 'Marie, where is Lizette?'

" 'Wait,' she answered with a quivering voice; and as the band again began the chorus, she sang from under her mask.

"Was it again wishful thinking? No, for now he noticed, through the narrow slits in the mask, two dark black eyes, while Marie's were blue; and, as she reached the words, 'As you desire me, I come to you!' He reached over and gently tore the mask from her face.

"He forgot he was king, forgot he was on a float, and did not see that thousands of inquisitive, startled eyes were upon them; nor did he note that the noise of the roaring crowd had been subdued so that only the creaking of the wagon wheels could be heard. She humbly said, 'Philippe, darling, I meant every word of it.' Quickly removing his mask and placing his crown on the seat, he clasped her to him, raining kisses on her fair and happy face."

PART THREE

"THE GREAT REVELATION"

CHAPTER I

Revelation

"Now I know you girls are happy."

"Happy, yes, that they were married; but, Emile, what I want to know is what became of them, for no one, not even elderly people know; and now, don't tell me that you don't."

"No, Petite I won't, for I do know; and if you will bear with me, I'll satisfy your curiosity."

"Were they happy, darling?"

"Yes, Grace, as happy as the two proverbial birds. For ten months they seemed to live only for each other; Philippe's every move, every action, was in adoration of Lizette, who in the near future would present him with a child. Both families made preparation."

"What preparation, darling? Baby clothes and so forth?"

"Not entirely, Grace, for that is almost secondary with us Creoles. Petite, will you explain about the pictures to Grace, while I send one of my slaves with the carriage on a very important errand?"

"Certainly, Emile. Now, Grace, it is a superstition that a birth mark is caused by some incident that happened while the mother was pregnant. For instance, I personally knew a man that was born with what might have resembled a rat tail across his forehead; and he assured me that at one time his mother had been frightened by a rat, having only seen its tail; and placing her hand to her forehead, she naturally marked the coming baby with a rat tail. The doctors that I've consulted are unanimous in denying that this is possible, stating that the moment of conception definitely determines all features and characteristics of the child. Let me tell you of a personal case. When my mother conceived me, she had occasion to visit my father's mother. On arriving she found the family drinking coffee, and naturally they invited her to drink with them. Mother says she refused, whereupon they insisted three or four times, knowing her condition and fearing her desire for coffee would mark the child. It seems

that their constant offering did create the desire; but after
refusing repeatedly, she felt ashamed to accept and, placing her hand on the back of her neck, she unconsciously
rubbed there with her finger. Realizing, Grace, what she
was doing, she quickly removed her finger, and, upon returning to her mother, my grandmother, explained what had
happened, and was assured that the child, that is I, would
carry a coffee mark."

"And, do you, Petite?"

"Yes; and mother says that when I was born, and since
the coffee incident had remained clearly in her mind, I was
placed on my stomach immediately after delivery, and there
was the mark. What Emile wants me to tell you is that in
Lizette's room as in all Creole rooms where an infant is
expected were pictures of beautiful babies and children,
bought, borrowed, and lent, on account of pre-natal influ-
ences. But wait, here he comes now."

"Have you finished, Petite?"

"Yes, Emile, but did they choose blondes or brunettes?"

"Well, Lizette always admired the blonde that she was
jealous of, the one who had brought her to her senses the
night of the parade at Marie's home. As Philippe gave her
her choice, she chose a blonde; hence her room was littered
with beautiful children of that type. However, whether influenced by those pictures or through heredity from her
father, the baby was a blonde."

"Was she pretty?"

"I wouldn't know when she was born, but I have a picture of her when she was a year old. Here it is, and I think
she is beautiful, for she inherited the expressive blue eyes
and blonde hair of her father, and the handsomely chiseled
face and full shaped lips of her mother."

"My, she is sweet; and look, Petite, how chubby."

"But, Emile, the face is familiar—and yet—I can't place
it."

"Yes, Petite, it is not only familiar to you, but you know
her. However, before you question me, when she was about
two years old, a catastrophe occurred that affected the child
for years; yes, and it still does even to this very day."

"My, and such a pretty baby!"

"Yes, I remember her even before that picture was taken, for before they disappeared it was my custom to hold her on my lap, as I was her god-father; she was christened at the Cathedral. I was older than she, and I learned to love her as a sister. When I grew older I would, at every opportunity, beg, borrow, or buy everything that pertained to her or her parents, hence this entire shelf of momentoes and records, including this Holy Bible which was not theirs originally, although they believed it to be theirs."

"But, there are two Holy Bibles, one in the secretary and one on the table. Was one of them Philippe's originally?"

"Yes, Petite, the one on the table belonged originally to the white de la Tour family and the one in the secretary belonged to the colored family of the same name. In this one is recorded the birth of a boy whose father was the original de la Tour who landed here in 1758, his mother being a free woman, an Octaroon; a common practice that exists to this day in our little French city.

"When this child was born, and since it had the appearance of being white in every respect, the grandmother conceived the idea of rearing him as a white child. To do this, she moved, with his mother and the child to north Louisiana near where Monroe is located today.

"So as to prove further that the child was white, she, having access to the de la Tour home, exchanged Bibles, since large Bibles of that day were fac-similies, all coming from France. So she had the Holy Book as proof that the child's parents were both white. Having the recordation of de la Tour's legitimate child, it was an easy matter, with this proof, to call that child their ward in the new community.

"Now, Henri de la Tour, the father of the colored child must have learned of the exchange, for Philippe found that page firmly glued to another; evidently this had been done with the intention to conceal the record."

"One would imagine that he would have destroyed that page."

"I thought so too, but evidently he didn't, for Philippe on opening the Holy Book to enter the name of his daughter noticed that all former entries were on a page that had been marked 'continued'; and further examination revealed that

after page three came page six and that pages four and five
had been glued together. As he had become curious, he
heated a sad-iron and applied it to those pages, separating
them.

"Imagine his surprise when he noticed, in the handwrit-
ing of a priest, since colored women at that time did not
know how to read or write, the word 'colored' behind the
boy's name.

"Since there was only one de la Tour family in this small
section at the time, and since he was ignorant of what I'm
telling you, he believed his granddarent had been colored
and naturally that would place him in that same category."

"But how did you obtain the original Bible?"

"Well, many of my friends knew that I was endeavoring
to solve the mystery; so one of them having heard of the
colored de la Tour family immediately wrote me, furnish-
ing me with their address. Then I took a coach, located the
grandmother, and for a good price, obtained possession of
that precious Bible, including the story as I've told it to
you."

"You have searched diligently, Emile."

"Yes, Petite, and I've been repaid a thousand times since."

"But, I don't understand."

"You will in less than an hour."

CHAPTER II

A Momentous Decision

" 'Lizette—I started to say darling, but I don't deserve calling you—'

" 'Please, Philippe, if there is colored blood on your side, I swear, darling it will never dampen my love nor my admiration for you. Further, my love, I give you my word that if I had known it before we took those sacred vows at the Mardi Gras ball, it would not have influenced me one iota.'

" 'But, sweet, we have our baby girl to think of; and she is according to my figures over ninety-nine per cent white. If you would have married me with ninety-eight per cent white blood, then no white man should hesitate to marry her.'

" 'That is true, Philippe; but you know the laws of this state.'

" 'Then we shall move into another.'

" 'Yes, but our moving, without a good explanation, and the fact that we know that that notation in the Holy Bible has been seen by some of the slaves who can read, since it disappeared for over two weeks, and told to those that can't, why, wherever we go, that fact will follow.'

" 'Yes, I realize that; and the only solution that I can possibly think of—God, I hate even to think of it.'

" 'Be brave, darling; our life is half over. But hers is just beginning.'

" 'Well, the only solution I know of would be to send her to a northern convent after we disappear from here.'

" 'Separate me from my baby—Oh! no, not that; anything but that.'

" 'But, sweet, suppose we sleep over it and maybe tomorrow we shall discover a better solution.'

"Grace, my sweet; I am going to recall, especially to you, since Petite, born and reared here knows the many sacrifices that the Creoles make for their children, a comment which I made when I related the story of our old French city."

"I remember the story in general."

"Well, I said speaking of a Creole woman that there are certain things about them that impress everyone, their honesty of purpose, a morality which is second to that of no other class of woman, and a love for their children and grandchildren that causes them to go to many senseless extremes. I continued with, 'in fact, that brings to mind a secret I've known for years', and—And then you asked, 'A secret, Emile?' My answer was, 'Yes, Grace, and I'm going to tell it to you and Petite as such, although I'll mention no names. Petite will understand this, knowing these women, or rather, practically being one herself; but I'm afraid, you Grace, will find it somewhat incredible.' "

"I remember that; in fact, I remember what followed. You said, 'I have known personally a married couple that resided on Esplanade Avenue, and I've heard of many others that resided in the same house, although in different rooms, ate at the same table, and yet for years—never spoke one word to each other. This incompatability of husband and wife in name only was a closely guarded secret. To separate or divorce was to cast a reflection on the children.' "

"Grace, you have a good memory."

"Yes, darling, I do; and further I understand those extremes better now, especially since I've learned that many families remain together even though the wife knows that her husband continues to be a protector of his former quadroon—all for the sake of the children. And, darling, what was their decision?"

"Well, girls, it is quite a story, however, I'll be as brief as possible. You see, when French people or their descendants live in this damp, lowland country, they are subject to lung disease, as is evidenced in the death of two of Philippe's grandparents on his mother's side and one on the side of Lizette's mother. In fact, this disease, or consumption, is so prevalent that I've taken precautions in the form of chest exercises."

"But, darling, I'm not of French descent and yet you insist that I, too, take those exercises."

"Only as a precautionary measure. But, Grace, don't be too certain that you are not of French descent. However, Mrs. de la Tour had been advised to leave the city for a dryer climate before she became a grandmother; but, so as not to leave the children, she remained until it was discovered that she was living with one lung and that the constant coughing of two of her children was diagnosed as the beginning of the white plague. Then it was that they decided to leave for France where they had relatives, and to leave the plantation in charge of Philippe, who had intended to remain. But now that they knew what the Bible contained, Philippe and Lizette, after many sleepless nights and much discussion, decided that they too would visit France, especially since Lizette, whose physical condition was weakened by her constant worrying and crying, also began to cough."

" 'Better, to make a mistake than to remain in suspense,' said Philippe one day. So then they decided, with much sadness, to send the baby to a northern convent where it would be free from the white plague environment. In a year or two they could recross the Atlantic to visit it secretly. Of course, one can imagine the heartaches they experienced while packing the little one's small clothes, and the shaking hand of the grandfather when he signed the document before a Notary Public, leasing his plantation for two years, the proceeds of which were to transport them to the land of their ancestors.

"Finally, after a stormy voyage, they reached their destination; and things immediately began to grow worse. First, it was the beginning of the Second Revolution when King Louis Philippe ingloriously abdicated the throne and the people with the National Guard marched on the Tuilleries. It was the same year that the Baroness Pontalba in fear of her life fled from Paris back to New Orleans to build the two large apartment buildings that flank that most cosmopolitan of places, Jackson Square.

"After three years had passed, they had lost everything and had discontinued corresponding with friends here who believed that the baby was with them. To make matters worse, Mrs. de la Tour died; and believing that their plantation was seized for taxes in the panic of that year, they just seemed to fade into oblivion, the baby with them."

CHAPTER III

Mine

"One day when I was in my teens, I had just returned home from the Civil Court where I had been emancipated for the sole purpose of receiving power of attorney for their estate. Although I was not related, and since I was the baby's godfather, I had paid the yearly taxes, so as to prevent its seizure, thus fulfilling the vow which I had made in the St. Louis Cathedral to act towards that baby as its second father; always hoping to locate that child. On my arrival I was accosted by a slave with, 'Marster Emile, that slave woman, Marie, is dying and wants to see you.' I hurried to the woman and saw that she was dying of old age, having nursed Lizette and her family. When I entered the shack I noticed a candle burning beside that picture of the baby; and as I walked on the floor, covered with crushed brick, it crackled its superstitious purpose of hoodoo prevention. Reaching her bed and sitting in an old chair by her side that she motioned me to, I asked, 'How are you feeling, Marie?'

" 'Going to my Maker, Marster Emile.' Resting a minute she continued, 'You're going to handle the plantation?'

" 'Yes; I've just returned from court where I've been granted full charge.'

"Then I saw her smile and she said, 'The Lord will bless you.'

"Again she rested. As I saw that respiration was becoming increasingly difficult, I feared that she wished to tell me something important; so I asked, 'Marie, is there something you wish to tell me?'

"Her old worn form trembled. And as she whispered 'The baby is in a seminary up North', she passed away. Now I knew she had loved the child—it was the last one she had nursed, and the last one she had proudly carried to the Cathedral for christening when I had vowed to protect and care for it should the occasion arise. I later became aware of the fact that all her spare money had been spent for candles

that burned before a statue of the Virgin Mary in the Church
and before the picture in her shack, for the child's spiritual
welfare.

"I saw that Marie had a proper burial and that she was
placed in a crypt in the slave quarters of the St. Louis cemetery. On leaving the cemetery I immediately repaired to the
rectory where I was closeted for over two hours with the
priest who had christened the baby. Then began a hunt, con-
ducted by us both that lasted for almost a year.

"With my father's aid, I had been very successful with
the plantation and had a neat sum in the bank in the name
of the baby, with myself as executor. One evening, on reaching home, I was informed that the priest desired by presence. Forgetting that I was hungry, I went without supper
and raced towards the rectory.

"I had gathered much of the information that you see in
the secretary and was elated to find that the good priest, all
excited, had had a letter from the Sacre Coeur Convent in
Philadelphia, where the baby had been for years.

"I opened a correspondence with the Mother Superioress,
not explaining what I had found in the first Holy Bible—the
second I had not yet learned of. I made it clear that I had
money for the child, and that she was to want for nothing.
I further made it clear, through the priest, that our correspondence was to be kept secret, as it was for the good of the
child who was now a young lady; and in the near future,
she must try to induce her to come to New Orleans, giving
the address of a woman friend of mine.

"From that time I placed someone in charge of the plantation and devoted myself exclusively to solving the mystery. Through Mr. Grosjean's son who was sent to France to
become a surgeon, I had located Philippe and Lizette and
written them a letter which I thought they would heed, having sent them money, for I knew that they were very poor."

"But, Emile, what became of the baby, I mean the young
lady?"

"Well—but wait, for I hear the horses—and pardon me while I see—"

"Emile! My God, man it's good to see you."

"It's good to see you too; and you Lizette—let me hug you, girl."

"Please, Emile, have you seen our baby?"

"Now, not so fast."

"Then, you have seen her—Please, is she well?"

"Yes, Lizette, she is well and happy; and now, let me introduce two sweet women who could not wait, but followed me through the door to meet you two. This is Petite; I'm sure you remember her?"

"Yes, I do, though she was small. My, Petite, you're beautiful. And who is this young lady with the sweet face that holds you around the waist?"

"She is my darling wife, Lizette, and always rushes to me when she meets strangers. Now, let us all go into the house."

"This old home, Emile, it brings back the old happy days!"

"Yes, I imagine so. But tell me, have you eaten?"

"No, but we're not hungry."

"Then, Philippe, read from that open Bible that was once owned by a colored family."

"Why, that's the same Bi—"

"No, the one you have reference to is on the upper shelf."

"Then we are white?"

"Yes, as white as I am. And Philippe, your plantation is in perfect shape, but has become exceedingly valuable since they have cut a wide street through it and named it after the first American governor, C. C. Claiborne. You will further find that homes surround the plantation and that real estate men will pay any price for it."

"But, Emile, how can I ever repay you?"

"And, Emile, where is my baby?"

"Well, to answer your question first, Philippe—I've done that at a terrible cost to you."

"Now my question, my baby?"

"That has been the cost, not yours any more but mine; and Grace, discontinue edging towards Lizette and Philippe and come to me."

"But, darling, there is an irresistible something that seems to—"

"Yes, I know; but raise your sweet face,—that's it,—and now, my little wife, kiss me and remember, YOU ARE MINE! always MINE, regardless of what those two strangers say. Now sweet, go to and kiss those two good people that would sacrifice anything for you, your loving mother and father."

CHAPTER IV

Gratitude

Many hours later, Emile had gotten into his flannelette night shirt while Grace escorted her mother and father and Petite to the spare bedrooms. A huge fire that had been made hours before by the maid had heated the room to a comfortable temperature, casting pleasing shadows, and in general, making it appear cheerful and pleasant.

No roof in the entire Vieux Carre that night covered more happiness, a happiness that was complete, although during the "Good-night" conversation, Lizette had said, "But, Grace, four years married and yet no little body to hold to your breast, no little feet to hear running through these rooms; no—"

"No, Mother; we might compare this to a little white fleecy cloud in an otherwise bright blue sky, a cloud that will soon evaporate under the bright, life-giving sun. Now, if you three care to continue talking, and you do seem too excited to sleep, Petite might explain how Emile solved the problem, reuniting us; and you know, Mother, I've always loved Emile, but tonight—why I just can't express my feeling."

"I know, and those same virtues that led us to choose him as your godfather, cause those emotions. Kiss me goodnight, my daughter, and go to him."

Emile was lying on his back, his pale blue night shirt in pleasing contrast to the spotless white linen, while his head rested on both hands that had sunk into the large, soft down pillow, while the fire crackled and illuminated Grace's beautiful figure as underthings were removed. Although always adoring each other, this night seemed different, for she experienced a sense of gratitude and humility; and he, a feeling of accomplishment and charity.

This night he didn't hear, as usual, "Emile, close your eyes"; or, "Sweet, turn your head," as the last piece of raiment left her milk-white body that seemed to glow a dainty pink, the curving, shapely lines of which seemed to be highlighted by the brilliantly burning coals.

Although eager to go to Emile, she seemed to remain in this condition much longer than usual, for she felt that she had done him a great injustice in the last four years; and thinking of what she called selfishness, the lines said by Petite came to her mind, when before the Holy altar in the St. Louis Cathedral, Petite was wed. "That God is to be a partner, three persons, man, woman, and God; and that as a partner, He is to guide us and to cause the mutual self-surrender of two persons, who are to be fused into one; in the house, man is the head; woman, the heart."

Emile was looking steadfastly at her as she pensively gazed at the flaming coals. Presently, she donned her gown, entered the bed, and lying flat on her stomach rested her chest on Emile's chest; he remained on his back with his head resting on his hands.

"Emile, you know I've loved you always, don't you?"

"Yes, sweet, I do."

"Well, tonight, I feel as if my very soul is yours; you, my godfather, my everything. While I rest on your chest, while your breath mingles with mine, while your face is in my hands, I feel a gratitude—no, that isn't the word—Emile, my darling, I feel as though I am of you, as though I am melting right into you, as though with a great desire I'm becoming a part of that loving, sweet, pure heart of yours. And, Emile, my love, the fear of having a child has left me completely, a fear you knew, and one that has prompted the protection you gave me in the past. Oh, darling, for the mother and father you've given me, I promise, with those tears that are falling on your loving face, to be more obedient, more—"

"Now, now, no crying, for even though I know them to be tears of joy, I dislike seeing you in that condition. Now, raise your head. Let me wipe your wet face; and, Grace, my Creole sweet, you could not possibly be more obedient more humble and loving than you were with your mother and father all evening, loving them. How they did kiss you and squeeze you! Why Petite and I seemed completely forgotten."

"I didn't mean to forget you two, but desiring a kind mother and father all of my life, having even prayed as a youngster for them, and all of a sudden, with their entire past before me, that mother's cholera and that father's prayer; 'As You Desire Me,' on that parade float; their great sacrifice for me—why, Emile, my heart seemed as if it were bursting and I just loved them. And when they took me to them, I seemed to swell, to become hysterical; and darling, Lizette, my mother, took me on her lap and gently forced my head to rest on her chest. But listen, they are playing their music box: Oh, Emile, what a beautiful tune, one I've never heard before!"

"Yes, it is beautiful; and now that it nears the chorus I will sing it for you. Listen:

Mine, when the dawn is breaking;
Mine, in my dreams at night.
Mine, when the birds are waking;
Mine, when the stars shine bright.
Mine, when the leaves are falling;
Mine, with a glory divine,
Mine with a love never dying,
You're mine, now, and always mine."

FINIS

3 ⁰⁰